KU-599-043

Climatic Change in Later Prehistory

Climatic Change in Later Prehistory

A. F. HARDING
Editor

Edinburgh University Press

Edinburgh University Press
22 George Square, Edinburgh

Set in Linoterm Plantin
by Speedspools, Edinburgh
and Edinburgh University Press
and printed in Great Britain by
Redwood Burn Limited
Trowbridge

British Library Cataloguing in Publication Data
Harding, A. F.
Climatic change in later prehistory
1. Palaeoclimatology
I. Title
551.69 QC884

ISBN 0-85224-425-8

Contents

Preface

The papers in this volume were mostly presented at the International Conference on Climatic Change in Later Prehistory held at the University of Durham on 19, 20 and 21 March 1981. The conference was conceived as a means of bringing together scientists from various fields with a common interest in, or knowledge of, Holocene climatic change, and prehistoric archaeologists interested in the relationship between such change and observed alterations in archaeological configurations. It was attended by some 130 participants, including botanists, quaternary geologists, geographers, soil scientists, and both environmental and cultural archaeologists.

All the papers included here were initially presented at the conference with the exception of those by Shennan, Magny, and Jäger and Ložek. Shennan's paper replaces one by Michael Tooley on 'Sea-levels and climate', which was already promised elsewhere; those by Magny and Jäger and Ložek are included because they present material and/or viewpoints that are not widely known to Anglo-Saxon readers and are highly relevant in the present context. The conference was further privileged to hear a paper by J. F. van Regteren Altena, entitled 'The archaeology of the Dutch coastal areas: food for climatologists', which its author decided against printing here, referring the reader instead to the paper by L. P. Louwe Kooijmans, 'Archaeology and coastal change in the Netherlands', in F. H. Thompson (ed.) *Archaeology and Coastal Change*, Society of Antiquaries Occasional Paper New Series 1, 1980, 106–33.

A particularly thorny problem encountered in preparing these papers for publication was that of how to express dates. Absolute, historical and radiocarbon dates are all used here by different contributors, and different conventions govern the use of each. Whenever possible, dates have been expressed as BP, taking AD 1950 as the present, in accordance with the decision of the 9th Radiocarbon Congress held in 1976. Since, however, the use of this convention alone would mask the fact that some dates are absolute, while others are little more than guesses (including some arrived at before the advent of radiocarbon dating), the date in this or the preceding era is also given in brackets where appropriate, using the convention of bc/ad for uncalibrated radiocarbon dates, and BC/AD for calibrated, historical or 'guess' dates. It is hoped that by this means both the physical scientist, accustomed to using BP dates, and the archaeologist, who has difficulty in thinking in terms other than of BC and AD, will be able to orientate themselves without difficulty, even if the method of expression is a little cumbersome.

It is a pleasure to be able to acknowledge the help and support, both moral and financial, of the following individuals and institutions: first and foremost to the University of Durham Publications Board, for a generous grant which has enabled this volume to be published; the British Council, for sponsoring the visits of the overseas contributors; the Royal Meteorological Society, for printing and distributing publicity material for the conference; to Judy Turner, Michael Tooley, Michael Alexander and Russell Davies, who advised the editor on numerous technical matters concerning the content of the volume; to Lesley Forbes, for translating the article by Michel Magny; to K.-D. Jäger, V. Ložek and M. Magny for allowing their work to be translated and reprinted here; and above all to the contributors themselves for producing their texts with a minimum of badgering. It remains to express thanks to Archie Turnbull and his colleagues at Edinburgh University Press, whose professionalism has ensured an easy passage through the press.

A. F. Harding, *Durham*, July 1981

Introduction: Climatic change and archaeology

'The same parts of the earth are not always moist or dry, but change their character according to the appearance or failure of rivers. So also mainland and sea change places and one area does not remain earth, another sea, for all time, but sea replaces what was once dry land, and where there is now sea there is at another time land. This process must, however, be supposed to take place in an orderly cycle . . . Cold and heat increase and decrease owing to the sun's course, and because of them the different parts of the earth acquire different potentialities; some are able to remain moist up to a certain point and then dry up and become old again, while others come to life and become moist in their turn. As places become drier the springs necessarily disappear, and when this happens the rivers at first dwindle from their former size and finally dry up . . . But these changes escape our observation because the whole natural process of the earth's growth takes place by slow degrees and over periods of time which are vast compared to the length of our life, and whole peoples are destroyed and perish before they can record the process from beginning to end. Of such destructions the most extensive and most rapid are caused by war, others by disease and famine . . . In the same way we must suppose that the time of the first settlement of the various peoples in places that were in process of change from wet and marshy to dry has been forgotten . . . This has happened in Egypt. This is a land which is obviously in the process of getting drier, and the whole country is clearly a deposit of the Nile . . . For as places dry they improve, and places that formerly enjoyed a good climate deteriorate and grow too dry. This has happened in Greece to the land about Argos and Mycenae. In the time of the Trojan War Argos was marshy and able to support few inhabitants only, while Mycenae was good land and therefore the more famous. Now the opposite is the case for the reason given above: for Mycenae has become unproductive and completely dry, while the Argive land that was once marshy and unproductive is now under cultivation. What has happened in this small district may therefore be supposed to happen to large districts and whole countries.'

Aristotle, *Meteorologica* I.xiv
(Loeb edition, translated by H. D. P. Lee, 1952)

The scientific study of climatic change may be said to have begun with this passage of Aristotle, written around the middle of the fourth century BC. Records of unusual climatic events are known much earlier than this, and observations of various natural phenomena had been made by the Egyptians long before, but Aristotle has the distinction of being the first to have gone beyond mere observation to the level of speculation on the causes of the observed meteorological effects; and this in a work the contents of which have been said to have an 'intrinsic lack of interest', Aristotle being 'so far wrong in nearly all his conclusions' (Lee, *loc. cit.*). However true that may be for the rest of the work, Aristotle clearly showed in the passage quoted an awareness of many important aspects of climate and climatic change: a) its spatial variation; b) its temporal variation; c) the interconnectedness of different parts of the climatic system; d) the effects of climatic change on human history; e) the fact that human settlement responds to environmental conditions; f) the long time-scale of some types of environmental change; g) the potential of studying selected areas for reconstructing an environmental history of wider regions.

It is with these considerations, among others, that the papers in this volume are concerned.

The effects of climatic change and its relevance to archaeology

'Climate' is an abstract concept. Most observers experience climate in the form of 'weather', that is, particular effects of precipitation, temperature, air movement and cloud cover. Indeed, to most people it is the more or less favourable combination of these factors that constitutes their view of climate. Climatology is concerned with these particular effects but also with their overall patterns, both spatially and temporally, and their interconnectedness or otherwise – that is, the extent to which they constitute a system. Climatology is a highly technical subject, yet like certain others (such as archaeology) it is one in which the layman, because of his extensive first-hand experience of the effects of climate, feels able to contribute significantly. Any mention of climatic change or causation in the past sparks off a feeling of awareness as to what is involved. You need only to have visited an upland hillfort to feel that a desertion of those sites through climatic causes was wholly understandable – more than that, that to have occupied them in the first place was flying in the face of climatic fact.

Archaeologists have adopted the idea of climatic change as a causative factor with some enthusiasm. 'Worsening climatic conditions within the sub-Atlantic type [*sic*] may have prompted a degree of migration south from Scandinavia and the Baltic area of the ancestors of some of our well-known tribes of Germanic history . . . The 6th and 7th centuries . . . represent a quiet period in Scandinavian political history, probably associated with the beginnings of a period of climatic amelioration' (Loyn 1977, pp.10–11; cf. Carpenter 1966, or for a more judicious use of climatic evidence, Burgess 1974, pp.195–7). The general mechanism propounded is: change of climate (typically drought or flooding), leading to crop failure over a period of years; a hungry population seeking new pastures in adjacent (or sometimes distant) lands, perhaps after having overthrown their own social order first; the result, war, migration, upheaval, supposedly recognisable archaeologically by new artifact types in given areas. An alternative result is, of course, starvation and consequent population decline. Which of these two possible sequences of events (or any variation on them) is likely to apply in particular instances is rarely considered. It is perhaps even more worrying that climatologists have on occasion drawn on such archaeological reconstructions to lend support to views of climatic change which the archaeologist had assumed were independently proven.

On the other hand, the importance of climatic change, particularly in marginal areas or for undiversified economies, should not be underestimated. Indeed, a whole science is now named after the study of 'the impact of the weather and climate on humans and their environment (animals and plants)' – biometeorology, formerly known as bioclimatology, of which the leading exponent is S. W. Tromp (1980). The effects of climate on all aspects of the biosphere have been exhaustively studied. In the present discussion, one might expect that its impact on flora and fauna would be of most importance, but one should not forget that climate affects human beings directly as well. Heat has been shown to cause an increase in blood pressure and changes in the physico-chemical properties of the blood (Tromp 1980, p.9). Various other parts of the body produce particular adaptive responses to the thermal environment, the best known being those affecting the skin (sweating) or the muscles (shivering) (ibid., pp.88–90), while the principal heat regulatory centre, controlling all aspects of the body's response to temperature, is the hypothalamus (ibid., pp.59ff.). Lest one is tempted to dismiss these facts as of purely medical interest, it is worth quoting the fact that climatic temperature can have direct social effects. Tromp (1980, p.10) quotes the race riots of 1965–7 in Los Angeles, Chicago and Newark (N.J.), which all took place after extended heat-waves; or the Amsterdam riots by construction workers in 1970.

The effects of climate on animals are well known (Tromp 1980, pp.263ff.). The common domesticates are variably equipped to cope with extremes of hot and cold, depending on (for instance) the number of sweat glands they possess, the thickness, colour and sheen of their coats, and so on. Cattle and pigs are ill equipped to deal with high ambient temperatures, quite apart from their drinking water requirements: neither animal sweats much, if at all, which means that they must rely on respiratory ventilation (panting), in the case of temperate cattle, raising the heart rate steeply in temperatures above 25°C. Young pigs, on the other hand, are highly susceptible to cold and are nowadays reared in hot (30°C), humid conditions. Sheep are also susceptible to the cold while young, but are by contrast much better able to cope with heat, apparently because of their ability to reduce brain temperature by panting. It is also of interest to note that animal diseases can be to some extent climate-dependent. The foot-and-mouth disease virus, for instance, 'does not easily survive excessive sunlight and high temperatures; damp cold weather favours survival and spreading' (Tromp 1980, p.309). The same is true for many plant diseases. It is worth remembering, therefore, that historical accounts of famines may be connected with climate only indirectly in this way.

The effects of climate on plants have probably been utilised most of all in the consideration of climatically induced change. Whittle, for instance (below), deals particularly with the effects of relatively small temperature and precipitation rate changes on moorland pasture. Parry (1978) has considered in detail the effects of climate on marginal land in Britain, especially for south-east Scotland in the Medieval period. It is well known that much of Britain's marginal land was intensively cultivated in the Bronze Age, but has since then been unavailable for anything more than rough pasture. In plain language, arable agriculture becomes impossible where temperature, rainfall and length of growing season do not combine favourably (cf. Parry 1978, pp.81–2). Nor should one forget that such unfavourable conditions can relate either to cold/wet situations or to warm/dry ones.

This brings us to consider the social and economic effects of prolonged periods of such conditions, which for the historian and archaeologist is the most significant aspect of the whole business. We may start by considering the two opposite and extreme (though not necessarily long-lasting) cases of climatic change: drought and flooding. That both are still factors of major importance is clear to us from our newspapers, if nothing else. The most widely publicised drought of recent years has been that in the Sahel zone of Africa, south of the Sahara (Lockwood 1979, pp.205ff.). Between 1968 and 1972 rainfall along the desert fringe was only 40 to 60 per cent of the 1931–60 average. The discharge of the Niger river declined by 50 per cent, of the Senegal river by 70 per cent; Lake Chad was reduced in area by 65 per cent. The result has been widespread starvation and population displacement. Cattle losses varied between 50 and 100 per cent, and total *per capita* food production fell by 35 per cent. Millions of people were affected, and hundreds of thousands died.

A less dramatic but equally telling case is that of United States grain yields, which fell drastically during the hot, dry years of the 1930s (Parry 1978, pp.71–2). Comparable effects have been seen in recent decades in the Soviet Union, China and India (Lamb 1977, pp.14–15).

These are modern cases of drought, but of course ancient ones are attested too. Among the most famous we may mention the story of seven years' plenty and seven years' famine recorded in Genesis 41, or the drought successfully brought to an end by Elijah in the reign of Ahab (874–853 BC) recorded in I. Kings 18. Archaeologically, interesting evidence for drought in the late eighth century BC has been adduced by Camp (1979), who bases his theory on both physical and archaeological (or literary) evidence. The latter is circumstantial in the extreme (gaps in early seventh-century cemeteries, peak of offerings at the Sanctuary of Zeus Ombrios on Hymettus, the foundation of Brauron for the cult of Braurian Artemis), but the former, namely the evidence of the large number of wells in the Athenian Agora which went out of use in or around 700

BC, is highly suggestive. Another well-known theory in which drought plays an important part concerns the decline of the Mycenaean civilisation around 1200 BC. Carpenter (1966) was the first to present a detailed argument linking a presumed drought with the undoubted fact that Mycenaean material culture declined and eventually disappeared, though his arguments were general and not reinforced by detailed meteorological (or any other) data. This gap was to some extent filled by Bryson, Lamb and Donley (1974), who showed that a modern precipitation pattern (that of January 1955) did indeed fit the supposed drought pattern of 1200 BC. While the archaeological complexities of the matter were generally underestimated (Dickinson 1974), climatic factors remain attractive as at any rate a contributory cause, but it must be stressed that we totally lack direct evidence for this.

These matters are considered more fully in archaeological contexts by some of the contributors below, for example Bouzek, and Jäger and Ložek.

The effects of sudden excessive rainfall, leading to flooding, are much more immediately dramatic and can be just as disastrous in terms of human survival. One of the best-known recent cases is the 1966 Italian flood disaster. On 4 and 5 November continuous heavy rain caused floods affecting one-third of the total area of the country, flooding two million acres of farmland, causing rivers to burst their banks, and cutting off large areas especially in the Dolomites. An estimated 50,000 animals drowned, including 80 per cent of total livestock in Tuscany; vineyards there and in other provinces were ruined. The village of Mezzano di Primiero in the Alto Adige had to be evacuated because an avalanche of mud and rubble descended on it. In all, 112 lives were lost; the floods were described as the 'worst in the recorded history of Italy' (Keesing Contemporary Archives, 3–10 December 1966, pp.21743–4). Many other comparable cases could be cited, ranging from such major disasters as those affecting Bangladesh in recent years, to episodes like the Lynmouth affair (Bell, below).

These are sudden, dramatic events; but dampness of climate and/or coldness can be just as important for its longer-term effects. I have already referred to the situation in the marginal areas of Britain, but the effects of climatic dampness are felt in many areas not today regarded as marginal. Continuing cool damp weather in the summer significantly reduces the quality and quantity of grain yields, by causing sprouting on the ear, mildew or rot, and flattened crops. Care must be used in speculating on the precise parameters of past climates, however; the summer of 1980, universally regarded by the British population as a bad one, in fact produced a record harvest.

The archaeological record provides evidence for flooding in plenty. Most notable are lake-shore settlements as for example in the Alpine area (cf. Joos, below). One thing that is quite clear about most of these sites is that they came to an end with an episode of lake-level rise. Preserved sites are overlain by lake muds and often contain huge amounts of cultural material including new and unused objects. It surely seems appropriate to suggest that flooding episodes of the 1966 variety are responsible for this archaeological situation: a period of prolonged rainfall saturated the ground and raised river and lake levels; this was followed by a storm which rapidly flooded the entire lake-shore site in a few hours. Such discontinuities are indeed only to be expected. Significant though such desertions are, they tell us little about the real nature of either climate or society in the periods in question. We should for this be looking to much more widespread effects; one of the main lessons of these researches has been that it is dangerous to extrapolate from one or two sites to whole regions where climate is concerned.

Climatic changes can, then, be assumed to have operated in prehistory at least as frequently as they do today, and with consequences that were much more alarming to the people who lived through them. We have seen that on the one hand there were general climatic trends which led to significant changes in mean temperatures, rainfall or attendant effects, and lasted for several decades or more. The Little Ice Age is a classic instance of this. On the other hand, there were sudden, dramatic and short-term – a few years or less – variations in temperature, rainfall or wind direction, such as are discernible in flooding episodes and site desertions in numerous parts of the archaeological (and contemporary) record. But between these two extremes there are all sorts of intermediate stages: in particular, one should not underestimate the speed with which major climatic shifts can occur. A displacement of normal air-flows which disrupts the westerly wind reaching north-west Europe (to take one example near home) can have a dramatic effect in only a few years as cold water and air from the polar regions move southwards (cf. Lamb, below). It is a popular misconception that major climatic shifts take a long time to develop, such that one man in his lifetime would hardly notice the difference. When, as actually happens, these shifts bring about significant cooling or warming episodes, especially when they are connected with insufficient or excessive rainfall, the effects rapidly become noticeable, and each year that they are repeated compounds the magnitude of the socio-economic implications.

Change of climate in later prehistory: principal sources of evidence

The papers in this volume are specifically concerned with a segment of time in the Holocene between about 8000 and 2000 years ago. 'Later prehistory' in this context means, broadly speaking, the Neolithic, Bronze and Iron Ages. While scientifically the logic behind such a chronological restriction may seem fallible (and indeed many palaeoclimatologists, including some contributors to this volume, would regard this span of 6000 years as no more than the filling of a very thick sandwich) archaeologically it makes sense in that groupings, prior to the postglacial warm period, are of a quite different nature to those after it; while the advent of historical sources renders the nature of the archaeology practised very different. The Neolithic, Bronze and Iron Ages constitute a segment of human development that is internally consistent in its sources of evidence and the way people use them; they are, moreover, periods for which – unlike the Palaeolithic or Mesolithic – few detailed climatic data have been adduced.

Lamb (1977, ch.13, and below) has considered the sources of evidence for past climate in exhaustive detail. Many of the sources he lists, however, are not applicable to the period under review, for instance the direct climatic records maintained by scientific observers over the last 300 years, or even casual mentions of weather phenomena such as occur in earlier writings. Such records do, however, serve a very useful function as controls when we come to consider the indirect, or proxy, data which are our principal informants. They also serve a useful analogical function.

Of the methods derived from physical science, tree-rings, lichen growth, varves, ice-sheet stratigraphy and flow are all primarily dating tools which have, however, been studied for their climatic potential (cf. Pilcher and Hughes, below). A variety of techniques also exists that bears directly on past climates, including especially isotope ratios. Oxygen isotope measurements, for example, relate directly to ocean temperature, whether measured on deep sea cores, sea water, or ice; carbon isotopes (C_{13}/C_{12}) have also been used to demonstrate environmental (and specifically climatic) change in the Post-glacial (Mörner and Wallin 1977). Water and sediment chemistry may hold some hope for postglacial climatic reconstruction, as Pennington and Lishman (1971) have shown for the English lakes.

Water levels in seas, lakes and rivers form another broad category of evidence. The evidence of sea-levels is undoubtedly relevant to our period but the complications have so far outweighed the positive results (cf. Shennan, below). The broad outline is clear; it is the detailed interpretation and correlation of smaller fluctuations that remains problematical (but for an interpretation that relates to the British Isles as a whole, and is written in fairly definite terms, see Tooley 1981). Lake levels, on the other hand, are more directly connected with climatic phenomena since lakes are fed by rivers that drain hills and mountains and should therefore be related to precipitation over the catchment area (cf. Joos, below). For river levels there is little direct evidence bearing on later prehistory: the best known is the series of Egyptian records going back to the Old Kingdom recording the flood level of the Nile (Bell 1970, 1971). Related to these water levels is the question of glacier variation, alluded to by Beug and Joos (below), and demonstrated by Manley (1966, 1974) to show good correlation with temperature records in recent times.

Other methods derived from physical science concern the development of soils and sediments, which are discussed by Bell, Keeley, and Jäger and Ložek (below).

The evidence for climatic change derived from biological science is perhaps better known, and may be dealt with more rapidly. Paramount here are the related disciplines of pollen analysis and peat stratigraphy, both of which have made crucial contributions to the period in question (Beug, Barber, below). The study of insects, beetles and molluscs also provides environmental data (Osborne, Ložek, below) for which climatic interpretations are possible.

Synthesis

The archaeologist who seeks to make use of the scientific information contained in this volume will inevitably find that it can both confirm and contradict his hypotheses. If one were to take all the possible pointers to climatic change in later prehistory and attempt to correlate them with observed cultural changes, success of some sort would be assured since such pointers are very numerous. Similarly, correlations between indicators of climatic change derived from different sources appear to have a high chance of success. Such correlations have traditionally been used by archaeologists seeking background data to the periods under study; and have often appeared in the literature as hard fact. That this is not the case can be seen very clearly from a number of these papers. Pollen diagrams, for example, typically show continuous fluctuation in most species. Of the various factors influencing the pollen rain, climate is one of the most important, but climate change cannot easily be used as an influencing factor of equal potency in every case. Especially in a post-Mesolithic context the influence of human activities has constantly to be borne in mind, and to attribute all pollen fluctuations to climatic causes alone would be most unwise. Even in the Mesolithic and earlier it is common for pollen analysts to seek out what are supposedly the most significant points of change on their diagrams, where either one species changes drastically, or several species change concomitantly on a smaller scale. Even then it is not always possible to be sure that some of the effects are not rather due to the increase-climax-decrease cycle of particular species in particular environments, or to the method of presentation most commonly employed, in which all values in a given spectrum are interdependent. Certainly it would be naive to suppose that climate could constantly be invoked, and in later prehistory it would be rash indeed to underestimate the effects of human activity. Extreme caution is necessary, therefore, in applying any of these results to archaeological data, but this is not to say it should not be done. The outline of the gross changes has been reasonably clear for many years – for instance the start of the Sub-atlantic; it is the finer fluctuations which are the harder to pin down, and the more so as those fluctuations are by no means represented in all the types of record available, or at all locations (though climatologists seem to agree that significant climatic changes do occur on a more or less world-wide scale, even if some of the correlations are inverse). In this connection, the fluctuations of lake-level in the subalpine region are of especial importance because, as Joos makes clear, they reflect the precipitation rate over the lake catchment, and they clearly affected human settlement on the lake margins. The movements of glaciers in the same region have also been shown to be closely connected with mean temperatures and offer great scope for palaeoclimatic reconstruction.

No attempt will be made here to provide a synthesising summary or chart which would distil the results of this and other conferences. Frustrating though this may be for the archaeologist seeking to know the definitive answer to questions of ancient climate, it would, for the reasons outlined above, be

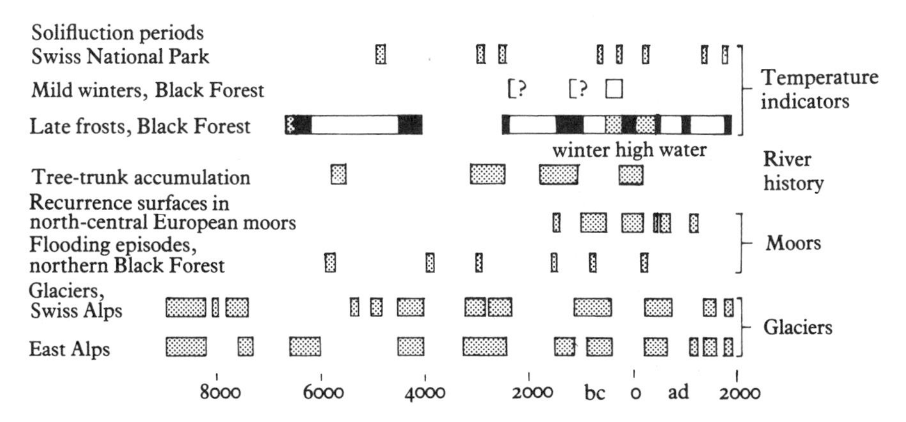

Figure 1. Climatic fluctuations in the Holocene in south-west Germany according to Frenzel (1978). Shaded areas represent cool/wet episodes according to a variety of different sources, as indicated.

methodologically indefensible. Instead, for a demonstration of how the combination of techniques can lead to the building up of a picture of climate of at any rate local application, the reader is referred to the work of Frenzel (1966, 1978), who has made a specialism of summarising Holocene climatic change. Figure 1 presents one of his recent summarising charts for central Europe (south-west Germany and adjacent areas), where the evidence from various different indicators is assembled in summary form. As far as the European Neolithic, Bronze and Iron Ages are concerned, we may note two significant cool/wet phases during the Neolithic (4500–4000 bc and 3200–2400 bc, with smaller fluctuations), one during the middle of the second millennium bc (Middle Bronze Age, cf. Joos), and another (the start of the Sub-atlantic) starting around 1000 bc and continuing to about 400 bc. These may be the broad outlines of the period, but they are hardly sufficient for assessing archaeological effects; for that, evidence such as Jäger and Ložek present will be indispensable. Indeed, it may yet be that archaeology has a crucial role to play in assisting climatologists in the correlation of climatic episodes. The flooding of an archaeological site took place in a very short space of time and is potentially exactly datable by means of dendrochronology. Most climatologists, on the other hand, are dealing with cooling and warming periods which available indicators would spread over a period of many years, even centuries. The data of archaeology and of palaeoclimatology are not closely comparable, yet each can provide the other with surprising insights.

To the extent that climate was only one of a number of environmental variables which operated on prehistoric living systems, climatic change should not be overestimated as a potential moulder of human socio-economic development in prehistory. The pervasive nature of climate, however, and its potentially far-reaching effects ensure that human adaptations, today as in the past, must bear regard to climatic factors even if they were not solely a response to them. In this respect climate is truly a part of the system for which data must actively be sought.

REFERENCES

Bell, B. (1970) The oldest records of the Nile floods, *Geogr. J.* 136 (4), 569-73.

— (1971) The Dark Ages in ancient history, 1: The first Dark Age in Egypt, *Am. J. Archaeol.* 75, 1-26.

Bryson, R. A., H. H. Lamb & D. L. Donley (1974) Drought and the decline of Mycenae, *Antiquity* 48, 46-50.

Burgess, C. (1974) The Bronze Age, in Renfrew, C. (ed.) *British Prehistory: a New Outline*, 165-232. London: Duckworth.

Camp, J. McK. (1979) A drought in the late eighth century BC, *Hesperia* 48, 397-411.

Carpenter, R. (1966) *Discontinuity in Greek Civilisation.* Cambridge: University Press.

Dickinson, O. T. P. K. (1974) Drought and the decline of Mycenae: some comments, *Antiquity* 48, 228-9.

Frenzel, B. (1966) Climatic change in the Atlantic / Sub-boreal transition on the northern hemisphere: botanical evidence, in Sawyer, J. S. (ed.) *World Climate 8000-0 BC*, 99-123. London: Royal Meteorological Society.

— (1978) Postglaziale Klimaschwankungen im südwestlichen Mitteleuropa, in Frenzel, B. (ed.) *Dendrochronologie und postglaziale Klimaschwankungen in Europa*, 297-322. Wiesbaden: Steiner.

Lamb, H. H. (1977) *Climate: Present, Past and Future. 2. Climatic History and the Future.* London: Methuen.

Lockwood, J. G. (1979) *Causes of Climate.* London: Edward Arnold.

Loyn, H. R. (1977) *The Vikings in Britain.* London: Batsford.

Manley, G. (1966) Problems of the climatic optimum: the contribution of glaciology, in Sawyer, J. S. (ed.) *World Climate 8000-0 BC*, 34-9. London: Royal Meteorological Society.

— (1974) Central England temperatures: monthly means 1659-1973, *Q. J. R. Meteorol. Soc.* 100, 389-405.

Mörner, N.-A. & G. Wollin (1977) A palaeotemperature curve from Gotland, Sweden, *Palaeogeogr., Palaeoclim., Palaeoecol.* 15.

Parry, M. L. (1978) *Climatic Change, Agriculture and Settlement.* Folkestone: Dawson.

Pennington, W. & J. P. Lishman (1971) Iodine in lake sediments in northern England and Scotland, *Biol. Rev.* 46, 279-313.

Tooley, M. J. (1981) (Sections on sea-levels) In Simmons, I. G. and Tooley, M. J., *The Environment in British Prehistory.* London: Duckworth.

Tromp, S. W. (1980) *Biometeorology. The Impact of the Weather and Climate on Humans and their Environment (Animals and Plants).* London: Heyden.

Reconstruction of the course of postglacial climate over the world

Introduction : the climate system[1]

The continual changes of weather extend to all time-scales. So the climate too is forever changing. Sometimes the changes are slight, sometimes big. Sometimes they are gradual, but sometimes sharp. To understand how these things happen, and how we can reconstruct in outline the past record, we must first look briefly at how climate is generated and how the system works.

The climate of any place is produced by:

i) *the radiation balance,* that is the local balance of gain and loss of heat by radiation – which varies with the angle of elevation of the sun and the length of day, in other words with latitude and season.

ii) *the balance of heat, and similarly the moisture, brought and carried away by the winds and ocean currents.*

iii) *characteristics of the locality,* such as

a) *aspect,* that is slope towards or away from the midday sun and the prevailing winds.

b) *thermal characteristics* (specific heat and thermal conductivity) *of the soil and vegetation cover,* particularly as regards moisture content which, if it is high, makes for only sluggish changes of temperature.

c) *reflectivity* (or *'albedo'*), that is what proportion of the incoming radiation is reflected away and how much is absorbed. The greatest differences arise between the low reflectivity of most vegetation-covered surfaces (sometimes under 10 per cent) and the higher figures for parched grasslands and especially deserts (up to 40–45 per cent) and fresh snow (80–90 per cent).

d) *topographical effects upon the winds,* that is friction and channelling, uplift and downward eddies. Among the vertical motions caused by the topography we may include thermal uplift due to unequal heating of different slopes and the downslope drainage of dense cold air formed by night cooling of the upland surfaces under clear skies. The latter sometimes produces accumulations of very cold air in valley bottoms (frost hollows) and formidable wind strengths where the downward flowing air converges in narrow valleys. And the whole pattern of uplift and downdraught on either side of hills and mountains has very strong effects on the cloudiness and amounts of rain and snowfall.

The most important part of the mechanism of climate and climatic changes

1. Because of the wide range of topics covered in this paper full referencing is not provided. The reader is referred to Lamb (1972) and (1977), where extensive bibliographies may be found.

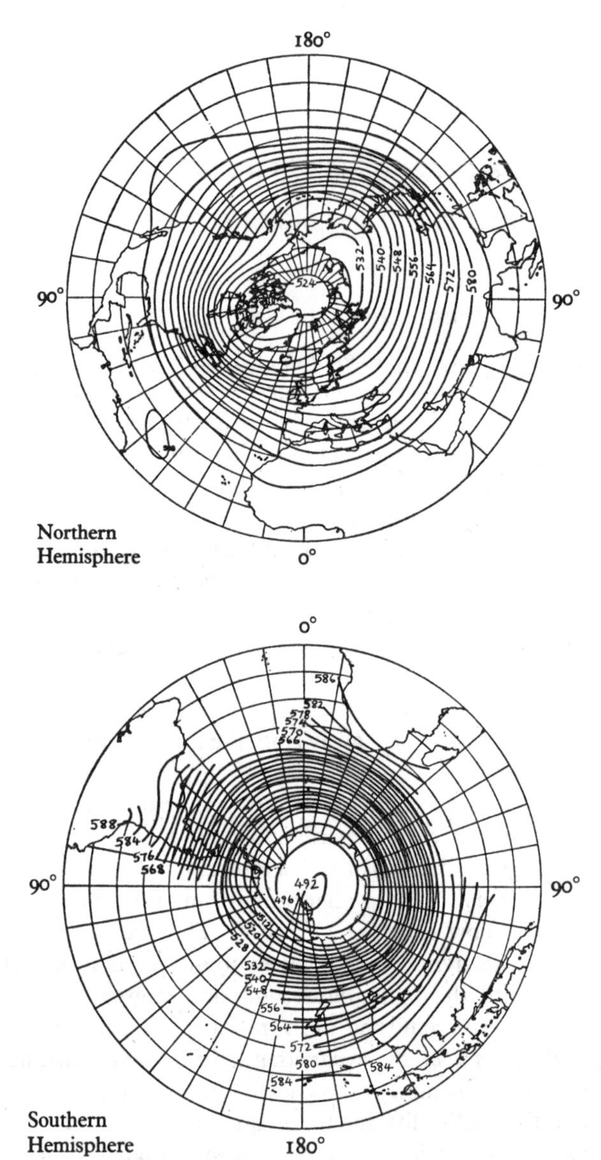

Figure 1. The circumpolar vortex, shown here by the contours (decametres) of the 500 millibar pressure level, averaged over several years in the 1950s. The winds blow anti-clockwise around the low pressure in the northern hemisphere, clockwise in the southern hemisphere, giving upper westerly winds over the middle latitudes of both hemispheres.

is the wind circulation (see, e.g., Lamb 1972).

Air, like most other substances, expands when it is heated unless extra pressure is exerted to prevent expansion. Hence, the upper layers of the atmosphere are lifted over the warmer parts of the Earth and sink over the cold zones. This produces the simple pattern of atmospheric pressure in the upper air seen in figure 1, with high pressure over the tropical zone and lower pressure over the polar regions, north and south. This lifting of the upper atmosphere over the most strongly heated regions is how the incoming radiation puts potential energy into the wind circulation. But on the rotating Earth the winds flow not so much from high to low pressure as along the lines of constant pressure. So the maps in figure 1 define a circumpolar vortex or flow of the upper winds from west to east around both hemispheres. The strongest flow is generally over middle latitudes, where the pole-to-equator temperature gradient is strongest. And, because the pattern is so similar through a great depth of the atmosphere from about 2 to 15 or 20 km above the Earth's surface, this is the main flow of the atmosphere, carrying most of the momentum.

The more complex and more numerous features of the surface pressure map, the anticyclones and depressions or cyclones, are created by local piling up or 'pumping out' of air caused by imbalance between the flow of air in the vast upper vortex and the forces acting upon it – places where the air departs somewhat from flow along the lines of constant pressure, where the curvature is too great or the gradient changes. On average, surface low pressure systems (depressions, cyclonic storms) are generated in, or near, the zone of strongest upper flow and end their lives near the cold flank of the upper wind system, maintaining on average low surface pressure there. Surface pressure is generally high along the warm flank of the zone of strong upper winds. There is also high surface pressure over the polar regions further away from the strong upper wind zone and particularly where the low air is very cold and dense. Comparison of figure 2 with figure 1 shows these relationships. And this determines the prevailing surface winds (figure 3), which blow rather more across the isobars towards the lower pressure regions, especially over land where the friction is strong. There are prevailing westerlies over middle latitudes and easterlies over low latitudes (the Trade Winds) and more variable easterlies over high latitudes.

The circumpolar vortex is subject to variations in the strength and latitude of the main flow, both seasonally and over longer and shorter periods when heating or cooling of the Earth contracts or expands the regions of polar cold. It also displays a wavy, meandering form owing to the effects of mountain barriers, heating differences within the latitude zones, and the dynamics of the flow itself. Very vigorous surface wind systems distort the temperature distribution and therewith distort the pattern of the circumpolar vortex itself. So the amplitude or range of latitudes swept by the waves (or meanders) of the upper flow varies. And this changes for the time being the whole pattern of prevailing winds, cloudiness and weather, and steers the developing storms (and the anticyclones) on different tracks. Some types of variant of the circumpolar

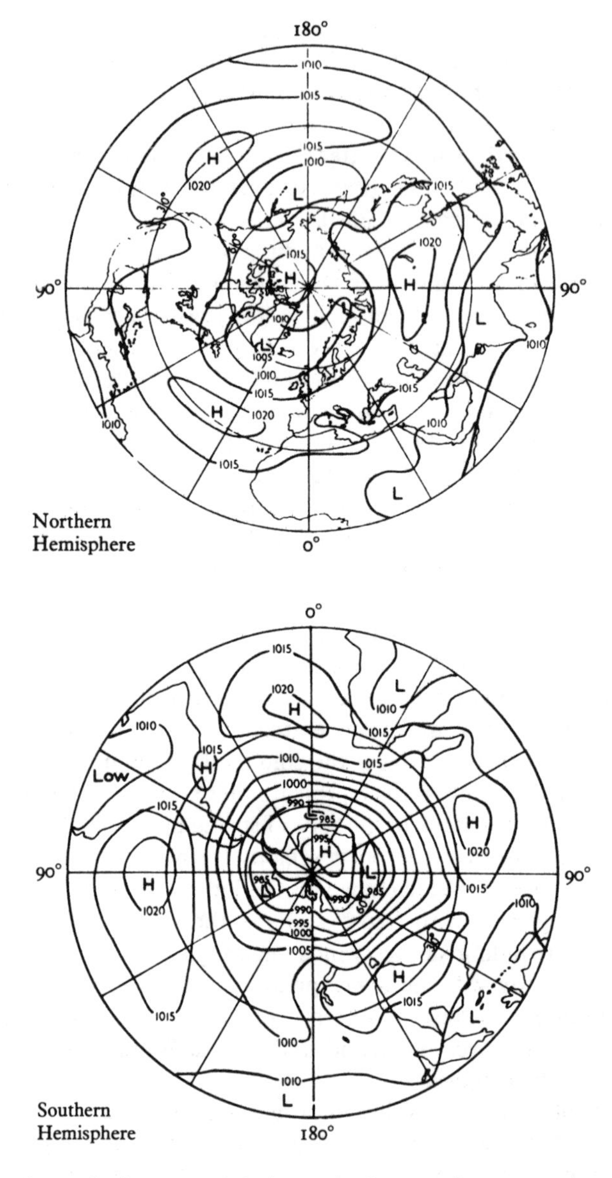

Figure 2. Atmospheric pressure (mbar) at sea level, averaged over approximately the first half of this century.

vortex are shown in figure 4. In the case of the sharpest, biggest amplitude 'troughs' and 'ridges' in the flow the upper winds can hardly be said to be westerly at all. Surface weather systems may be steered northwards or southwards or may become nearly stationary for long periods. Such stationary situations are called 'blocking patterns', because the usual upper westerlies over middle latitudes appear blocked or diverted, and surface winds from the east may actually prevail over parts of the middle latitudes. Northerly and southerly winds also become more prominent in parts of the middle latitude zone, bringing spells of unusual cold or warmth, and, if the systems are displaced somewhat from one spell (or one year) to the next, unusually big variations occur.

Great changes from normal also occur in the winds, weather and cloudiness owing to the displacement of the storm tracks leading to prevalence of winds from the other side of some coasts, hills and mountain chains. An example of the pattern of one particular season with large amplitude waves in the circumpolar vortex is shown in figure 5.

Despite these variations, the spacing around the hemisphere of the waves in the upper flow downstream from the major disturbance, anchored for the time being by a mountain barrier such as the Rockies, or by a large region of anomalous warmth in the ocean or of snow and ice on one of the continents, is governed by a simple dynamical law. The wave length, or spacing, increases as the upper flow gets stronger or moves to higher latitudes. So the wave length to be expected can be calculated, and so indeed can the probable development of surface low and high pressure systems. And it is the simplicity of form of the circumpolar vortex and its variations, as well as the intimate associations between it and the prevailing surface pressure pattern and developments, that make it possible to reconstruct in outline the whole global (or hemispheric) pattern of past climates from fragmentary and sparsely scattered data.

To complete this section, we must also notice the general circulation of the surface ocean currents (figure 6). The similarities to the pattern of wind circulation are due to the fact that the ocean circulation is largely driven by the drag of the winds on the ocean surface. And so, when the wind pattern shifts or changes, there are shifts and changes in the movement of the water on the ocean surface. And at some points such shifts may cause big changes in the current pattern. One example is where even a 1 or 2° of latitude shift, north or south, of the Trade Wind systems fanning the Equatorial current across the surface of the South Atlantic, as has happened over long periods within the last 150 years, must make a big difference to the supply of equatorial water moving north of the nose of Brazil (Cape of São Roque) into the Caribbean to feed the Gulf Stream. Another example, much closer to Europe, is the shifts of the boundary between the warm, saline Gulf Stream water and the cold, less saline polar water in the north-east Atlantic (Lamb 1979). A history of the dramatic displacements of this boundary is seen in figure 7.

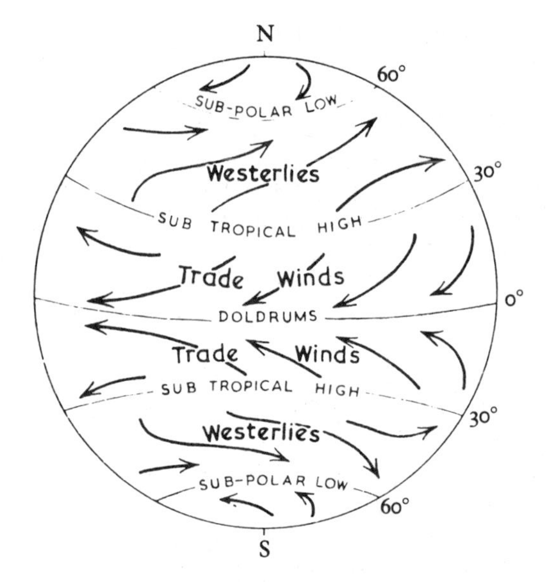

Figure 3. Prevailing surface winds in different latitudes, simplified.

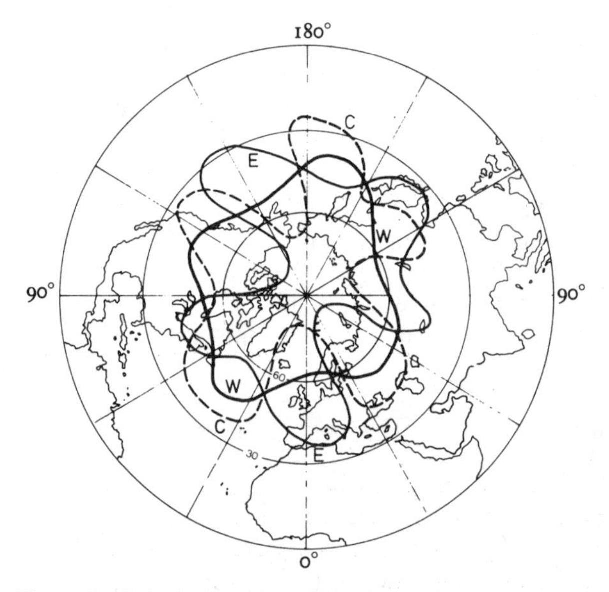

Figure 4. Types of variation in the pattern of wind flow in the circumpolar vortex, illustrated by the course of a constant pressure line in the middle of the zone of strongest flow on individual days (schematic). The line marked W (westerly) is about as near an approximation as ever arises in practice to a smooth 'zonal' flow around the latitude hemisphere in a nearly constant latitude. The other patterns illustrated are two different 'blocking' patterns, marked C and E, distinguished from each other by the positions of the (cold) troughs and the (warm) ridges. The classification is a Russian one, by Wangenheim and Girs. Most 'blocking', or 'meridional', patterns are less extreme – not such long stretches of northerly and southerly flow – as in this schematic illustration.

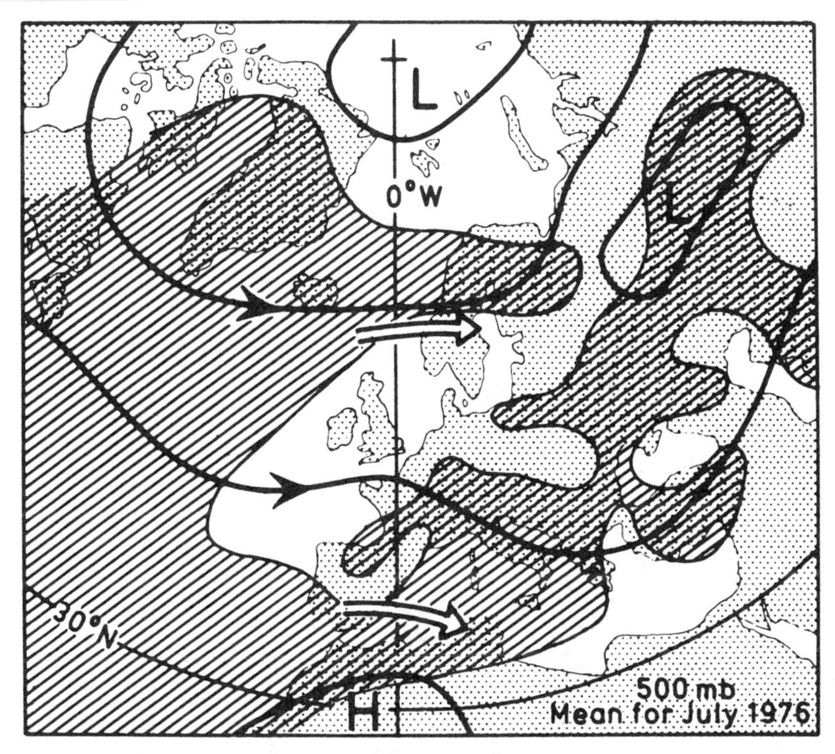

Figure 5. The average flow pattern in the part of the circumpolar vortex over the northern Atlantic, Europe and the Arctic in July 1976, an historic warm month in and near the British Isles. The areas of diagonal hatching had above-average rainfall – note their association with the 'troughs' in the circumpolar vortex in this map and in figure 4. Map by J.S.A.Green, reproduced with his kind permission.

The evidence of past climates : general

The kinds of evidence for past weather and climate (Lamb 1977) – although multifarious because nearly every aspect of our lives and environment is affected by weather – may be classed in just three groups:

i) Regular observations using meteorological instruments.

ii) Descriptive reports – not including instrument measurements – of the weather by observers living at the time, entered in diaries, in some cases in specially kept weather registers, and in various annals, chronicles, account books and state papers, also daily in the logs of ships at sea or in port.

iii) Fossil, or 'proxy', data rendered into derived climatic indications by the physical and biological sciences.

Deductions from written human history and archaeology can only be used in a very few cases where the physical implications are unambiguous. Examples of such cases are, for instance, where a former route of communication becomes cut off by the development of desert or marsh, glaciers or increasingly stormy seas. Thus, there is no danger of arguing in a circle or inventing

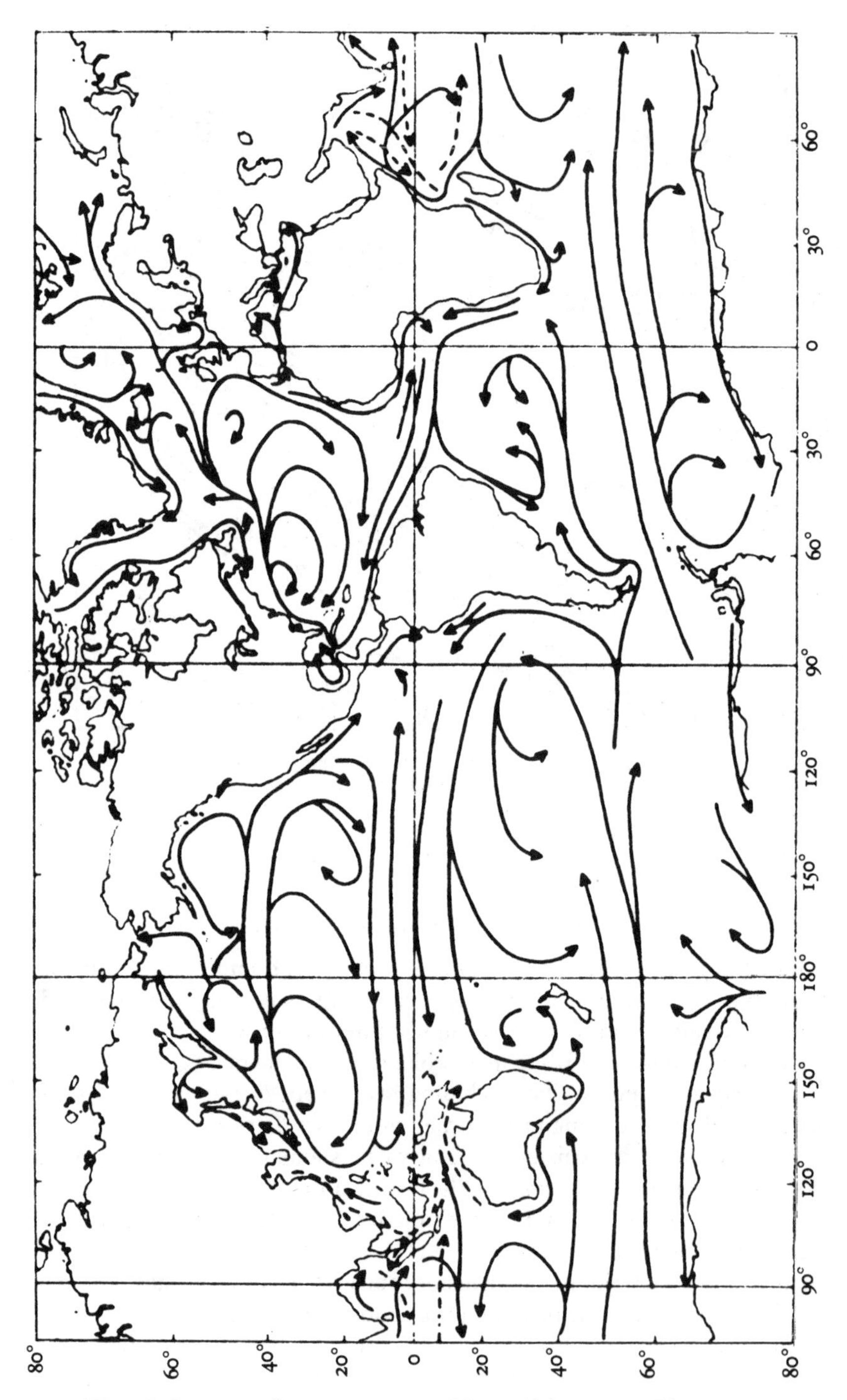

Figure 6. Average surface ocean currents of the world (present epoch).

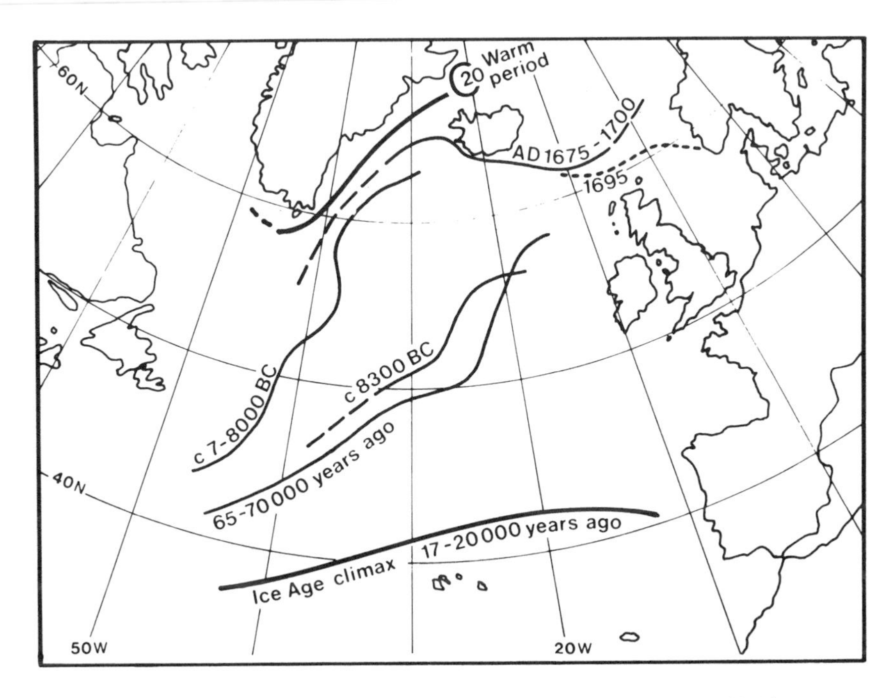

Figure 7. Average positions of the boundary between warm saline water of Gulf Stream origin and the polar water in the surface of the North Atlantic Ocean at various epochs.

climatic changes to explain the changes in human history.

In general, Man and the larger animals are too adaptable and too mobile for safe deductions about climatic changes to be made from their actions, though such things as the abandonment of settlements and tillage may provide confirmation of changes diagnosed by other means, and may throw light on how climate history affected human affairs and the economy. Such records as the prices of wheat and rye may also be added to the types of proxy climatic data that are useful, provided enough is known about the record to identify and eliminate variations due to other than climatic causes (such as wars, depopulation by disease or civil unrest, etc.).

Instrument records

The main meteorological instruments – barometer, thermometer and rain-gauge – first came into use in Europe during the seventeenth century (see Lamb 1977) and the longest continuous records of their measurements start in a few areas from just a few decades after their invention or first use. A tremendous amount of very prolonged, painstaking work has been involved in critical scrutiny of the behaviour and exposure of the earliest instruments (Manley 1953, 1974), the units used and other practices of the observer, and

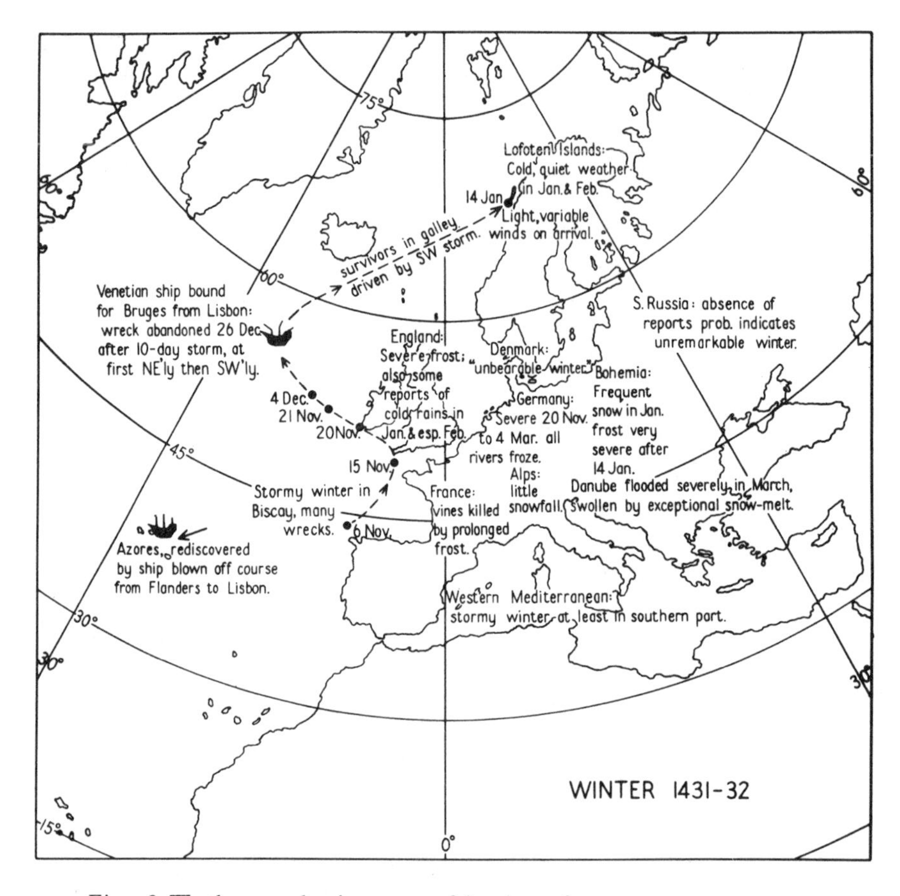

Figure 8. Weather map showing reports of the winter of 1431–2.

the comparison of records overlapping in time from places not too far apart, to obtain standardised, acceptably homogeneous records of temperature, rainfall and barometric pressure, representative of this or that area back to the seventeenth or eighteenth century in a few parts of the world – mostly in Europe (Rudloff 1967) but also from isolated points in eastern North America and the Far East. Fortunately, these areas from which the longest records come are in the zone of the northern hemisphere westerlies and they can be used to derive indications of the behaviour of that major wind system – essentially the patterns of the circumpolar vortex.

It should also be possible to produce a record of the Indian monsoons back to the late eighteenth century, and by using descriptive reports indicating the dates and broadly the abundance of the monsoon rains, this record may be extended to the seventeenth century, for both India and the Far East (China, Korea and Taiwan). The rain-gauge and the wind-vane were invented long before the other instruments. Both were used in parts of the Roman world in

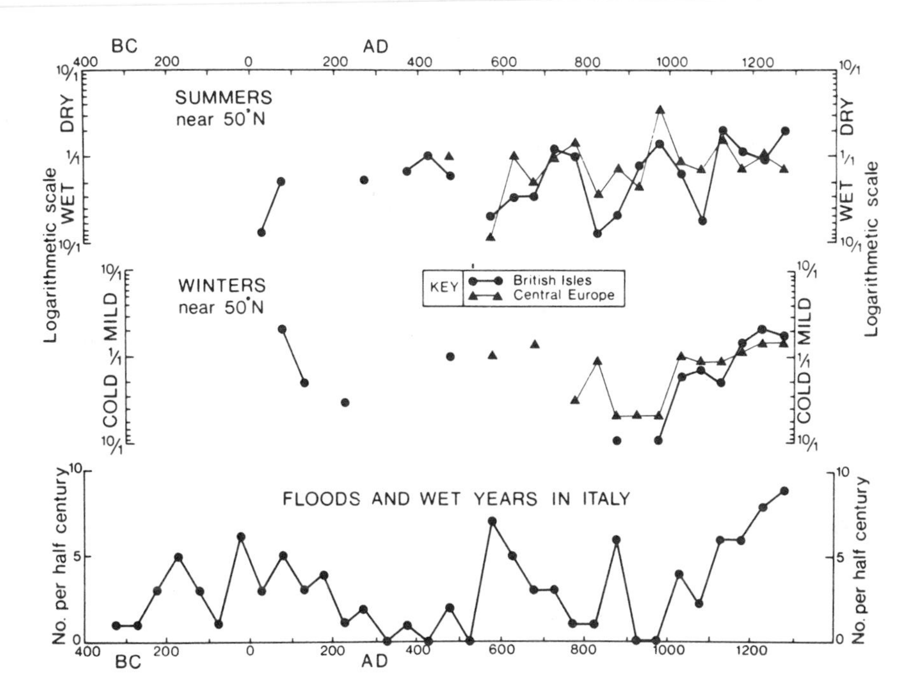

Figure 9. Prevailing character of the summers and winters reported in Europe in the first millennium AD, and the frequency of reports of floods and wet years in Italy from 350 BC to the Middle Ages, by half centuries.

classical times, and rain-gauges are known to have been used in parts of India and in Korea in early times, but the records of their measurements have been lost.

The longest instrument record which we have is that of the temperatures prevailing in central England since 1659.

Daily weather registers enable us to view the changing frequency of days of westerly winds, often regarded as the most basic feature of Britain's so-called maritime climate but actually subject to long-term variations of 50 per cent or more. The complete daily record of weather maps covering the British Isles goes back to 1861, with the addition of six complete years in the 1780s and some sixty days based on the descriptive reports in ships' logs etc. from the historic Spanish Armada summer of 1588. A complete daily record of surface winds observed in the London area goes back to 1668 and this can be extended from various types of indicator and occasional daily records in nearby parts of Europe back to the daily record of observations – without instruments, of course – by the Reverend Father Merle in Lincolnshire from 1340 to 1344.

Descriptive accounts

An example of the possible use of records of seasonal weather and its effects in historical documents is shown in the assembly of reports of the winter of 1431–2 in Europe and the North Atlantic in figure 8. The winter was clearly a severe one dominated by anticyclones over Scandinavia and bitter-cold easterly winds over the European plain and British Isles. There were six or seven winters in that same decade with spells of weather of this type.

Indices (Lamb 1977) defined by the relative frequency of reports of unambiguously very cold or very mild winters, and of summers marred by serious droughts or flooding, in various parts of Europe from east to west, make it possible to trace shifts of the influence of the repeated occurrence of troughs or ridges in the upper westerlies and the weather systems they generate. From these, the prevailing length and positions of the waves in the upper westerlies, and hence the strength and the latitude of the strongest flow (and storm tracks), can be assessed back to AD 1100 and perhaps even earlier.

Some descriptive accounts of the weather exist for the previous millennium. Although the reports are too sparse for great confidence or much detail to be derived, they do seem to give a consistent account of the weather sequence (figure 9) which is confirmed by various types of fossil data.

Proxy climate records : fossil data types

Data under this heading are of many types, so many that it is impossible here to mention more than a few of the most important kinds (for more extensive discussion, see Lamb 1977). There has been a great development of new kinds of data and techniques since about 1950, and of data-gathering enterprises, so that our information is enormously increased. Perhaps the most important development has been that the diversity of data now offers many opportunities for the independent corroboration of conclusions which the analysis of each had suggested.

Furthermore, numerical methods and computation facilities have greatly facilitated the conversion of proxy data to probable values of temperature or rainfall etc., with their margins of uncertainty; one should beware of claiming too much for this, however, since proxy records registering the effects of climate are often produced by combinations and sequences of developments such that the facts observed could have been produced in several different ways.

Our first knowledge of the course of postglacial climatic development was obtained from pollen analysis (usefully summarised in, for instance, Iversen 1973). One of the longest of such records of vegetation is from near the Vosges Mountains in Alsace (Woillard 1978) and extends back in great detail right through the last ice age. A typical result indicating, at least, in broad terms, the history of the vegetation in East Anglia (Godwin 1975) since early postglacial times is shown in figure 10. It is obvious that an early predominance of birch trees was followed successively by pine and then elm and oak, and soon the

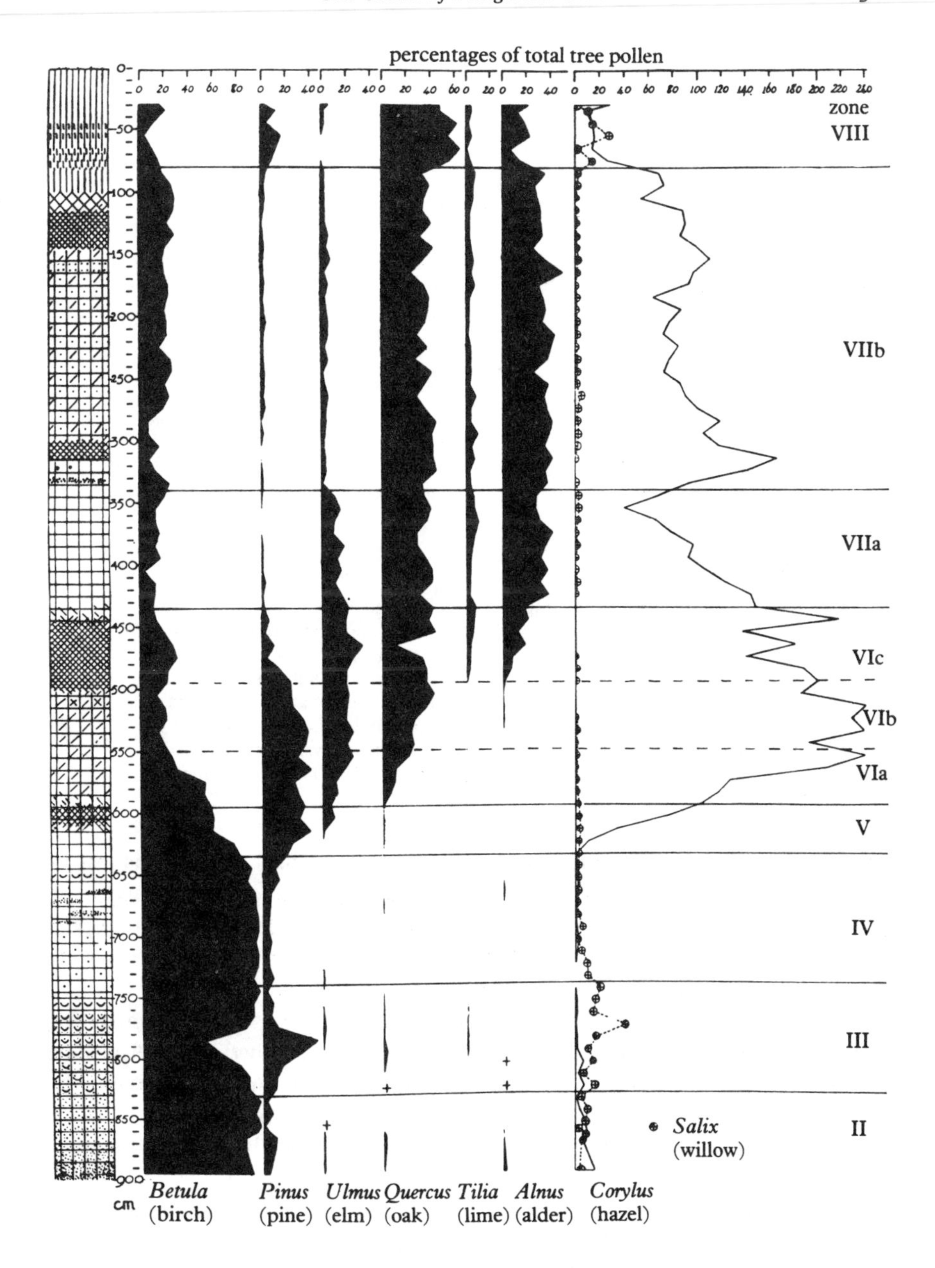

Figure 10. Variations in pollen frequency at different depths (age increasing downwards) deposited in Hockham Mere, East Anglia, through postglacial times.

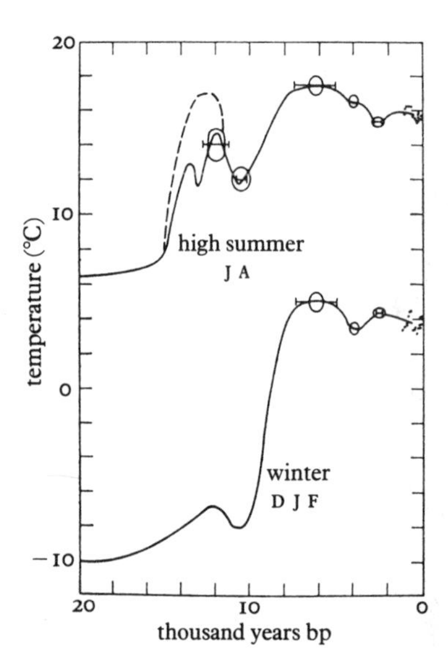

Figure 11. Temperatures prevailing in central England over the last 20,000 years, mainly from pollen analysis before the last 1200 years, when statistical analysis of reported weather, and after 1659 thermometer readings, have been used. The broken line shows an adjustment suggested by G.R.Coope's analysis of beetle fauna. Oval plots indicate the range of uncertainty of temperature values and radiocarbon dates, horizontal bars show the apparent duration of the régime indicated by the plots, and dots are mean temperatures derived for individual centuries in the last millennium. JA = July/August, DJF = December/January/February.

addition of much alder. Ever since mid-postglacial times the elm has lost its earlier position; indeed, adjustments which are now understood as necessary for the different pollen productivity of different tree species make it appear that not oak but elm, and in Denmark elm and lime (linden) trees, were dominant in the forests in this latitude before the decline of the elm. It is also now understood that the thermal climate suitable for these warmth-demanding trees may have existed in England and Europe generally north of the Alps long before the trees arrived from their Ice Age refuges far away beyond the mountains. An indication of how quickly the temperatures rose after the Ice Age may be better given by the quicker response achieved by the insect faunas, as indicated in figure 11.

Great advantages for diagnosis of climatic conditions lie in the study of the abundance of insects, pollens and micro-organisms, which are entirely at the mercy of the environmental conditions in which they find themselves; because of the large numbers in which they occur they lend themselves to statistical studies. In the best cases, where the geographical limit of certain species is climatically determined, probable values of the temperatures or rainfall implied can be deduced.

Similarly, studies of the distributions of different species of marine micro-organisms (foraminifera, radiolaria etc.) in the deposits on the ocean bed yield information on the probable sea-water temperatures prevailing either at the surface or in the ocean depths, depending on where the creatures lived. Such studies on thousands of ocean bed sediment cores have made possible global surveys of past ocean surface temperatures and water temperature histories at many points.

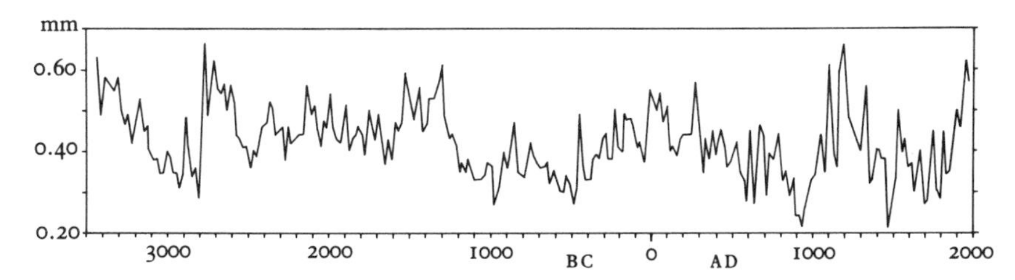

Figure 12. Variations of growth (20-year means from 3431 BC) in Bristlecone pine trees near the upper tree line on the White Mountains, California. (From work by V.C.LaMarche, Laboratory of Tree-Ring Research, University of Arizona, Tucson.)

An essential part of all these studies is the dating of the samples of the deposits, whether on land or sea, that are being studied. Radiometric methods, such as radiocarbon tests, are subject to error margins and calibration difficulties, which in some cases affect the ages by 10 per cent or more. Another limitation arises from the difficulties of time resolution within the column of a slowly accumulating deposit. Pollen analysis of samples from peat bogs can seldom be referred to a date with an error margin of less than 100 to 200 years. In ocean bed deposits the sample must more usually be taken to represent conditions averaged over a period of one to two thousand years. This is because of the usually very slow accumulation rate of the deposit and the activity of boring animals which effectively stir up the uppermost layer.

Since some climatic changes in the past seem to have taken place astonishingly quickly, and changes in the prevailing winds and occurrence of blocking today are observed to be more or less instantaneous, any types of 'fossil' evidence which reveal as discrete layers the events of individual years assume special importance. The most obvious types are tree-rings, varves or year-layers in lake-beds, and the year-layers in ice-sheets. Studies are necessary to establish just what climatic conditions produce the responses registered in any record of these types, and interpretation is by no means always straightforward. But the dating is in some cases reliable to the particular year, and it may at best be possible to diagnose changes within the seasons of an individual year. The longest of these precisely dated records is that of tree-growth at the upper tree-line in California (figure 12) back to 3431 BC. It is surprising that the possibilities offered by records of these types have not so far been used to analyse the course of events year by year during some of the quickest and most drastic climatic changes known, which show up well here (as around 1350 to

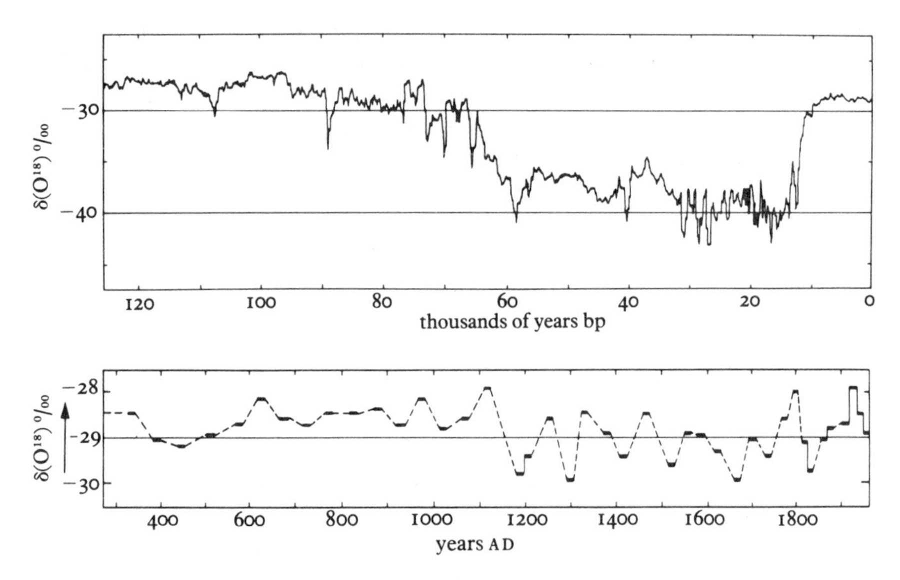

Figure 13. Oxygen-isotope measurements from dated levels in cores taken from the Greenland ice sheet, arranged to be read as proxy temperature records (increasing upwards): (a) at 200-year intervals over the last 125,000 years; (b) from AD 300 to the present (from work by W. Dansgaard and colleagues).

1000 BC and perhaps on to 500 BC, AD 250 to about 600, 850 to 950 and 1190 to 1470 and from then on to 1700).

Most of these records can also be studied in terms of isotope measurements. For instance, the relative abundance of the heavier and lighter isotopes of oxygen O^{18} and O^{16} in the water molecules deposited as snow on the Greenland ice sheet depends on the temperature at which the snow was formed from water vapour in the atmosphere over Greenland. Measurements of the isotope ratio are, therefore, to a first approximation, a fossil record of those temperatures.

Unfortunately, there are complications since the ratio also depends on the relative abundances of the two isotopes in the water vapour in the first place and, therefore, on the temperatures prevailing and the abundances of the isotopes in the ocean or wherever the water was evaporated. Nevertheless, series of isotope measurements in Greenland clearly do give an interesting record (figure 13a, b), which shows the whole of the last Ice Age and the warmer and colder periods of postglacial and historical times in Greenland. There is broad agreement with the climatic history, as it has been pieced together from diverse data, for Europe; but also there are some interesting differences which need to be studied synoptically.

Another item of some interest that has been examined in deep cores at two points in the Greenland ice-sheet is the quantity of sulphuric acid originating in the sulphur dioxide from volcanic eruptions occurring in the northern hemisphere and deposited in the year-layers in the ice-sheet. This gives a year-by-year chronology of volcanic activity back to AD 553 and less closely dated back to the last Ice Age (Hammer *et al.* 1980). Two points of note emerge: there was greatly enhanced volcanic activity all through the development of the cold Little Ice Age climate in the late Middle Ages and on into the nineteenth century, and there was remarkably little volcanic material deposited through the warmest millennia of postglacial times. It seems certain that the effect of volcanic aerosol in the stratosphere in screening off some of the incoming solar radiation must have contributed to the development of the Little Ice Age, and a lack of volcanic matter in the atmosphere presumably played a part in the warmth of the climate about five thousand to seven thousand years ago as in the warmest decades earlier in the present century. It may be that much current work in meteorology and climatology takes too little account of the volcanic effect in comparison with the assessment of the importance of carbon dioxide.

The climate record summarised

Let us now briefly survey the record of postglacial times. I suggest that the salient features are:

i) *The rapidity of the warming in the earliest postglacial times*, as seen in figures 11 and 13. This was accompanied by a northward shift of the forest and other vegetation zones of the northern hemisphere and a great rise of the level of the upper tree-line on the mountains in all parts of the world. The northward spread of the forest was rapid in North America, where there were no barriers; but in Europe it entailed a succession of the dominance of different species drawn out over several thousand years. The arrival of the birch and later the pine forest was, however, so quick that in southern Norway reindeer hunting folk seem to have found it easier to inhabit the plateau over 900 m above sea-level – on Hardangervidda by 5500 BC or earlier[2] – than the densely wooded valleys below within about a thousand years of the disappearance of the ice-sheet from the heights. (This information comes from the interdisciplinary studies of the area south of Hardangervidda by the Arkeologisk Museum in Stavanger – see also Selsing and Wishman 1978.)

Sea-level rose very rapidly as the ice-sheets melted, averaging one metre per century over a long period. This submerged coastal plains everywhere, notably the broad, inhabited plain which became the North Sea, and by 5000 BC or earlier isolated the islands of Britain, Ireland and Denmark from the continent. The submergence doubtless proceeded erratically, advancing in a long series of storm-flood incidents which probably cost many lives.

There seems to have been at least one very rapid phase of the postglacial development, involving temporary dislocation of the northern hemisphere climatic pattern, between about 6000 and 5500 BC, as the sea got into Hudson's Bay and rapidly (perhaps within 100 years) cleared the huge mass of the remaining ice-sheet there (Andrews *et al.* 1972). Before that stage North

2. These dates, like others in this section, are based on enough radiocarbon dates to fix the time-scale in outline, but have been converted to calendar dates. A few dates are points where the time-scale has cross-references to archaeological dating.

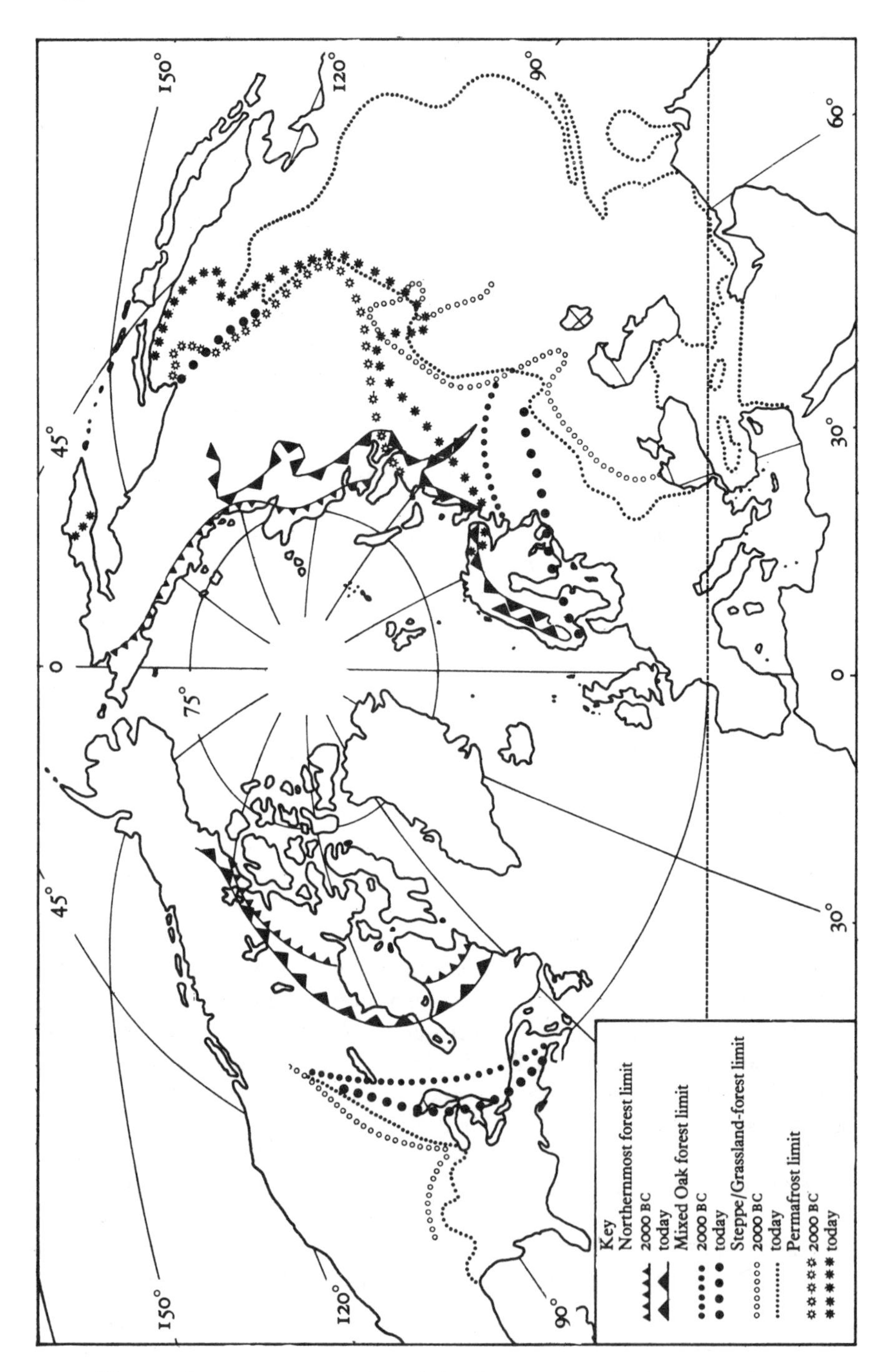

Figure 14. Forest and vegetation boundaries about 2000 BC and today compared. The permafrost boundary positions are also shown.

America, with the continuance of a massive ice-sheet over most of Canada, was lagging far behind Europe and all other parts of the world in the postglacial development. But even after this event substantial areas of ice remained in northern Canada either side of the Bay and were not all gone from the mainland until around 3000 BC.

ii) *The prevailing characteristics of the warmest postglacial times:* for much of the world these occurred between about 7000 and 2000 BC, but especially between around 4500 and 3500–3000 BC.

Sea-level was still rising, though towards the end less rapidly; and the polar ice and glaciers were generally receding, though also not without shorter term fluctuations.

The most remarkable difference from our own times was the much moister régime in the desert zone (Flohn *et al.* 1979; Nicholson *et al.* 1980) – there were some permanent rivers even in the Sahara and probably also in the other deserts – and stronger development of the Indian summer monsoon. The moist regime was interrupted for 900 to 1500 years by a very dry interval in the Sahara between about 6000 and 4500 BC, though apparently not, or by no means so markedly, in the deserts further east. The event seems to have been related to the clearance into the Atlantic Ocean of the massive amount of ice from the Hudson Bay portion of the North American inland ice.

The moist régime allowed human settlement and cattle-herding in the Sahara, and wild animals (elephants, hippopotamus, rhinoceros etc.) to roam there.

With the first cooling events in higher latitudes after about 3500 BC, and especially after 2800 BC, the moist régime began to decline. Ultimately the animal and human populations were essentially confined to the oases and the river valleys (Nile, Mesopotamia, Indus, Hoang-ho); and it may be suggested that the civilisations in those valleys came about through the need to organise irrigation to provide food for the increased population, while the refugees presumably provided the slave labour to do it. During these same millennia the forests were spreading further north, until the limits were in some places 300 km north of today's (figure 14) and 200 to 250 m higher on the mountains (Lamb 1974, 1977).

iii) *The climatic fluctuations and decline since the earliest historical times.* The warm régime of global climate with moisture in the desert zone, which seems to have been very stable before 3500 BC and gave summer temperatures in middle latitudes averaging 1 to 3°C higher than today's, was prolonged sufficiently to support the river valley civilisations mentioned until around the middle of the second millennium before Christ. There were, however, some important fluctuations, and winter temperatures (which in China are thought to have been 5°C higher on average than now) became more variable. So, later on, did the monsoons in India. And there is evidence of sharp variations from century to century of wetness in Europe.

The demise of the Indus valley civilisation seems from pollen analytical studies (Singh 1971) in Kashmir (figure 15) to coincide with a drop of about 70

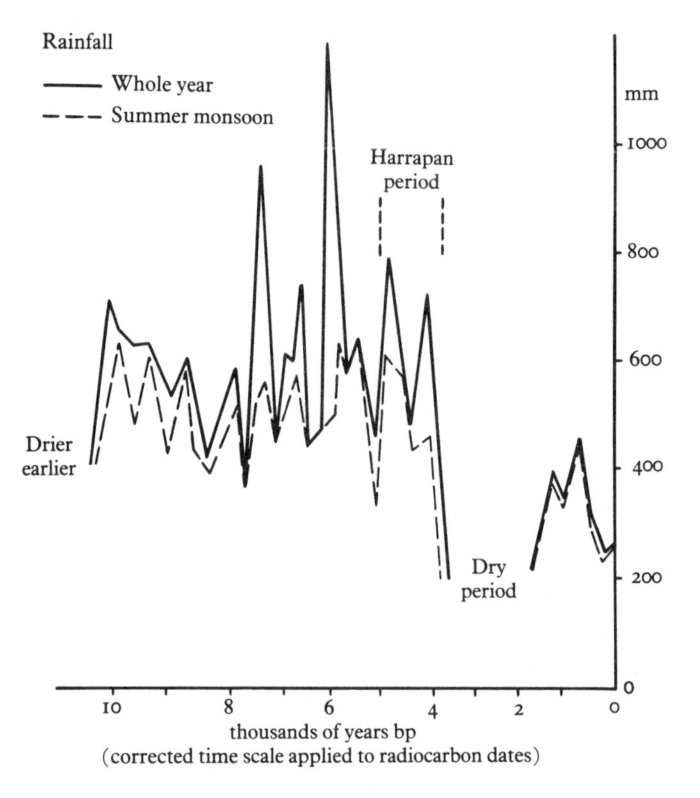

Figure 15. Rainfall variations in Rajasthan, north-west India, over the past 10,000 years, estimated by R. A. Bryson from pollen studies by G. Singh (1971).

per cent in the yield of the monsoons in the north-western part of the Indian subcontinent, leading to the development of the Thar desert. And between about 1300 and 900 BC prevailing temperatures in the middle latitudes of the northern hemisphere seem to have declined by about 2°C, a fall from which there has been no full recovery since. The advancing glaciers at various dates closed the high-level mines in the Alps (e.g. gold mining in the Hohe Tauern) and apparently ended the traffic across some passes. The upper forest limit also declined.

Around 2000 to 2200 BC the forest had reached the very shores of the Atlantic in the British Isles from Cornwall to north-west Scotland, with some woodland near the coasts even in the Hebrides and Orkney, but this receded soon afterwards. Within about 200 years during the second millennium BC the forest receded 200 to 400 km to its present limit (or even somewhat south of it) right across northern Canada; and equally quickly further south oak forest was replaced by pines. (This information is from Dr Harvey Nichols, of the Institute of Arctic and Alpine Research, Boulder, Colorado.) Forest fires seem to have played a part. Also around 2000 BC the evidence of trading links and the spread of similar megalithic monuments seem to indicate much seafaring activity along the western fringe of Europe to latitude 60°N or beyond: this, like the proximity to the coasts attained by the forest, evidently indicates an era of calmer seas, which also seems to have ended in the second millennium BC.

It is now well known that a sharp deterioration of the climate occurred in the present millennium, heralded by a marked increase of the Arctic sea ice and storminess in northern waters from around AD 1200. After some improvement for a while around 1500 in Europe (but probably a century earlier in Iceland) this climatic development culminated in the Little Ice Age of the period between 1550 and 1900, with greatly advanced glaciers in all parts of the world, colder winters and very variable summers in Europe, and pronounced storminess at times in these latitudes. The average growing season in England probably shortened by five or six weeks, and the upper limit of cultivation came down by 150 to 200 m. The writer believes that this, and the superposed variations from year to year, was (even more than the Black Death) the background to the Highland troubles in Scotland, the lasting abandonment of farmland and settlements and unrest and constitutional changes in many parts of Europe. The bigger and longer-lasting variations are indicated in the temperature values derived for different centuries in the last millennium plotted in the right-hand part of figure 11.

For a few centuries in the High Middle Ages, between the 900s and 1200 AD (and on to around 1300 in Europe) the temperatures in middle latitudes generally had returned almost to the level of the warm times before 1500 BC. (There were some differences in the timing of the climax of this warmth, which seems to have continued later in western and northern Europe than elsewhere and may have peaked as early as 900 in China and about 1100 in Greenland and North America.) The deterioration which followed was accompanied by an evident increase of the westerly winds in middle latitudes, increasing storminess on the North Atlantic, and spreading the 'rain shadow' of the Rockies further east over the plains and prairies of North America, where a long drought caused the collapse of the Indian agricultural settlements and migration southwards.

There are probably important analogies between this development and the events in the first and second millennia before Christ. Indeed, researches over the past thirty years have increasingly forced recognition that the glaciers in various parts of Europe advanced to positions more or less comparable with those of the recent Little Ice Age around 1600 to 1850 in the middle centuries of each of the last three millennia. Some evidence of the cooling about the time of the end of the Roman Empire in the west may be seen in figure 9, and it may be that this was an important complication in the historical events of those times, just as it is certain that there were times of great drought in the pasture lands of the nomads on the steppes of Asia and European Russia, which may reasonably be thought to have started the barbarian movements around AD 300.

REFERENCES

Andrews, J. T. & Ives, J. D. (1972) Late- and postglacial events (<10,000 B.P.) in the eastern Canadian Arctic with particular reference to the Cockburn moraines and break-up of the Laurentide ice-sheet, in *Climatic changes in Arctic areas during the last ten-thousand years*, Oulu, Finland (*Acta Universitatis Ouluensis, Series A, Scientiae Rerum Naturalium* 3, *Geologica* 1), 149-74.

Flohn, H. & Nicholson, S. E. (1979) Climatic fluctuations in the arid belt of the 'Old World' since the last glacial maximum; possible causes and future implications, *Palaeoecology of Africa* 11 (publication pending). Cape Town: Balkema.

Godwin, H. (1975) *History of the British Flora* (2nd edition). Cambridge: University Press.

Hammer, C. U., Clausen, H. B. & Dansgaard, W. (1980) Greenland ice sheet evidence of postglacial volcanism and its climatic impact, *Nature* 288 (5788), 230-5.

Iversen, J. (1973) *The development of Denmark's Nature since the Last Glacial.* Copenhagen (Geological Survey of Denmark, V series, No. 7-C).

Lamb, H. H. (1972) *Climate: Present, Past and Future.* 1. *Fundamentals and Climate Now.* London: Methuen.

— (1974) Climate, vegetation and forest limits, *Philosophical Transactions of the Royal Society of London, A.276,* 195-230.

— (1977) *Climate: Present, Past and Future.* 2. *Climatic History and the Future.* London: Methuen.

— (1979) Climatic variation and changes in the wind and ocean circulation: the Little Ice Age in the northeast Atlantic, *Quaternary Res.* 11, 1-20.

Manley, G. (1953) Mean temperature of central England, 1698 to 1952, *Q.J. R. Meteorol. Soc.* 79, 242-61.

— (1974) Central England temperatures: monthly means 1659 to 1973, *Q.J. R. Meteorol. Soc.* 79, 389-405.

Nicholson, S. E. & Flohn, H. (1980) African environmental and climatic changes and the general atmospheric circulation in Late Pleistocene and Holocene, *Climatic Change* 2, 313-48.

Rudloff, H. von (1967) *Die Schwankungen und Pendelungen des Klimas in Europa seit dem Beginn der regelmässigen Instrumenten-Beobachtungen, (1670).* Braunschweig: Vieweg. (*Die Wissenschaft*, Band 122).

Selsing, L. & Wishman, E. (1978) An approach to the understanding of the summer climate 7000-6000 B.P. in Ryfylke, southwest Norway, in *Proceedings of the Nordic Symposium on Climatic Changes and related problems (organised by the Danish Natural History Society and Danish Meteorological Institute)*, Copenhagen (Danish Meteorological Institute, Climatological Papers No.4), 145-53.

Singh, G. (1971) The Indus valley culture, *Archaeology and Physical Anthropology in Oceania* 6 (2), 177-89.

Woillard, G. (1978) Grande Pile peat bog: a continuous pollen record for the last 140,000 years, *Quaternary Res.* 9, 1-21.

Atlantic and Sub-boreal: dampness and dryness?

A recent study of climatic history in the subalpine zone during the Neolithic and early historic period (Magny 1978) has provided the opportunity of re-examining the character of the climate generally attributed to the Atlantic and Sub-boreal periods. Indeed, these two climatic fluctuations, known from pollen analysis, are often identified as corresponding to damp and dry phases respectively. However, the conclusions reached relating to the evolution of climate in the subalpine zone for these periods would have relevance for this global intepretation. In fact, it would appear that certain factors used previously as proof of Sub-boreal dryness can mask a different palaeoclimatic or ecological situation.

We shall look here at the notion of Atlantic dampness and Sub-boreal dryness again, and emphasise the need to modify the climatic divisions established initially in northern Europe on the basis of pollen cores before applying them to temperate regions.

History of research

It is the work of Blytt, a Norwegian, taken up again by another Scandinavian, Sernander, which today serves as the basis of the climatic divisions in the Postglacial (Pre-boreal, Boreal, Atlantic, Sub-boreal and Sub-atlantic). While certain chronological differences have appeared between northern Europe and temperate Europe in the middle latitudes (France, Switzerland etc.), it is nonetheless clear that these divisions are soundly based: palynologists working in central and western Europe as well as in the Mediterranean zone have been able to distinguish the five phases characterised by Blytt and Sernander. There can thus be no doubt that they correspond to climatic fluctuations.

It is still necessary to understand how to qualify these same fluctuations, that is to what sort of development in temperature and precipitation régimes they correspond. For this, Blytt and Sernander relied on the ecological demands of the various vegetational combinations characterising each of these palynological phases. They thus succeeded in establishing that in Northern Europe the Atlantic corresponds to a warm and damp phase, while the Sub-boreal is marked by a cooling and drying of the climate.

The first problem concerns the application of the Scandinavian system to central Europe. On this point de Lumley *et al.* (1976) distinguish clearly between chronological and climatic aspects, while Chaline (1972), following the Nordic system, proposes that we should recognise temperate, mild and humid climate during the Atlantic and a slightly less warm and drier climate during the Sub-boreal in both eastern and western Europe. This is thus a general problem, but it becomes much more delicate in the subalpine zone where the intervention of archaeological research has led to still greater confusion.

If the first palynological analyses allowed one to propose an initial climatic approach to the Postglacial in Scandinavia, archaeological research, conducted simultaneously in the subalpine zone (eastern France, southern Germany, Switzerland, northern Italy, Austria) had also to raise the question of the development of climate in this zone during the Neolithic and early historic period. Indeed, during the winter of 1853–4 Dr Ferdinand Keller of Zürich produced evidence for the first time of the lake-dwellings on the edges of the Swiss lakes. These dwellings had been occupied during the Neolithic and Bronze Age. However, their discovery at once stirred up a passionate debate: most of these settlement traces were in fact submerged below the present-day level of the subalpine lakes and it needed the exceptional dryness of the winter of 1853–4 for the posts of these ancient constructions to emerge. Was it then a case of houses on piles, after the manner of contemporary lake-villages in Indonesia, Africa or America, or were they simply villages built on dry land?

For Keller and his followers it was a matter entirely of constructions on piles, which were fixed below water: the level of the subalpine lakes had thus never changed. But Reinerth then refined Keller's interpretations from the time of his research undertaken on the Federsee and on Lake Constance, while in 1958 Paret strongly attacked what he called the 'myth of the lake-villages'. According to him, there was no doubt that all the prehistoric dwellings found on the edges of the subalpine lakes had been founded on dry land, the water-level at that time being much lower than it is today. This lowering could only represent a significant period of dryness. And as one could distinguish two phases in the occupation of lake-shore sites (Neolithic-Early Bronze Age on the one hand, and Late Bronze Age on the other), so one could identify two phases of dryness: the first happening between 2200 and 1800 BC and the second between 1200 and 800 BC. The general abandoning of the lake shores between 1800 and 1200 corresponded to a very damp period.

These conclusions, however, are not as satisfactory as they might seem at first sight.

On the one hand, the Atlantic-Sub-boreal transition is marked in pollen diagrams by the retreat of mixed oak forest to the benefit of the beech-fir forest, which represents a climatic deterioration (lowering of temperature and increase in dampness). These palynological findings will be studied in more detail below.

On the other hand, recent excavations conducted with greater attention to detail have substantiated Paret's views. Whether at Zug-Sumpf, at Wauwilermoos or at Thayngen-Weier, the structures discovered were certainly those of dwellings constructed on dry land. One is thus forced to suppose that the level of the subalpine lakes was lower during the Neolithic and Bronze Age and that the climate then was dryer: lake-dwellings can only be explained by the dryness of the Sub-boreal phase, interrupting the dampness of the Atlantic and

Sub-atlantic. Besides, does not the beginning of the Sub-atlantic correspond to the definitive desertion of the lake-shore sites? Furthermore, the climatic divisions proposed by the Scandinavians corroborate these views perfectly.

The problem of the lake-dwellings explains why one finds the idea of Sub-boreal dryness appearing again and again in the work of numerous archaeologists, palynologists and palaeoclimatologists around the subalpine zone. It will suffice to quote certain significant examples.

In their masterly history of climate in central Europe in the Postglacial, Gams and Nordhagen (1923) rely on the low level of the subalpine lakes to identify the Sub-boreal with a long phase of dryness. From then on, one notices the difficulties which various authors meet with in truthfully justifying their conclusions: archaeologists appealed to palaeoclimatologists, who in turn had recourse to archaeological discoveries to support their hypotheses.

In his history of climate through the ages, Brooks (1950) notes likewise this idea of Sub-boreal dryness from the time of the lowering of the subalpine lake-levels during this period: the climate was supposed to have been warm and very dry.

In a recent article by Olive (1972) about the palaeoclimatology of the Lake Léman region, one reads that 'the lake dwellings were built between 5000 and 3000 BP. This era corresponds precisely to the Sub-boreal. The climate was relatively dry. This form of settlement must thus have been brought about by necessity. In fact during this period the climate was the driest since populations settled down in the Mesolithic. From then on, people were probably drawn towards the lakes which constituted a permanent reserve of water'.

From the stratigraphy of the site of St Paul's Abbey in Besançon, Petrequin (in press) attempted to reconstruct the frequency of flooding of the river Doubs during the Postglacial: 'general dampness must have been acute at the end of the Boreal and Atlantic, minimal during the Sub-boreal and again rising during the Sub-atlantic, which corresponds to our ideas on climate generally from pollen diagrams. . . . From the climatic point of view, the deposition of silt by the Doubs and the formation of lake muds in the lakes of the French Jura appear to have occurred simultaneously'.

Millotte (1963) was more careful. For, while he notes that many factors combine to assign the Bronze Age to a dry phase, he is curious about the possible existence of several climatic fluctuations during the Sub-boreal from studies made in the peat-bogs of Britain, north Germany and Scandinavia.

Lüdi (1951) tried to establish a correlation between the findings of palynology and the hypotheses put forward by archaeologists about lake-side sites. In fact he makes the most of the difficulties. There is actually no doubt that the spread of the beech-fir forest represents a worsening of the climate by comparison with the Atlantic, with a lowering of mean annual temperatures and an increase in precipitation. He remarks only that the Bronze Age, among other periods, corresponds to a definite retreat of the white fir to the benefit of the beech, which could according to him indicate a drying of the climate. One notices again here the concern to iron out all contradictions between pollen diagrams and archaeological reality. While modifying the conclusions of Paret, who supposed there had been significant phases of dryness, Lüdi wanted to find in pollen analysis evidence of dryness which would explain and confirm the lowering of the subalpine lake-levels during the Neolithic and Bronze Age.

Palynological results

Can one really say on the basis of pollen diagrams that the Sub-boreal *in the subalpine zone* corresponds to a drying of the climate by comparison with the preceding Atlantic and the subsequent Sub-atlantic? It is impossible in this brief study to retrace the vegetational history of the whole area under consideration: suffice it to take the example of the Jura massif. This region has been particularly thoroughly studied in this respect (Firtion 1950, Wegmüller 1966, Matthey 1971); what is more the Jura has varied relief composed of plateaux and folded zones rising one above the other progressively from west to east. This unusual structure has the advantage of better encompassing the various gradations of climatic development. Today the climate of the Jura shows a marked tendency to continentality. The annual temperature range reaches 18 to 20°C, while the range between absolute minima and maxima lies around a mean figure of 46°, over an observation period of more than a century (Quantin 1935). Besides, while the temperature range remains important from the western foothills across to the eastern peaks, the harshness of the climate increases from west to east with the altitude. This last factor also has a decisive influence on the intensity and distribution of precipitation. Generally the precipitation is abundant but there is an important relative divergence between the plateaux and the folded High Jura: the former receive 1200 to 1500 mm precipitation while on the latter it exceeds 2000 mm.

The vegetation follows this climatic zonation (figure 1) and it rises in tiers from west to east as one gains height towards the High Plateaux and the Chaînons in the east. Up to a height of 600 m one finds hornbeams, limes and oaks. Then beeches come to the fore, soon taken over in their turn by white fir. Above 1000 m is the domain of the beautiful Jura spruce forests dominated by spruce (Quantin 1935, Guinier 1932).

Pollen diagrams allow one to trace the vegetational history as follows:

Atlantic (5500–3000 bc): the forest comprises mixed oak extending to 1300 m. The extension of oak beyond its present-day limits testifies to a milder temperature than today. During the early Atlantic one even finds lime in the inhospitable Joux valley. Fir and beech are represented from the beginning of the late Atlantic (4000 bc).

Sub-boreal (3000–800 bc): it is characterised essentially by the rise of the beech-fir forest at the expense of mixed oak which no longer goes beyond an altitude of 600 m. Spruce increases while ivy and mistletoe disappear (as far as indices of climatic deterioration are concerned). The mean annual temperatures are lower and precipitation increases. It is this that explains the increase in fir and beech, species favoured by cloud and dampness, in the regions of the Jurassian chain which are least favoured climate-wise and thus most sensitive

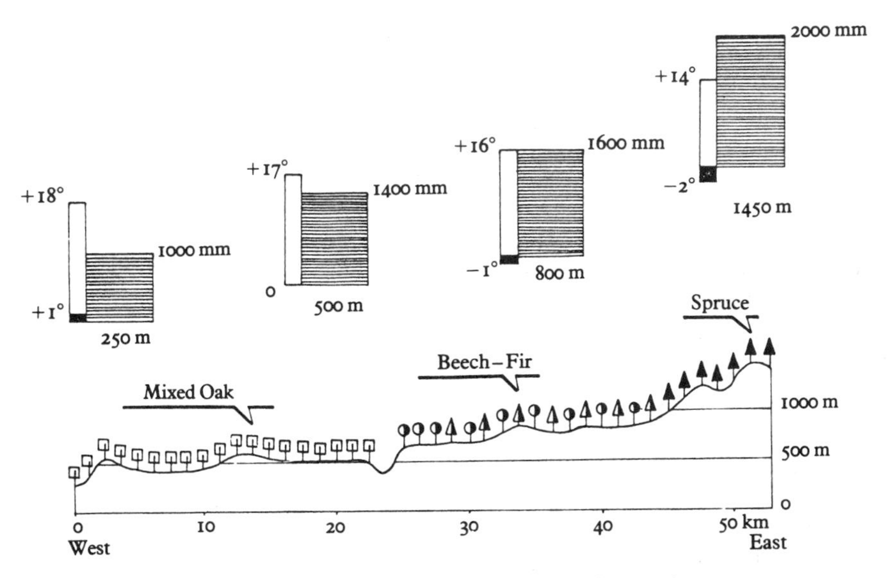

Figure 1. Vegetational stages in the Jura, in parallel with altitude and meteorological conditions. Left column: lower number represents mean January temperature, upper represents mean July temperature. Right column (horizontal hatching): total annual precipitation.

to a transformation of atmospheric conditions. It is difficult to establish a more detailed periodisation: the curves for beech and fir cross many times without any constant factor being discernible across the different pollen diagrams.

However, besides this long-term tendency (over millennia) to climatic deterioration in the Sub-boreal, we have stressed the existence of shorter-term climatic fluctuations (over a century or several centuries) characterised by the improvement of atmospheric conditions (increase in temperatures, lessening of precipitation). And these secondary fluctuations are found to correspond to the different phases of occupation of the lake-sites (Magny 1978).

Sub-atlantic: corresponds to an accentuation of the deterioration of the climate, marked by an increase in spruce.

The long-term tendency of climatic development from Atlantic to Sub-atlantic is thus one of slow deterioration (lowering of mean annual temperatures and increase in precipitation). However, palynological research (Markgraf 1974) and glaciological research (Le Roy Ladurie 1967) both show that there is no cause to envisage catastrophic changes in climate in the latitudes in question: temperatures are lower by 1 to 2 degrees and precipitation increases over a margin not exceeding 10–15 per cent of the annual total.

Lastly, let us note that the study of pollen diagrams allows us to distinguish phases where the deterioration of the climate is accentuated, essentially in the highest places which are the most sensitive (around 3500 bc, 2400 bc, and 1600 bc – Magny 1978).

Forest history in the Jura shows also that it is difficult to assign the Sub-boreal to a dry climatic phase between two damp periods that would be the Atlantic and Sub-atlantic. This evolution is not specific to the Jura massif and one can find numerous parallels to it. Research carried out in other parts of France are significant in this respect (Guilaine 1976). In the Hautes-Pyrenées and Pyrenées-Atlantiques the Sub-boreal is marked by cooling and an increase of dampness. In the Massif Central the Sub-boreal corresponds to a cooling, the Sub-atlantic is fresh and wet. In the southern Alps the Sub-boreal is characterised by a cooling. In the northern Alps a cooling takes effect in the Sub-boreal and the climate stays damp. The Sub-atlantic accentuates this deterioration (fresher and wetter). In the Vosges the Sub-boreal is characterised by an increase in dampness and a lowering of temperatures.

Low lake-levels in the subalpine lakes during the Neolithic and Bronze Age

The contradiction between the findings of palynology and those of lake archaeology quickly becomes apparent. On the one hand, the development of the beech-fir forest at the expense of the mixed oak gives indisputable evidence of a climatic deterioration (lowering of temperatures and progressive increase in wetness). On the other hand the low level of the subalpine lakes, which allowed the occupation of the lakeside sites in the Neolithic and Bronze Age, has brought about the notion that the Sub-boreal corresponds to a phase of marked dryness. Hence the recourse to the climatic periodisation established in Scandinavia. But even if the rhythm of climatic change is the same, one cannot reasonably appeal to the development of Scandinavian climate to explain a phenomenon observed in the subalpine zone. We will return to this question in detail.

Actually, these two alternatives do not offer a real choice. In fact if the peat borings carried out in the subalpine zone allow one to recognise with certainty a progressive and continuous tendency towards climatic deterioration from the Atlantic on, we must revise this climatic explanation of low lake-levels in order to refine it.

A recent study concerning precisely these lake-level fluctuations during the Neolithic and early historic period (Magny 1978) brings out that the low level of the subalpine lakes results in part from a long geomorphological development in progress since the Late Glacial. A lake is only a chance effect in the profile of a water-course and because of this is integrated in the whole dynamic of the profile's development. Now the flow-level of European rivers and streams was lower during the Neolithic and Bronze Age. The example of the Rhône valley is particularly significant in this respect. Borings taken in the Valais (upsteam from Lake Léman) and in the marshes of Lavours (near Lake Bourget) have provided evidence, at more than 8 m below the present-day flow level, of the existence of peat beds dating from the Sub-boreal, although this type of formation characterises dry-land situations! One can cite other examples leading to the same conclusions, relating to the valleys of the Rhine, Danube and Saône. From the beginning of the Sub-atlantic the development would be inverted, involving a progressive aggradation of the valley bottoms and a raising of the flow-level. In the future it will be necessary to study the development of the hydrological network more precisely: it seems, in fact, that the explanation of the low level of subalpine lakes could also be envisaged in this type of scenario and not just according to a strictly palynological set-up.

In addition one must emphasise that it was a mistake to explain this low lake-level exclusively by means of a drying in climate in the Sub-boreal after the damp Atlantic. In fact certain lake-side sites were occupied well before the beginning of the Sub-boreal (e.g. the Federsee, lakes of Zürich and Clairvaux) and occasionally even in the full Sub-atlantic (the site of La Tène). Lake Neuchâtel was at a low level from the late Atlantic, and Ammann (1975) was surprised at this lowering occurring in the middle of a period believed to be wet.

Pollen diagrams illustrate well a long-term tendency to climatic deterioration, with a revival of dampness indicated from the beginning of the Sub-boreal. As for the low level of the lakes during the Neolithic and Bronze Age, it is the result of geomorphological phenomena on the one hand, and of a temporary improvement in the climate even in the heart of the Sub-boreal on the other. It is these secondary fluctuations which explain the occupation of the site of La Tène in the full Sub-atlantic.

Palynology of northern Europe and of middle-latitude Europe

It remains to pose questions about a final contradiction which has appeared in the course of the preceding discussions. If in Scandinavia, as in the subalpine zone, the Sub-boreal corresponds to a lowering of mean annual temperatures, one can also note that Scandinavian palynologists identify the Sub-boreal with a phase of dryness while in central Europe (France, Switzerland, southern Germany) the beginning of the Sub-boreal marks a return to dampness. Furthermore, we are talking about the same climatic fluctuations occurring according to the same general rhythm in northern Europe and in lower latitudes.

In fact there is no contradiction if one makes reference to the mechanics of atmospheric circulation which determine the climate at different European latitudes. North and central Europe are subject to different influences:

Polar influence: this is marked by the descent towards low latitudes of air masses originating in the polar regions. This cold air is more or less damp according to whether we are talking about maritime air-masses (maritime polar air, cold and wet) or continental air-masses (continental polar air, cold and dry).

Tropical influence: tropical air climbs towards the north either from the Atlantic (tropical, wet and mild air) or from the Sahara (tropical, warm and dry air).

Polar front influence: this is the name of the contact zone between the polar and tropical air masses. The opposition of these two air-masses are responsible for the disturbances which move from west to east and bring abundant rain.

A climatic deterioration corresponds to a descent in latitude of the cold polar air masses and thus also to a parallel descent of the polar front. This movement entails a fall in mean annual temperatures (the influence of the cold polar air). But on the north of the front there are two possible situations for western Europe: either it is subject to maritime polar air masses and in this case the lowering of temperature will be accompanied by an increase of dampness (the oceanic influence) or it is subject to the continental polar air masses and in this case the lowering of temperatures will be accompanied by a diminution of dampness (the continental influence).

Climatic amelioration corresponds to a rise in latitude of the cold polar air masses and in the same way to a displacement of the polar front to the north, while the tropical air masses rise in latitude. This movement thus brings on an increase in mean annual temperatures: the influence of polar air diminishes to the benefit of tropical air. But at high latitudes, this increase of temperature goes hand in hand with a revival of dampness owing to the influence of the polar front.

In the light of this system of atmospheric circulation, it would seem easier to understand the evolution of the climate from the Atlantic to the Sub-atlantic both in northern and in central Europe:

Atlantic: Europe is more and more strongly subject to the influence of tropical air, while polar air goes much less far southwards. The polar front is thus pushed back northwards. Northern Europe experiences a renewal of warmth, but is also much affected by the passage of depressions corresponding to the polar front. Hence an increase in dampness. The problem of the intensity of precipitation during this period in central Europe remains. This was probably less important in the Sub-boreal which corresponds exactly to the increase of the beech-fir forest, while in the Jura the beech and fir are continuously represented from the start of the Atlantic. On the other hand excessive cloud cover would no doubt have reduced the hours of sunshine and eventually brought with it a reduction in mean annual temperatures. Now the Atlantic corresponds exactly to the climatic optimum of the Postglacial; in fact one can see that the passage of the polar front depressions was displaced towards the north. However, it is a fact that the development of the alder in this period has often been linked with an increase in dampness. Unfortunately, it is very risky to make use of the presence of this species which, rather than a return to dampness, can mean on the contrary a drying-out of the peat-bog where the boring has been taken. The bog develops, and the colonising vegetation diversifies to the benefit of tree species or those characteristic of better drained situations. Thus a high percentage of alder is frequently attested in pollen diagrams for lake-sites at the level of the archaeological strata: this emphasises the drying of the site before human occupation began. It would be worth re-examining this question, notably by the study of plant macrofossils found in peat borings. This latter analysis would allow one to follow the general evolution of vegetation better (figure 2).

Sub-boreal: A displacement southwards of the various climatic zones brings about a deterioration in climate over the whole of Europe. The polar air mass

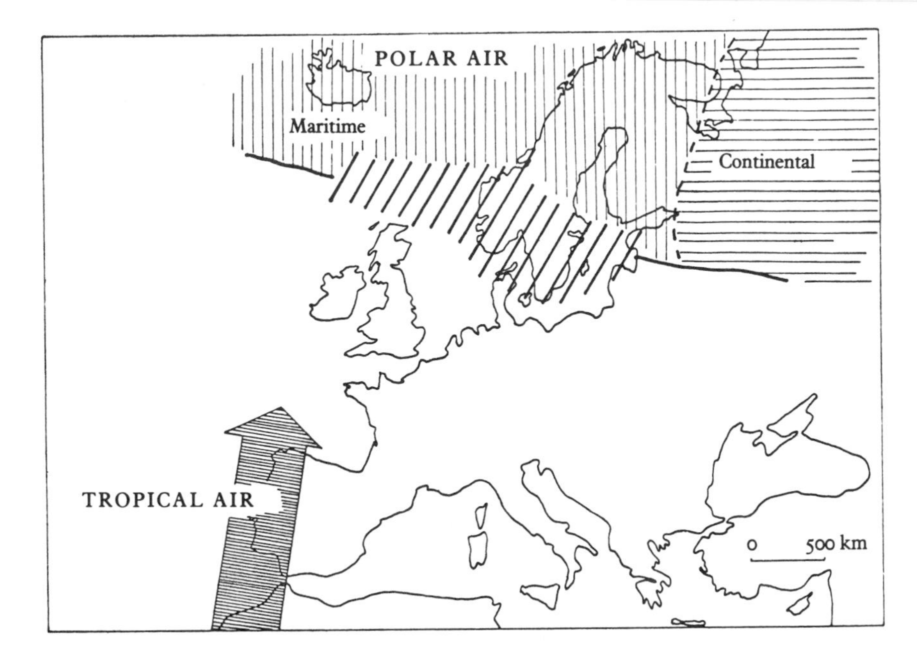

Figure 2. Type of atmospheric circulation over north and central Europe during the Atlantic period. The situation shown here (as in figures 3 and 4) is the one that seems to have had most influence on vegetational development, thus the one that best characterises the period. Oblique hatching indicates the perturbation zone (marked precipitation) corresponding to the polar front.

advances further southwards, while similarly diminishing the beneficial influence of tropical air. The polar front descends in latitude. A cooling thus affects the whole of Europe. But northern Europe becomes dry thanks to the descent in latitude of the polar front and the more marked influence of the continental cold and dry polar air. In central Europe, on the other hand, precipitation tends to increase: the passage of depressions from the polar front moves further south (figure 3).

Sub-atlantic: The movement begun during the previous period is accentuated. The cooling increases. However, northern Europe seems to be more under the influence of the maritime cold and damp polar air: this would correspond to the increase in dampness that is noted from pollen diagrams obtained from this region (figure 4).

There is thus no contradiction between the development of dampness observed in Scandinavian countries and what one can see in central Europe. It will be sufficient to place these two schemes in the more general framework of the development of atmospheric circulation in the northern hemisphere. The same changes in climate have different effects according to the latitude under consideration. The Scandinavian system is not immediately applicable to central Europe. To be sure, the chronological sequence is identical, given that it is the same general development of the atmospheric circulation of the

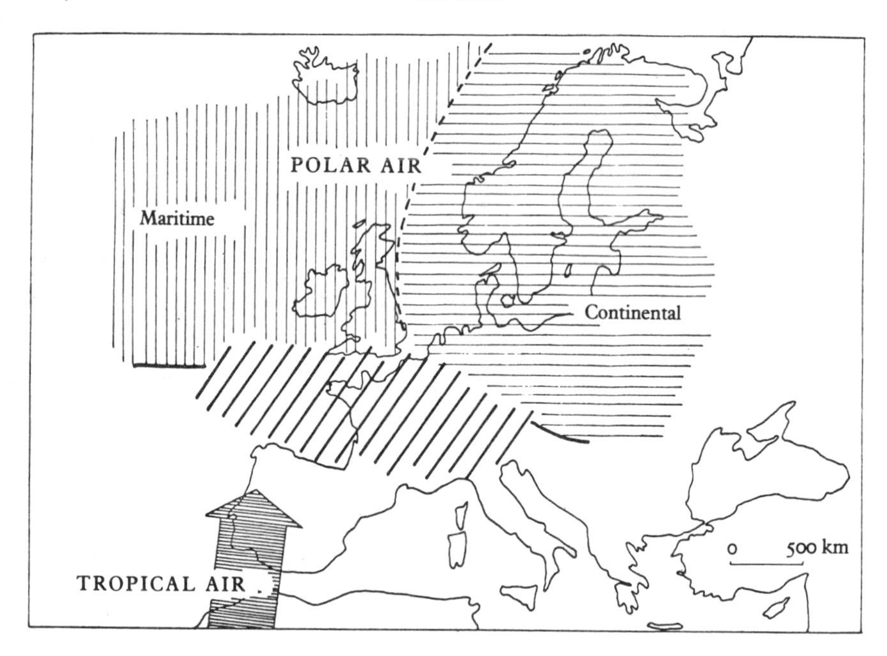

Figure 3. Type of atmospheric circulation over north and central Europe during the Sub-boreal period.

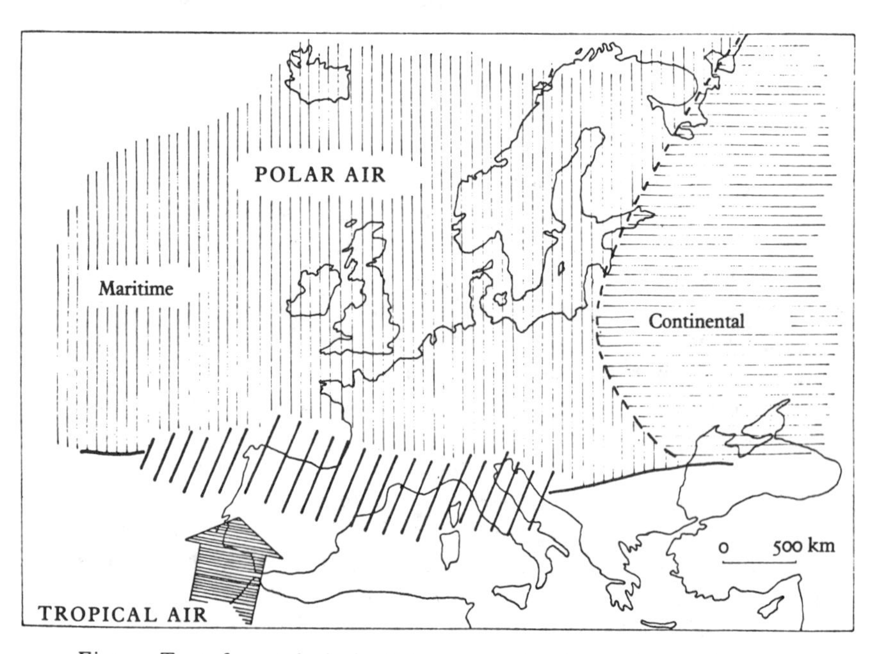

Figure 4. Type of atmospheric circulation over north and central Europe during the Sub-atlantic period.

northern hemisphere which is at the bottom of these climatic changes; but the development of temperature and precipitation régimes known from northern Europe cannot correspond in a systematic way to those of central Europe because we are dealing with two different climatic zones characterising two particular latitudes.

(Translated by L. E. Forbes and A. F. Harding. This article originally appeared in *Revue Archéologique de l'Est et du Centre-Est* 30/1–2, 1979, 57–65).

REFERENCES

Ammann-Moser, B. (1975) Vegetationskundliche und pollenanalytische Untersuchungen auf dem Heidenweg im Bielersee, *Beitr. geobot. Landes. Schweiz* 56.

Brooks, C. E. P. (1950) *Climate through the Ages*. London: Benn.

Chaline, J. (1972) *Le Quaternaire, L'Histoire humaine dans son environnement*. Paris: Doin.

Firiton, F. (1950) *Contribution à l'étude paléontologique, stratigraphique et physico-chimique des tourbières du Jura français*, Mem. Serv. Carte Géol. Alsace et Lorraine, 10. Strasbourg, thesis no.96.

Gams, H. & Nordhagen, R. (1923) *Postglaziale Klimaänderungen und Erdkrustenbewegungen in Mitteleuropa*. Munich.

Guilaine, J. (ed.) (1976) *La Préhistoire française. 2 : Les civilisations néolithiques et protohistoriques*. Nice: Actes du IXe Congrès UISPP.

Guinier, P. (1932) Les associations végétales et les types de forêts du Jura, *Comptes rendus congrès Soc. Sav. Sect. Sc. Besançon*, 269-79.

Le Roy Ladurie, E. (1967) *Histoire du climat depuis l'an mil*.

Lüdi, W. (1951) Problèmes relatifs aux palafittes, *Archives suisses d'anthrop. générale* 16, 129-59.

Lumley, H. de *et al.* (1976) Le cadre chronologique et paléoclimatique du Postglaciaire, in Guilaine, J. (ed.) *La Préhistoire française*, 2, 4-16. Nice: Actes du IXe Congrès UISPP.

Magny, M. (1978) *L'évolution du climat dans le domaine subalpin pendant le Néolithique et la Protohistoire : éléments d'approche*. Besançon: unpublished doctoral dissertation.

Markgraf, V. (1974) Paleoclimatic evidence derived from timberline fluctuations, in *Les méthodes quantitatives d'étude des variations du climat au cours du Pléistocène*, Colloques internat. du CNRS no.219, 67-78.

Matthey, F. (1971) *Contribution à l'étude de l'évolution tardi- et postglaciaire de la végétation dans le Jura Central*. Berne.

Millotte, J.-P. (1963) *Le Jura et les plaines de Saône aux Ages des Métaux*. Paris: Les Belles-Lettres.

Olive, P. (1972) La région du Lac Léman depuis 10000 ans: données paléoclimatiques et préhistoriques, *Rev. de géog. phys. et de géol. dyn.* 16/3, 253-64.

Paret, O. (1958) *Le mythe des cités lacustres*. Paris: Dunod.

Petrequin, P. *et al.* (in press) *L'habitat néolithique et protohistorique du quartier Saint-Paul*. Bescançon.

Quantin, A. (1935) Le climat du Jura, *Bull. Soc. Bot. Française* 105, 8-11.

Reinerth, H. (1936) *Das Federseemoor als Siedlungsland der Vorzeitmenschen*. Leipzig.

Reinerth, H. (1940) *Pfahlbauten am Bodensee*. Leipzig.

Wegmüller, S. (1966) Über die spät- und postglaziale Vegetationsgeschichte des südwestlichen Jura, *Beitr. zur geobot. Landes. Schweiz* 48.

Swiss Midland-lakes and climatic changes

Lake-sediments, level-changes and climatic fluctuations

The fact that lake-levels fluctuate has of course been considered before. The palynological pioneer W. Lüdi pointed out as long ago as 1935 that the lake-system of the western Swiss lakes shows many fluctuations in postglacial times.

Ammann (1975) took up this matter again and came to a similar but somewhat simpler curve than Lüdi. Winiger (1976) propagated the idea of level-changes and postulated a 'level-chronology'. I have shown (1979) that the principle of Lüdi's work is right but the fluctuations differ in detail considerably, as many chronologically fixed Neolithic and Bronze Age settlements at the lake-shores show. Magny deals with the same phenomenon in his thesis and in his later works (1979, 1980). Furger has enlarged and detailed variations for the Horgen period at Twann (Lake of Bienne). In every attempt at the reconstruction of fluctuation-curves archaeological dates have played an important role. I will come back to the subject, as we can now correlate sites from different lakes by dendrochronology, and I here postulate a direct connection of *lake-level fluctuations and climate*. If we are able to date these changes we are also enabled to erect a climatic time-scale.

Evidence of lake-level changes

Since the time of Ferdinand Keller's first *Pfahlbaubericht* in 1854 people have believed in lake-dwellings. In the early twenties of this century Reinerth argued that they might be lake-shore settlements, but he later helped to reconstruct a lake-dwelling museum at Unteruhldingen (Lake of Constance) where a village is sunk on piles into the lake in spite of knowledge to the contrary. So it was the late Emil Vogt who in 1954–5 celebrated the centenary of lake-dwellings by denying their very existence. Nowadays we have become more cautious and conciliatory with each other, and try to decide site by site if it was a construction directly on earth, raised above it, or of some other kind. As a matter of fact one has to be careful; certainty is impossible because settlements of all types of construction do really exist in all environments. I believe along with Strahm and Winiger, however, that they should – having regard to the strong annual fluctuation – have stood on fairly high foundations. The problem is that we know almost nothing of the constructional side of settlements because of the heavy destruction of houses along the shores, at least of the larger lakes; on small lakes, on the other hand, these variations occur over a much smaller range, and the dynamic of waves, winds and so on

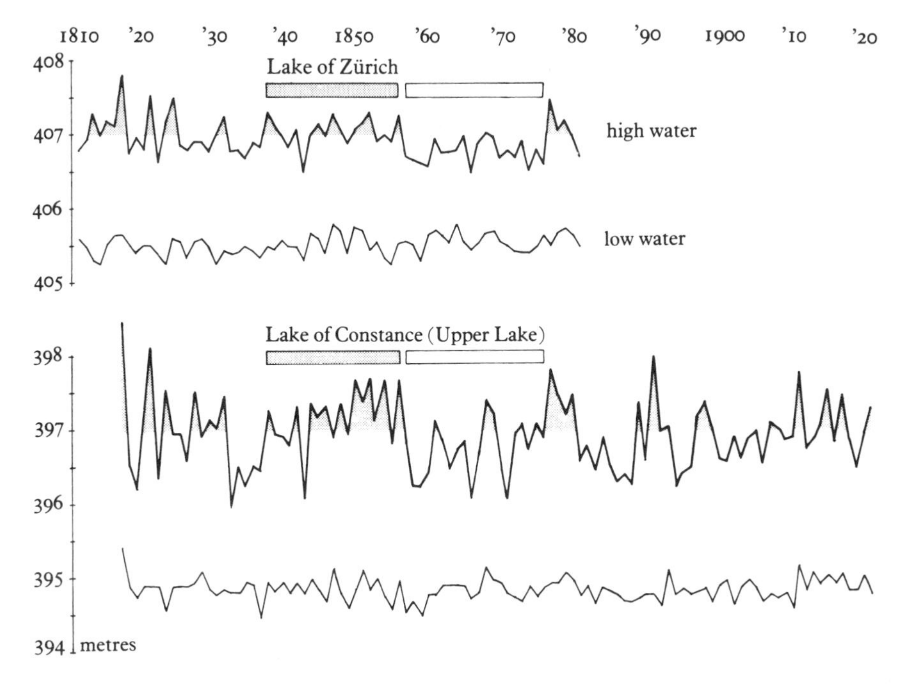

Figure 1. The behaviour of the levels of the lakes of Zürich and Constance in the periods 1811–80 and 1820–1960. The development of the fluctuations shows a certain correlation (after Ruoff 1976, Bertschinger 1967).

compared with those of the bigger ones has a much reduced effect.

In figure 1 we can see the lake-level changes of the last two centuries of two of the large lakes. Comparable data do not seem to be available for smaller lakes. Practically all the lake-systems analysed are controlled by man, so that the mode of variation and certainly the high water-levels are artificially influenced and have not developed in a purely natural manner. Small natural lakes, on the other hand, have not been analysed in recent years.

Low water-levels correspond to winter, whereas in spring levels begin to rise and in summer the lakes show their highest 'niveaux'. As the lakes in question are influenced by snow-melting they depend on the quantity of winter snow as well as moisture and wind throughout the year. It seems as if low-level periods correspond with slightly warmer and/or drier weather cycles (cf. Schweingruber *et al.* 1979, p.83, Schweiz. Verkehrszentrale 1979, p.43).

Stratigraphy of lake-settlements

Looking at the rather complicated stratigraphy of some sites in a generalised way, we find in a profile of lake-marl (or sandy loam) deposits of Neolithic and Bronze Age date. These demonstrate a constant moving of the lake-level for over 4000 years, if we agree that settlement took place during low levels while high levels interrupted settlement or pushed the sites inland. As shown by

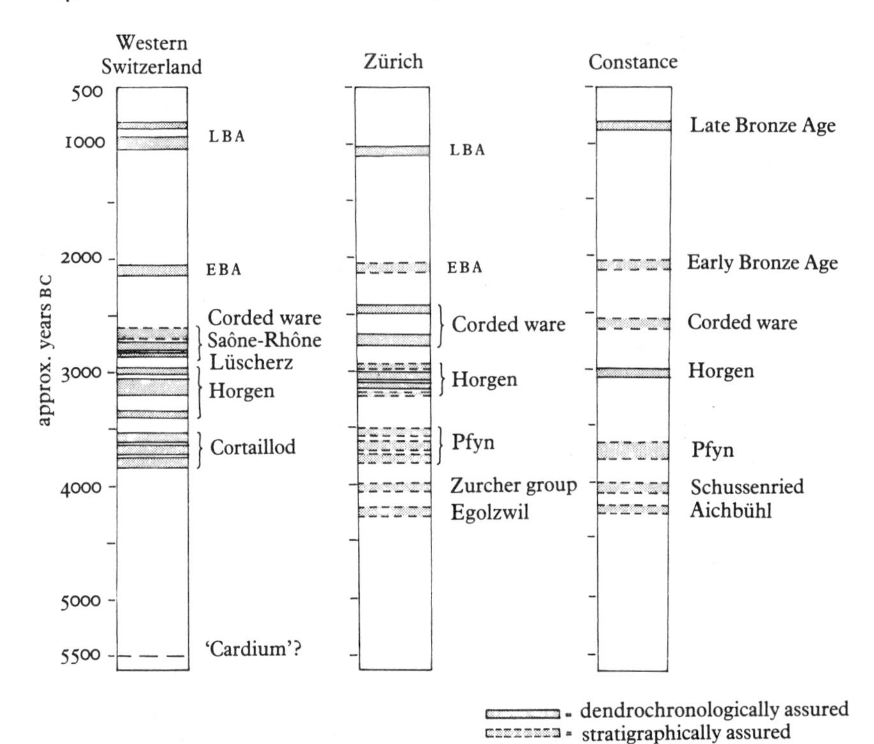

Figure 2. The chronology of lake-shore settlements in the Neolithic and Bronze Ages (mostly after Winiger).

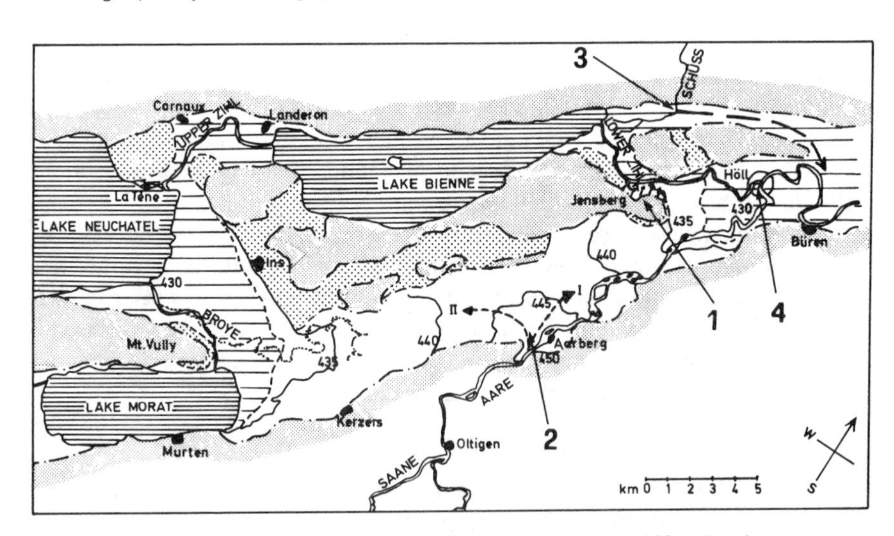

Figure 3. The western Swiss lake-system (Neuchâtel, Bienne and Morat) and the 'Grosse Moos', with the critical points: 1 Jensberg (landslide); 2 Aare (derivation); 3 Schüss (gravel accumulations); 4 Höll (gravel deposits). (Mostly after R.Müller 1973.)

archaeology as well as by sedimentology, low levels correspond with settled periods and high levels with unsettled periods of lake-marl production. We know very little of sites postulated to exist in high situations during flooding episodes, but in general, continuity of settlement is to be expected. Up till now it has not been possible to prove the absolute contemporaneity of settlement at one lake or one lake-system with another, because neither the typological classification nor radiocarbon dating provided an absolute correlation, which is of course a necessary postulate.

Lake-marl production in the littoral zone is also a very unreliable criterion because the normal ratio of 1 mm/year can very often change through erosion to a high rate of accumulation, so that no sure conclusion on an exact time-span can be made from the thickness of a layer. (I owe thanks for as yet unpublished information in figure 2 to H. Schwab and H. Egger.)

Reasons for lake-level changes

We can point to three main reasons for lake-level changes: one that we might call *geological*, a second *anthropogenic* and a third we believe to be *climatic*.

By *geological reasons* we understand events such as gravel transport, land-slip and landslide, river derivation and so on. High levels resulting thereby usually occur only locally, that is at one lake, and for a fairly short time. One can exclude climatic causation when the local character of a high lake-level is provable.

The behaviour of the Western Swiss lakes is, for instance, very complex. Landslides, gravel-accumulation and the filling up of the main drainage channel by sediments as well as river derivation all occur in this system. Landslides in the Jensberg are dated back to the Mesolithic period; the outflow of the Aare-river into the lake-system once or more than once leads to extremely high levels in the lake-system, whereas its blocking effects or alternatively the possible influence of the small river Schüss at the overflow-area of the Lake of Bienne are so far practically unknown. But on the long time-scale of the Neolithic and Bronze Age periods, these effects are probably not very important (figure 3).

Besides geological reasons there exist also *anthropogenic influences* such as woodland-clearance for cultivation or drainage. This human influence we estimate to have been relatively small in prehistoric times, though the channelling of a river, which must have been a possible form of interference, would in some systems have had a very pronounced effect. Becker (1977) has shown by dendrochronology that the accumulation of tree-trunks in the lower courses of the rivers Main and Danube in the Early Bronze Age, in Roman times and in the Middle Ages are due to this kind of activity, reducing the land's ability to retain water and leading therefore to river aggradation.

These may also exert a small influence on the lakes, but cannot be the only reason for the supposed high levels in the Middle Bronze Age; Neolithic axe technology was already of a very high standard, and it is unlikely that simply because of the new copper and bronze axe-technology of the late Neolithic and

Early Bronze Age excessive woodland clearing led for the first time to high lake-levels. It does not seem logical either that there should be low levels in the Early Bronze Age and Late Bronze Age and high levels only in the Middle Bronze Age. High levels in the Middle Bronze Age, incidentally, are not yet proven, only very probable, because no sites have yet been found at low levels. There are, however, many archaeological finds of Middle Bronze Age date along the lake shores (Osterwalder 1971, p.39). An important colonisation of the Alpine valleys falls in this period mostly because of ore prospecting and trade, but as most lakes draw on a very large hinterland, we cannot believe this would have made an important contribution to lake-levels.

The simultaneous fluctuation of a majority or even all lakes, we believe, originates predominantly in *climatic changes*. They are of a supraregional character and can increasingly be fixed in time by dendrochronology. Palynological and other scientific methods do not indicate climatic variation very exactly; lake-levels respond in a much more sensitive manner, as can be seen in lake-shore stratigraphy.

Climatic changes and lake levels

On the one hand there obviously exists a close relationship between the changes of climate, woodlimits and glacier-movements (Schweiz. Verkehrszentrale 1971, p.37). On the other hand there is a great danger in overvaluing individual measurements. While a minority of glaciers may retreat, a majority can advance. As a positive mass balance of the glaciers means a higher humidity and/or a colder climate, one should also find a reaction at the lakes being somehow the final 'reservoir' of such processes.

The retreat of a majority of glaciers between 1855 and 1875 at the end of the 'Little Ice Age' can be seen at the same time at the Grindelwald-Glacier in the Bernese Oberland as well as at the Rhône-Glacier in the upper Valais (figure 4). We have to interpret this as a result of a climatic change which is manifested by a higher mean temperature in this same period. Compared with the behaviour of the lake-levels at the lakes of Constance and Zürich, one finds relatively low water-levels at both lakes for the same span of time (figure 1). This coincidence is naturally not discernible on a year-by-year basis, rather in moving mean values over a certain length of time; we also have to consider the fact that since the Middle Ages lakes have been regulated to a greater or lesser extent.

Any lake which is connected with the process of snow-melting in the Alps – and all large lakes *are* connected with this phenomenon – of course shows a typical annual fluctuation with low levels in winter and high levels in summer. At irregular intervals of some years there result extreme inundations and at intervals of some decades these culminate in a catastrophically high water-level. But of more importance is the mean level trend which seems to be directed by climatic effects (figure 1). As an inland lake usually receives its water from a fairly wide area and from a number of different glaciers, random effects are eliminated.

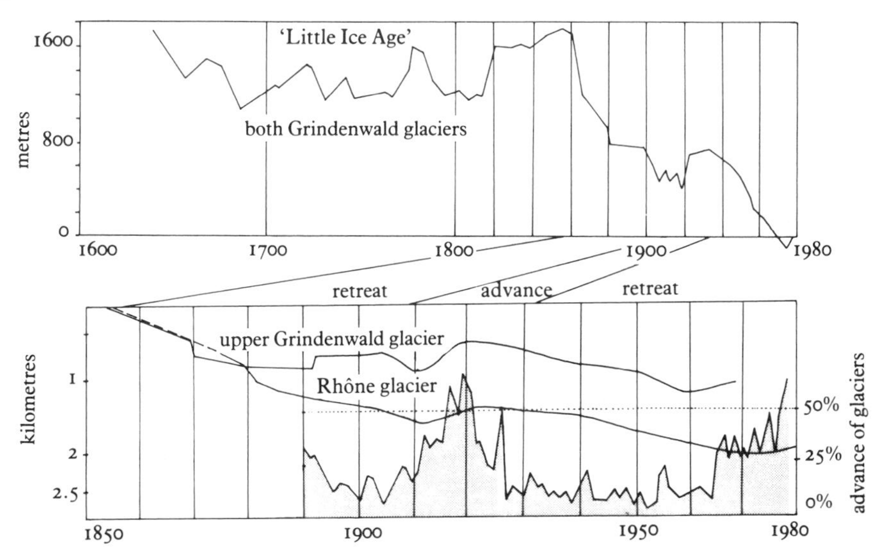

Figure 4. Comparison of two Swiss glaciers from the Bernese Oberland and the Upper Valais at the end of the 'Little Ice Age', between 1850 and 1875 in retreat, and between 1912 and 1922 advancing (compare figure 1). (Schweiz. Verkehrszentrale 1979.)

If we look closer at lake-shore stratigraphy, we find a lot of settlement-phases in the Neolithic and Bronze Age being interrupted by lake-marl deposition. From one lake to another we can see the same occupation phases, and by dendrochronological determination we are now increasingly able to correlate absolutely phases of simultaneous settlement. Nevertheless we are still unable to attribute many settled periods to geological factors. But several inundation-phases seem to be of much more local and/or short-term effect, for example geological and/or extreme meteorological conditions as Schindler (1971) has shown for Lake Zürich. We find only fairly short periods of low lake-levels in the Early and Late Bronze Age, whereas in the Middle Bronze Age we certainly have to reckon on high water-levels, there being no indication of settlement at the lake-shores for this period. On the other hand settlement in the hinterland is well demonstrated for the Middle Bronze Age.

Up till now published curves for lake-level fluctuations have differed very much from each other (figure 5), but we will soon be able to produce much more reliable curves as more and more data accumulate. In later periods archaeological dates for settlements become rather infrequent and we suffer from a lack of information. There were a few new activities on lake-shores, for instance in harbours or stonepits. This lack of information will probably soon change by means of dendrodensity-measurements, from which we can hope to obtain more detailed information on the palaeoclimate. Promising as this method looks, it would be only right to expect to find the same fluctuations both in lake-levels and in dendrodensity-measurements.

In the Hallstatt period we must mainly reckon on high levels, whereas in La

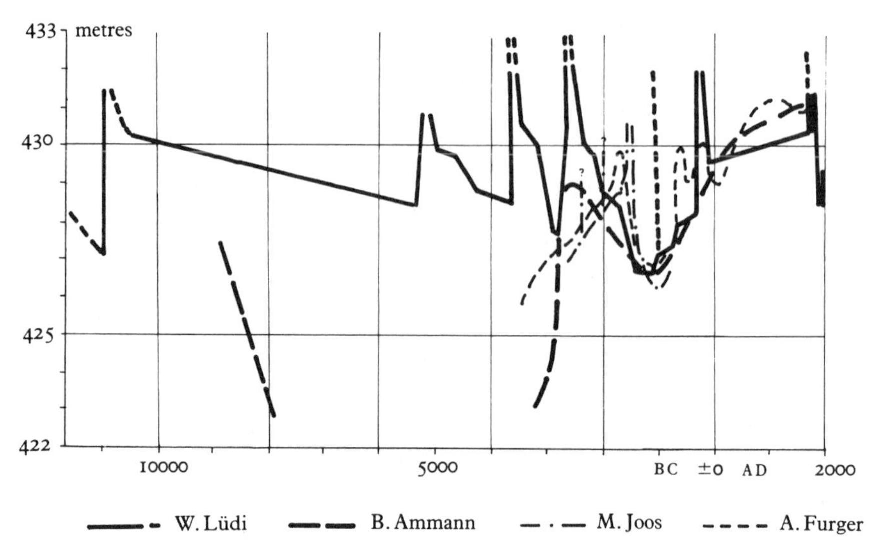

Figure 5. Fluctuations of the level of Lake Neuchâtel in the Holocene period according to various authors: W. Lüdi 1935, B. Ammann 1975, M. Joos 1976, A. Furger 1980.

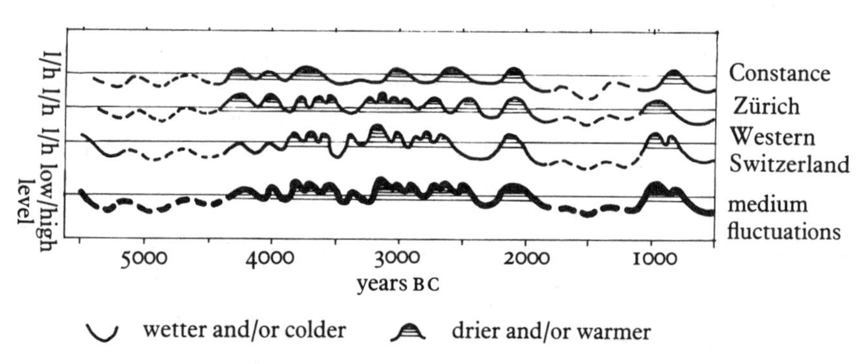

Figure 6. Attempts at a more theoretical curve of fluctuation created from the stratigraphic sequence of settled and unsettled periods (compare with figure 2).

Tène and during the Roman period we have several dates for both high and low levels. In the tenth/eleventh centuries AD, low lake-levels in Poland coincide with those in France at the Lake of Paladru near Grenoble (according to papers at the 2nd International Congress for the archaeological exploration of inland waters, Zürich, 12–14 March 1981, by M. Collardelle and M. Jasinski). These dates fit quite well into the Sub-atlantic optimum, whereas the following 'Little Ice Age' brings higher water-levels, and not only to the Swiss lakes.

Figure 6 presents a model of fluctuation of lake-levels for the Neolithic and Bronze Age periods in a rather simple way, without special regard to the common trend of lake-level evolution of the chosen lakes.

In my opinion we should continue to collect dates from the Atlantic to

Sub-atlantic periods, and this could help us greatly in increasing our knowledge of climatic changes in periods with a lack of 'conventional' information.

REFERENCES

Ammann-Moser, B. (1975) Vegetationskundliche und pollenanalytische Untersuchungen auf dem Heidenweg im Bielersee. *Beitr. geobot. Landesaufn. Schweiz* 56.

Ammann, B. *et al.* (1980) *Die neolithischen Ufersiedlungen von Twann, Band 6. Die Profilkolonne X/42.* Bern.

Becker, B. & Frenzel, B. (1977) Paläoökologische Befunde zur Geschichte postglazialer Flussauen im südlichen Mitteleuropa, *Erdwissenschaftliche Forschung* 13, 43-61.

Bertschinger, H. (1967) Bodenseeregulierung, *Terra Grischuna* 5, 259-62.

Furger, A. (1980) *Die neolithischen Ufersiedlungen von Twann Bd. 7. Die Siedlungsreste der Horgener Kultur.* Bern.

Joos, M. (1976) Geologische und sedimentologische Aspekte von Yverdon-Garage Martin, in Kaenel (1976).

— (1979) *Seespiegelschwankungen grösserer Mittellandseen.* Unpublished MS.

Kaenel, G. (1976) *La fouille du 'Garage Martin _ 1973'. Précision sur le site de Clendy à Yverdon (Néolithique et âge du Bronze).* Cah. d'Arch. Romande 8, Lausanne.

von Känel, H. M. *et al.* (1980) *Das Seeland in ur- und frühgeschichtlicher Zeit.* Bern.

Keller, F. (1854) Die keltischen Pfahlbauten in den Schweizerseen, *Mitt. Antiquar. Ges. in Zürich* 9, 67-100.

Lüdi, W. (1935) *Das Grosse Moos im westschweizerischen Seelande und die Geschichte seiner Entstehung.* Veröff. Geobot. Inst. Rübel Zürich 11, Bern.

Magny, M. (1979) Atlantique et Subboreal: humidité et sécheresse? *Rev. Arch. de l'Est* 115-16, 57-65.

— (1980) Fluctuations lacustres et paléoclimatologie postglaciaire, in *L'environnement naturel de l'homme préhistorique.* Geneva.

Müller, R. (1973) *Über die Wasserstände der Juraseen.* Freiburg.

Osterwalder, C. (1971) Die mittlere Bronzezeit in Mittelland und Jura, in *Ur- und frühgeschichtliche Archäologie der Schweiz* 3, 27-40. Basel.

Reinerth, H. (1922) *Pfahlbauten am Bodensee.* Stuttgart-Augsburg.

Ruoff, U. (1976) Tauchuntersuchung bei der Pfyner Siedlung Horgen 'Dampfschiffsteg', *Jahrb. der Schweiz. Ges. für Ur- und Frühgeschichte* 59, 57-75.

Schindler, C. (1971) Geologie von Zürich und ihre Beziehung zu Seespiegelschwankungen. *Vierteljahresschr. Naturf. Ges. Zürich* 2, 284-313.

Schweingruber, F. H. *et al.* (1979) Stand und Anwendung der Dendrochronologie in der Schweiz. *Zeits. für Archäologie und Kunstgeschichte* 36, 2, 69-90.

Schweiz. Verkehrszentrale (ed.) (1979) *Die Schweiz und ihre Gletscher.* Zürich.

Strahm, C. (1972-3) Les fouilles d'Yverdon, *Jahrb. der schweiz. Ges. für Ur- und Frühgeschichte* 57, 7-16.

Vogt, E. (1955) Pfahlbaustudien, in *Das Pfahlbauproblem.* Monogr. Ur- und Frühgeschichte Schweiz 11, 119-219. Basel.

Winiger, J. & Joos, M. (1976) *Feldmeilen-Vorderfeld, Die Ausgrabungen 1970/71.* Antiqua 5, Basel.

Winiger, J. (1980-1) *Der Stand der neolithischen Forschung in der Schweiz 1980.* Unpublished lecture script, University of Basel.

Problems of correlating Flandrian sea-level changes and climate

Sea-level changes may be regarded as a proxy record of climatic change, and notwithstanding the numerous problems of absolute dating there is a high positive correlation between ocean levels and temperature, generally reflected *via* the amount of water held within ice sheets, throughout the Quaternary Period when viewed at a suitable, generalised, scale. However glacial-eustasy and temperature are not the sole components of sea-level and climatic change (e.g. Mörner 1976a, fig.5; 1977, fig.12) and it is necessary to assess the relevant variables at different temporal and spatial scales. The stability of a system, the input to it and its output, the status of the variables and the controls of a system all vary through time (Schumm and Lichty 1965). Climate and sea-level changes during the past 10,000 years have not been uniform in either amplitude or direction over the whole Earth and it is necessary to assess the scales over which the reconstructions made from individual sites and study areas can be considered representative. Since the whole record will not be revealed at a single site, correlation of data is necessary at various stages of analysis. This requires the accurate definition of terms and for these terms to be used in different areas, before the first stages of correlation can be attempted. These requirements are rarely fulfilled, thus invalidating many conclusions which themselves become incorporated within subsequent models or as corroborating evidence for new models.

In this paper the problems of interpreting sea-level data are considered. They must be solved before any correlation with climatic variables can be attempted, otherwise the tendency is to adopt a circular argument while trying to find supporting evidence for a new hypothesis.

Operational definitions

The ambiguous use of basic terms must be avoided but unfortunately the few conventions that exist are not adhered to. The sea-level literature is full of references to the terms 'transgression' and 'regression', and there are various ways of referring to relative and absolute age.

'Transgression' and 'regression' are common terms in the description of sequences, processes and chronologies (e.g. Devoy 1979; Jardine 1975; Jelgersma 1961, 1979; Mörner 1969; Tooley 1974, 1978). Each author uses the terms in a slightly, but significantly, different sense (see Shennan 1980a for a more complete review) thus invalidating subsequent correlations of sea-level changes (e.g. Devoy 1979, fig.31; Tooley 1974, fig.11). It has been suggested by Shennan (1980a, 1982) and Tooley (1982) that the terms transgression and regression are totally unsuitable as formal chronostratigraphic terms and should be used only for process and lithostratigraphic descriptions. They are not synonymous with a rise and fall in sea-level and this is made clear by adoption of the terms 'transgressive overlap' and 'regressive overlap'.

Because of such basic inconsistencies most sea-level data cannot be used in their published form. Re-classification and re-evaluation of the data are required before meaningful correlations are possible. It can be argued that even if the sea-level data currently used for correlations between different areas (in some cases involving climate) were all defined in a suitable form, the techniques of correlation are rarely developed beyond the visual similarities of two or more curves upon a graph. More reliable techniques of correlation are required.

Time-series correlation of sea-level and climatic data

Numerous authors have presented diagrams claiming to show significant correlations between various sea-level chronologies and/or palaeoclimatic variables (e.g. Devoy 1979, fig.31; Fairbridge and Hillaire-Marcel 1977, fig.2; Geyh 1980, fig.5; Mörner 1973, fig.2; 1977, fig.11) yet no attempt is made to indicate the 'goodness-of-fit' between the various chronologies. This is regardless of the interpretation given to the apparent agreement between the variables.

Hillaire-Marcel and Fairbridge (1978, pp.121–2) present eight separate curves relating to changes in sea-levels and climate and claim 'a high level of coincidence' but no measurement of this coincidence is given. Furthermore it is unclear exactly what is being compared: 'It is notable that in the two curves . . . the major regressions and transgressions in excess of 2 to 3 m appear to coincide', yet according to the published diagrams, one curve refers to the altitudinal changes of eustatic sea-level while the other depicts the rate of sea-level change in the Hudson Bay area.

Theoretically, in view of the fact that this refers to the *rate* of sea-level change, the positions of zero-change, and not the peaks or troughs, should coincide with the maxima and minima of the first curve and the reasons why this should not be expected are not explained.

Equivocal statements regarding the correlation of sequences made by Devoy (1979) were noted by Shennan (1980a) and similarly the 'coincident minima' discussed by Geyh (1980) are given no statistical significance. All of these criticisms are in addition to the unreliability of the original data sets being compared. For example Tooley's (1974) sequence of marine 'transgressions', Lytham I–IX, is often quoted as lending support to other 'transgression/regression' sequences (e.g. Devoy 1979; Mörner 1976b, 1979; Hillaire-Marcel and Fairbridge 1978) yet owing to poor operational definitions and recent new information the chronology has been revised (Tooley 1982). Even without the new information the different operational definitions of transgression and regression by different authors should have inhibited further correlation a long time before 1980 when Shennan (1980a) first pointed out the inconsistencies.

These criticisms indicate that at present it is not reliable, or desirable, to use much of the sea-level data in correlation schemes with other palaeoclimatic data unless the reliability and significance of the original data are clearly understood. Few authors expressly state that sea-level data are only estimates, and therefore the reconstruction of past levels, processes and periods are also estimates of limited reliability. Mörner (1980) suggests that his curve is accurate to 0.1 m and that the time resolution is no better than 100–200 years. A similar age accuracy is given by Shennan (1980a, b, 1982) while the estimate of past levels from the Fenland of eastern England shows a much larger altitudinal error. This may be due, in part, to specific difficulties of interpreting the sediment suites involved. The resolution of these errors must be considered in the methods available for comparing sea-level curves from different areas.

Time series analysis

This is the most reliable method of comparing sea-level changes from different areas since the errors affecting the reconstruction of past altitudes (e.g. estimates of indicative meaning, past tide-levels, consolidation, local geotectonic factors, errors in measuring altitude) will obscure significant changes in dominant processes through time (Shennan, 1982). A similar argument was inferred by Mörner (1973) but nevertheless sea-level index points that are recording obviously different processes have continued to be represented by a smooth curve (e.g. Kidson and Heyworth 1978).

Streif (1979) and Shennan (1980a, 1982) have put forward the concept of 'tendencies of sea-level movement'. While it is unwise to interpret a single sea-level index point as representing a regionally significant process, each sea-level index point will reflect a tendency of sea-level movement. Cumulative tendencies of radiocarbon-dated sea-level index points showing the same direction of tendency of sea-level movement, with undated sea-level index points confirming the lithostratigraphic correlation where possible, can be used to identify periods dominated by positive tendencies of sea-level movement and others dominated by negative tendencies of sea-level movement (Shennan 1980a, b, 1982). While there is incontrovertible evidence that microfossil analysis of intercalated peats and marine clastic deposits can reveal periods of rising watertable and falling watertable, the relationship to regional sea-level movements is not necessarily so clear since the whole system is governed by the ecologically relevant hydrology, of which sea-level change is only one component (Streif 1979). Changes in the time and space environments, which can be measured in both horizontal and vertical dimensions in Flandrian sequences, must be assessed to get a reliable interpretation even of the tendency of sea-level movement.

The main discussion in present sea-level studies relates to the interpretation of the regressive overlap. There is little objection to a regressive overlap representing a relative fall in sea-level in space/time situations, apparently, other than within the sedimentary sequence of Flandrian age in a subsiding area (see Shennan 1980a, pp.222–5). It is worthwhile repeating Mörner's model relating eustatic and relative sea-level curves in which it becomes obvious that the registration of negative tendencies of sea-level movement in a subsiding area and the registration of positive tendencies of sea-level movement in an uplifted area are likely to have a regional, possibly eustatic, origin (Mörner 1969).

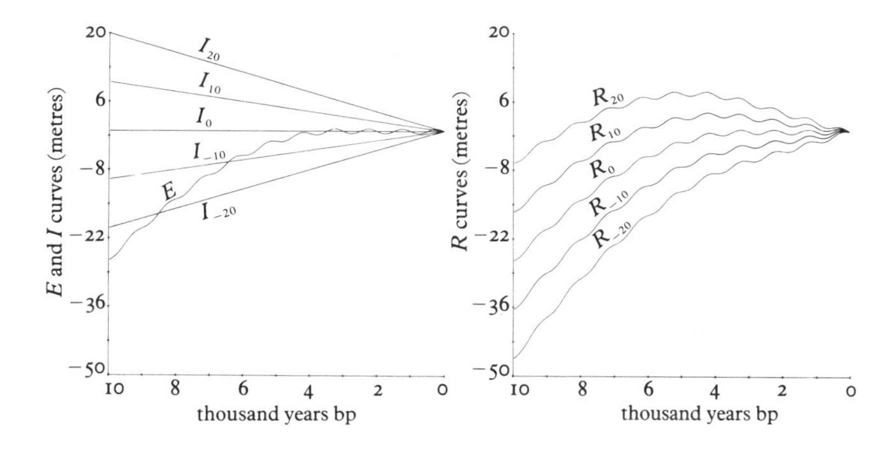

Figure 1. (a) Simulated eustatic sea-level curve (E) and five isostatic recovery curves ($I_{20} \ldots I_{-20}$) showing +20 . . . −20 m crustal movement over 10,000 years. (b) Resultant relative sea-level curves ($R_{20} \ldots R_{-20}$) calculated as explained in the text.

The model can be refined to aid the development of techniques for correlating sea-level chronologies from different areas. Figure 1 is an adaptation of the model using curves rather than straight lines in order to study the rate of change at suitable scales. Figure 1a shows a hypothesised eustatic curve and the isostatic curves for five regions. The isostatic factor is constant at +20, +10, 0, −10 and −20 cm/100 yr for the respective areas. These are not intended to model any particular 'real' areas. The eustatic curve is calculated from the following equations:

$$T < 3100 \quad E = 0.5 \sin(T\pi/500)$$

$$T > 3100 \quad E = 0.5 \sin(T\pi/500) + 50(\cos((T-3100)\pi/2000)-1)$$

where T = time in years BP and E = eustatic sea-level. The resultant curve approximates to a generally smoothly rising curve reaching present sea-level at 3100 BP with superimposed oscillations of 1 m amplitude and 1000-year wavelength. Figure 1b represents the relative sea-level curves, R_{20}, R_{10}, R_0, R_{-10}, R_{-20}, for the five areas calculated from the sum of the eustatic curve and the relevant uplift curve. Clearly the oscillations of the eustatic curve are represented in all five relative sea-level curves but their form varies from curve to curve and through time. In order to use a technique which can be applied to

Table 1. Periods of simulated positive and negative movements of sea-level in years BP. (Only the beginnings of the periods are shown, since the sequence is continuous.)

	Region				
Movement	R_{20}	R_{10}	R_{0}	R_{-10}	R_{-20}
−	360	300	250	200	140
+	640	700	750	800	860
−	1360	1300	1250	1200	1140
+	1640	1700	1750	1800	1860
−	2360	2300	2250	2200	2140
+	2640	2700	2750	2800	2860
−	3340	3290	3230	3190	3140
+	3680	3740	3790	3860	3970
−	4280	4230	4180	4120	4020
+	4750	4810	4870	10000	10000
−	5220	5170	5110		
+	5820	5880	10000		
−	6160	6100			
+	6890	10000			
−	7090				
+	10000				

'real' data sets the method of correlation should depend as little as possible on the need for accurate reconstruction of altitude. There will be only a few areas where the rate of change of sea-level movement can be accurately measured (e.g. Fairbridge and Hillaire-Marcel 1977, Mörner 1969) but the identification of periods dominated by specific tendencies should be possible in more areas (Shennan 1980a, b, 1982). The curves in figure 1b can be represented by periods of positive or negative movements of sea-level with no complicating local factors, such as variable rates of deposition or erosion or consolidation etc., which affect real data. These periods are given in table 1, and were taken from the original equations and rounded to the nearest 10 years.

The results from figure 1b and table 1 are obvious and predictable but not always considered. From subsiding areas only the periods of negative tendencies reflect true regional changes, but are shorter than the 'real' events and in uplifted areas only the periods of positive tendencies reflect true regional changes, and similarly underestimate the duration of the 'real' events. The degree of underestimation and the significance of the local oscillations depends on the position in time and the amplitude and wavelength of the sine and cosine functions given earlier. In the real world these would approximate to the different order cycles indicated by Mörner (1973). In a re-run of the simulation the amplitude of the sine curve was set at 2 metres and the greatest difference between the onset of the last period of negative tendencies was 100 years (cf. 220 years, table 1); the subsiding area R_{-20} recorded a first period of negative tendencies from 6080 to 5910 (cf. 4020 to 3970, table 1). Therefore, while only the time-series of different curves are being compared, the periods of agreement and disagreement indirectly reflect the relative amplitude for the shorter-term oscillations; high-amplitude oscillations should show greatest synchroneity.

Curves from two areas can be compared in the first instance by using a matching coefficient. This can be used when discrete states are compared, that is positive or negative tendencies, and the variables need not be in numerical form. The simplest coefficient of this type is the matching coefficient S_{sm} (Harbaugh and Merriam 1968) which is defined as the proportion of agreements to the total comparisons (agreements plus disagreements):

$$S_{sm} = m/n$$

where S_{sm} = the coefficient, m = number of matches, n = total number of comparisons. More than two curves can be represented by a matrix of matching coefficients. Using the present data comparisons could be made between two curves for every 10-year unit. The only case where $S_{sm} = 1.00$ would be R_0 vs E. Since R_{-20} is a subsiding zone only the periods of negative tendencies should correlate with regional events, and by limiting the comparisons to such periods then $S_{sm} = 1.00$ for R_{-20} vs E.

When $S_{sm} \neq 1.00$ then it is necessary to measure the possibility of the observed number of matches occurring by chance. An adaptation of the matching coefficient is 'cross-association' and this technique allows a χ^2 test to be carried out (Davis 1973, Harbaugh and Merriam 1968). These authors describe how cross-association can be used to compare two or more geological sequences by moving the overlapped sequences past each other until the position of greatest similarity is found. With absolute time series of sea-level chronologies only one position is being tested unless there is some reason for shifting the records, perhaps ±100 years to allow for the errors of age estimates. This shifting may or may not improve the correlation. In the context of comparing radiocarbon-dated periods of sea-level tendencies it is probably unrealistic to attempt correlations finer than the nearest fifty years. The cross-association tests have been applied to both simulated and real sea-level data using the following formulae:

$$Pr_m = \frac{\sum_{k=1}^{h} (X_{1k}.X_{2k})}{n_1.n_2}$$

$$Pr_{mm} = 1 - Pr_m$$

$$E_m = j.Pr_m$$

$$E_{mm} = j.Pr_{mm}$$

$$\chi^2 = \frac{(O_m - E_m)^2}{E_m} + \frac{(O_{mm} - E_{mm})^2}{E_{mm}}$$

where

h = number of possible categories into which observations can be classed,

X_{1k} = number of observations in the kth state of series 1,

X_{2k} = number of observations in the kth state of series 2,

n_1 = total length of series 1, i.e. $\sum_{k=1}^{h} X_{1k}$

n_2 = total length of series 2, i.e. $\sum_{k=1}^{h} X_{2k}$

Pr_{m} = probability of a match at any position of comparison in a random series equivalent to the series considered,

Pr_{mm} = probability of a mismatch etc.,

j = number of positions of comparison,

E_{m} = expected number of matches,

E_{mm} = expected number of mismatches,

O_{m} = observed number of matches,

O_{mm} = observed number of mismatches, and

χ^2 = chi-squared statistic (one degree of freedom).

Reasonable care is required in choosing the data sets to be compared. Individual peaks or troughs, or discrete events, can be analysed separately by using S_{sm} but when whole series are to be compared the length of the sequences analysed must be limited to where changes in category are recorded. For example, the comparison of the curves R_{-10} and R_{-20} for the whole 10,000-year period would be pointless since the significance of the similarity of the alternating tendencies after 4120 BP (2170 bc) would be unclear. This is because in the pre-4120 BP series neither sequence exhibits any change in tendency. The length of the sequences compared must be restricted to where changes in the discrete states occur.

The only data sets presently available for direct comparison are the Fenland / Wash sequence described by Shennan (1982) and the sequence of periods of transgressive and periods of regressive overlap from north-west England described by Tooley (1982). The latter are defined from 78 radiocarbon dates and the periods of overlap have been defined purely by the mean of the maximum radiocarbon date of a continuous run of dates on similar stratigraphic boundaries. The number of dates used to define a period varies between 1 and 10. There are gaps within the sequence since the periods of overlap have not been defined as periods of dominant tendency by detailed reference to the stratigraphy and micropalaeontological analysis. The Wash/Fenland sequence (Shennan 1980a, b, 1982) is continuous since the interpretational step to classify all the available evidence as tendencies of sea-level movement has been made. The two sequences are shown in figure 2. The Wash/Fenland scheme has been extended beyond 2500 BP (550 bc) but is not considered reliable beyond this date (Shennan, 1982) and the period 4200 to 3900 BP (2250–1950 bc) has also been omitted from further analysis since the dominant tendency appears to vary within the Fenland.

The first data set analysed consisted of each 50-year interval between 2500 and 6700 BP (550 and 4750 bc) for which both the Fenland and north-west England contain data. Coincident periods of positive tendency with transgressive overlap or negative tendency with regressive overlap are classed as a match and other combinations a mismatch. The overall matching coefficient $S_{sm} = 0.55$ and therefore it is necessary to use the cross-association test. This is given in table 2.

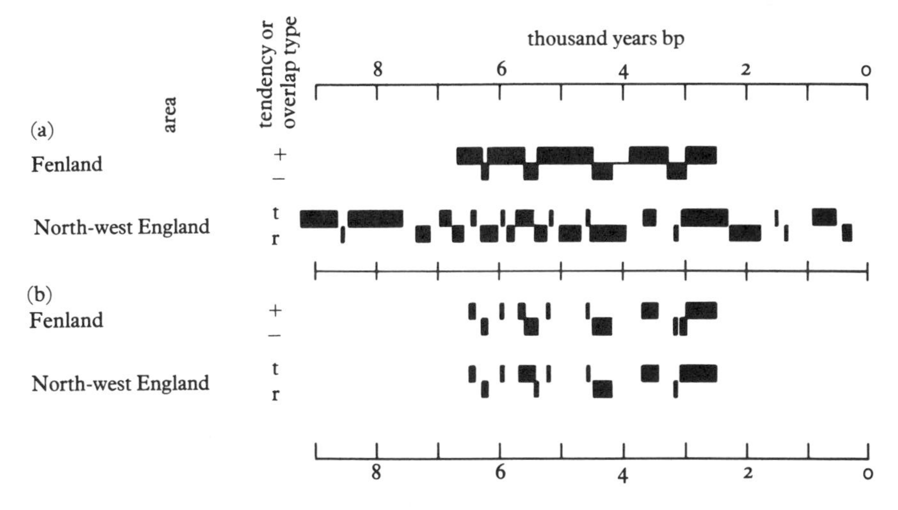

Figure 2. (a) 'Fenland' periods (negative tendencies of sea-level movement) and 'Wash' periods (positive tendencies) from the Fenland area (Shennan, in press) compared to periods of transgressive and regressive overlap from north-west England (Tooley, in press). (b) Periods of regional significance from figure 2a.

Clearly the χ^2 value is not significant at the 5 per cent level (indeed not at the 20 per cent level, see Davis 1973, table 3.16) and it must be concluded on the basis of this test that the observed number of matches between the two series is no greater than that expected from two random sequences of equivalent composition. For comparison a similar calculation was made for the simulated data for the period 2500 to 6700 BP (550 to 4750 bc) using R_{20} and R_{-20}. The results were $S_{sm} = 0.59$, $\chi^2 = 2.36$, which is not significant at the 10 per cent level but is significant at the 20 per cent level. This result was expected in view of the different uplift histories. For non-eustatic sea-level curves the regionally significant periods of positive and negative tendencies can only be evaluated when the crustal movements are considered. Therefore the simulated data from R_{20} and R_{-20} should only be compared when R_{20} indicates a positive tendency or R_{-20} shows a negative tendency. With this data set the result will obviously be $S_{sm} = 1.00$. The real data are complicated by local factors and problems of interpretation and a perfect fit cannot be expected, yet the regional effects can be identified by taking the known crustal movements into account.

The Fenland has been characterised by subsidence since at least 6500 BP

Table 2. Cross-association test between the Wash/Fenland sequence and the overlap sequence from north-west England (all data).

Category 1 = positive tendency or transgressive overlap
Category 2 = negative tendency or regressive overlap
Area A = Fenland
Area B = north-west England

	A	B	$X_{Ak} \cdot X_{Bk}$
1	45	28	1260
2	15	32	480
$\Sigma =$	60	60	1740

$Pr_m = 0.483$ $O_m = 33$
$Pr_{mm} = 0.517$ $O_{mm} = 27$
$E_m = 29$
$E_{mm} = 31$ $\chi^2 = 1.07$

For one degree of freedom, critical value for χ^2 at the 5% significance level = 3.84

(Shennan 1980a) while north-west England has undergone isostatic uplift for at least part of the Flandrian Age. As a working hypothesis only those periods where negative tendencies of sea-level movement have been recorded in the Fenland or where periods of transgressive overlap have been noted for north-west England should be considered. These are indicated in figure 2b. The matching coefficient $S_{sm} = 0.84$ and the cross-association test is given in table 3. This result suggests that the Fenland and north-west England chronologies represent non-random, therefore possibly regionally significant, tendencies of sea-level movement as given in table 4 (to the nearest 50 years). To aid

Table 3. Cross-association test: proposed regionally significant periods. Categories and areas as in table 2.

	A	B	$X_{Ak} \cdot X_{Bk}$
1	23	28	644
2	15	10	150
$\Sigma =$	38	38	794

$Pr_m = 0.55$ $O_m = 23$
$Pr_{mm} = 0.45$ $O_{mm} = 6$
$E_m = 20.89$
$E_{mm} = 17.11$ $\chi^2 = 13.12$

For one degree of freedom, critical value for χ^2 at the 5% significance level = 3.84

Table 4. Chronology of regionally significant periods

informal name	age (years BP)	S_{sm}	*n*
ppt1	6500–6400	1.00	2
pnt1	6300–6200	1.00	2
ppt2	6000–5950	1.00	1
ppt3	5750–5450	0.50	6
pnt2	5600–5400	0.25	4
ppt4	5250–5200	1.00	1
ppt5	4650–4600	1.00	1
pnt3	4500–4200	1.00	6
ppt6	3700–3450	1.00	5
pnt4	3200–3000	0.33	3
ppt7	3100–2500	0.83	12

description the informal names 'period of positive tendencies' (ppt) and 'period of negative tendencies' (pnt) have been used. There is overlap between ppt 3 and pnt 2 and between ppt 7 and pnt 4 but these fall within the estimated accuracy of ±100 years for the age limits.

This simple method of analysis offers a more objective method of correlating between time-series of discrete variables and when more data are available from both the Fenland and north-west England the identification of regionally significant tendencies can be extended. Similarly, correlations with other coastal units of the United Kingdom can also be attempted when the data have been adequately scrutinised. The technique should be viewed as the first stage in developing more reliable correlations between sea-level chronologies.

Time-altitude correlation

Statistical smoothing of time-altitude variates will not show absolute rises and falls of the sea-level surface because of the errors involved in estimating past altitudes given present techniques and methodology, yet time periods of local and regionally significant tendencies can be illustrated within a sea-level band (e.g. Shennan 1980a, fig.7.3; 1982, fig.4e). The representation of a series of sea-level index points by a smooth curve may be sufficiently accurate for certain studies but only when the confidence bands of the mean curve are known and taken into account. A single smooth sea-level curve can only be considered as misleading and certainly should not be used to differentiate between component variables within an altitudinal range of one or two metres (cf. van de Plassche 1980).

Time-altitude-space correlation

This method of environmental reconstruction remains a future aim for sea-level research when sequences of events can be compared spatially, including altitude, and through time. The exploratory work of van de Plassche (1980) represents a movement towards such analyses.

Histogram analyses

The analysis of radiocarbon data using cumulative histograms has been applied to the recognition of periods of coastline movement around the North Sea (Geyh 1969, 1971; Geyh and Streif 1970; Morrison 1976), to the solution of problems of Weichselian chronostratigraphy (Geyh and Rohde 1972), and to the age distribution of marine deposits of eastern Canada (Hillaire-Marcel and Occhietti 1977), and is likely to become an increasingly important technique, not just for sea-level studies, as more radiocarbon data become available. The method is essentially a time series analysis but differs from the techniques discussed earlier in two ways. First, the data need not always relate to any tendency of sea-level movement, and secondly the height of the histogram (or probability) as well as the representation of time must be analysed.

The basic technique is well known and has recently been summarised by Shennan (1980a). Once the histogram has been constructed the problems to be

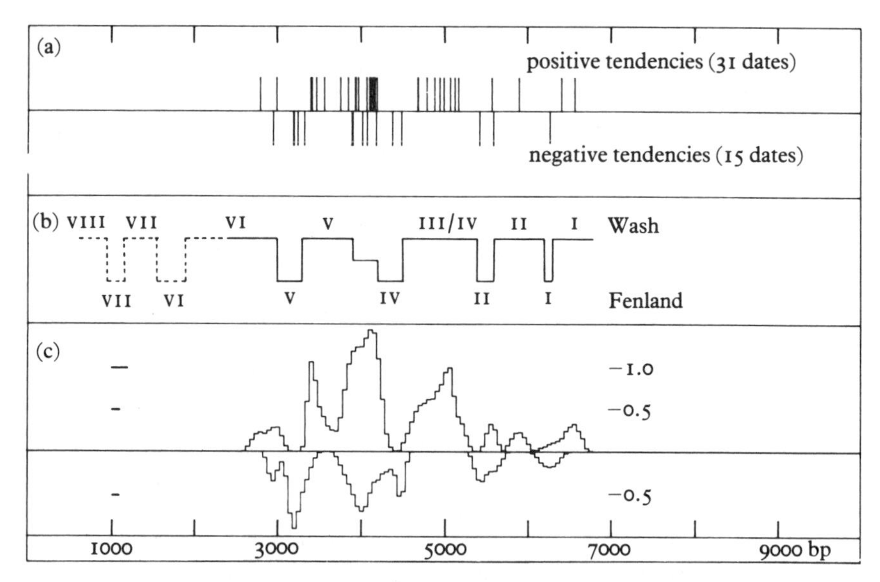

Figure 3. (a) Reliable radiocarbon data from the Fenland relating to positive and negative tendencies of sea-level movement. (b) Wash/Fenland chronology of positive and negative tendencies of sea-level movement. (c) Cumulative histograms of the radiocarbon data shown in figure 3a.

overcome are either statistical or interpretational. The former are in dealing with the problems of random fluctuations, the significance of the size of the maxima and minima and the number of radiocarbon data required (Geyh 1980, Shennan 1979). Further complications will arise with data sets exhibiting extreme positive or negative skewness or bimodality especially when the significance of maxima and minima are measured relative to an overall mean (cf. Geyh 1980) rather than some floating mean. The technique is still being developed but there remain too many uncertainties to allow conclusive statements regarding regional synchroneity of events to be made (Geyh 1980).

Once maxima and minima can be shown to be significant their geological interpretation must be assessed. The relationship of peat growth in the tidal flat and lagoonal zone to sea-level movement is not clear; it may form a regressive overlap but at the subsequent transgressive overlap relates to periods of rising water-levels. Histogram analyses may reveal regionally synchronous periods of peat growth in the tidal flat and lagoonal zone, but it is unclear how these relate to sea-level chronologies established by other methods. The technique also gives interesting correlations between the distortion of the radiocarbon time scale, regional, possibly global, sea-level changes, and climate (Geyh 1980) and therefore is a promising research technique for the future.

Morrison (1976) has used a quite different method of analysing radiocarbon histograms by separating the data into classes based on indicative meanings. The limitations and possible future developments have been discussed by

Table 5. Comparison of the original Wash/Fenland boundaries and those estimated by the histogram analysis

Original boundary	Period	Estimated boundary
	Wash I	
6300		6400
	Fenland I	
6200		6050
	Wash II	
5600		5750
	Fenland II	(5650 to 5550 + < −)
5400		5350
	Wash III/IV	
4500		4550
	Fenland IV	
4200/3900		4300
	Wash V	
3300		3350
	Fenland V	(3100 to 3000 + < −)
3000		2900
	Wash VI	

Shennan (1980a) and applied to the definition of periods of transgressive and regressive overlap and positive and negative tendencies (Shennan, 1982). Figure 3 represents the route followed by the analysis. There are at present 31 dates from the Fenland that relate unequivocally to positive tendencies of sea-level movement prior to 2500 BP (550 bc). Fifteen dates represent negative tendencies (figure 3a). By analysing these data along with other stratigraphic, micropalaeontological and radiocarbon data, a reliable chronology has been developed (figure 3b). Unfortunately few areas have been subjected to such reliable analyses even though there exist suitable series of radiocarbon dates. The radiocarbon data can be screened and classified and assuming that there is no extreme clustering of the data either through time or in space then the representation of the radiocarbon data as cumulative histograms may give a chronological scheme of positive and negative tendencies where the boundaries are defined by the points where the dominating tendency changes. The histograms are shown in figure 3c and table 5 compares the original boundaries (figure 3b) and those indicated by the histogram analysis. The agreement is generally good and suggests that where a lack of detailed stratigraphic and micropalaeontological data prevents the definition of limits to the periods of positive and negative tendencies of sea-level movement, then histogram analyses may give a scheme which can act as a working hypothesis for future research. In such a case the stage depicted by figure 3c would precede 3b.

Sea-level changes and climate

The preceding discussion indicates that the present state of sea-level research prevents detailed correlation of sea-level and climate. It is unrealistic to compare anything except the broadest changes while the altitudinal reconstructions of sea-levels lie within broad confidence bands. The palaeotemperature curve from Gotland (Mörner and Wallin 1976) may represent a significant advance in research but the variance of the original data (e.g. the isotope base data) deserves much more discussion.

Factors which complicate the correlation between sea-levels and climate include the unmeasured effects of changes in the geoid, frequencies of storms and surges, changes in sedimentation rates, consolidation of the different sediments, palaeo-tidal changes and associated changes in coastal geomorphology and processes, and changes in freshwater run-off. Some of these factors have occasionally been used to dismiss the regional significance of changes within coastal Flandrian sequences, particularly the significance of regressive overlaps or intercalated peat layers (e.g. Heyworth 1978; Kidson and Heyworth 1973, 1979; Jelgersma 1961, 1979).

If such periods are synchronous over wide areas and sea-level changes are refuted as being a major controlling variable, then widespread changes in any of the variables listed above would generally necessitate a change in some climatic variable. The problem is to isolate the relevant variables and the scales at which they control local and regional systems. Until reliable statements can be made regarding the basic sea-level data and the regional significance of similar sequences and tendencies the possibility of making detailed correlations with climatic changes does not exist.

Conclusions

The identification of past sea-level always entails correlation of data from individual sites through to correlation between regions. This correlation relates to age, altitude and location. Present methodologies do not allow all the errors to be considered and often the process of correlation is little in advance of visual comparison.

The scales at which the various data may be averaged are time-dependent and it is necessary to recognise the temporal and spatial scales at which the status of each variable is decided. Processes occurring over 10^1 years may be apparent but their absolute age, regional significance and correlation cannot be confirmed because of the analytical errors. Events occurring over periods of 10^2 years are likely to be more widely recorded yet dating techniques may still prevent unequivocal correlation.

Whether or not sea-level has fluctuated during the Flandrian Age is only important over the specific time-scale of the study, the area involved and the variables considered. Given the importance of recognising the predominant sea-level tendencies of a given period, and the fact that altitudinal synchroneity cannot be assessed for most regions, the associated altitudinal limits are totally dependent on the underlying problem. For time scales in excess of 10^3 years the sea-level band may be generalised and the alternations of periods of positive and negative tendencies may become insignificant as the time scale approaches 10^4 years, when the altitudinal data is only required in the most general terms. As the resolution decreases to 10^2 years the same variables reflected by the confidence band of the sea-level curve increase in importance yet their accuracy is unchanged. Generalisations that could relate to the longer periods can no longer be made. Long term variables may have changed their status from dependent to independent, the smaller-scale variables from indeterminable to dependent. As the time scale approaches 10^1 year the methods discussed in this paper become less applicable. The variance of the data is too great, the variables measured become independent and quite different research techniques are required. However, only by consideration of the relevant temporal and spatial scales can the applicability of research results be assessed.

At present it is only possible to indicate where the sea-level and climate records agree or disagree. Even if whole sequences correlate at a high level of significance the linkage in the system is not necessarily proved. The correlation may be *via* one or more other variables. Basic problems of interpretation of both sea-level data and the relationship between sea-level and climatic changes remain, for example global or regional changes of the same magnitude and/or direction, the effect of time-lags in process-response systems. Thus, while occasional correlations can be identified the linkages of the complex system cannot yet be measured. The statistical techniques presented here are basic. They only present the first stages of exploration of the data and need to be developed much further before sea-level changes can reliably be used as a proxy record of climatic change.

Acknowledgements

I am grateful to Dr M. J. Tooley, Mr B. A. Haggart and Mr M. J. Davis for their observations and criticisms during our discussions of this topic. I wish to thank Professor W. B. Fisher for the use of the excellent facilities at the Department of Geography, Mr D. Hudspeth for the photo-reduction of the diagrams, and Mrs M. Coffield for typing the manuscript. Much of the research of the Fenland data was carried out while in receipt of a NERC research studentship. Dr M A. Geyh carried out many new radiocarbon assays from the Fenland.

REFERENCES

Davis, J. C. (1973) *Statistics and data analysis in geology*. New York: John Wiley and Sons, Inc.

Devoy, R. J. N. (1979) Flandrian sea level changes and vegetational history of the lower Thames estuary, *Phil. Trans. R. Soc. Lond.* B 285, 355-410.

Fairbridge, R. W. & Hillaire-Marcel, C. (1977) An 8000 yr paleoclimatic record of the 'Double-Hale' 45yr solar cycle, *Nature* 268, 413-14.

Geyh, M. A. (1969) Versuch einer chronologischen Gliederung des marinen Holozäns an der Nordseeküste mit Hilfe der statistischen Auswertung von ^{14}C-Daten, *Z. dt. geol. Ges.* 118, 356-60.

— (1971) Middle and young Holocene Sea Level Changes as global contemporary events, *Geol. För. Stockh. Förh.* 93, 679-92.

— (1980) Holocene sea-level history: Case Study of the Statistical Evaluation of ^{14}C dates, *Radiocarbon* 22, 695-704.

Geyh, M. A. & Rohde, P. (1972) Weichselian Chronostratigraphy, ^{14}C Dating and Statistics, *Proceedings of the 24th International Geological Congress* (Montreal) Section 12, 27-36 (pre-print).

Geyh, M. A. & Streif, H. (1970) Studies on coastal movements and sea-level changes by means of the statistical evaluation of ^{14}C-data, *Proceedings of the Symposium on Coastal Geodesy (Munich)*, 599-611.

Harbaugh, J. W. & Merriam, D. F. (1968) *Computer Applications in Stratigraphic Analysis*. New York: John Wiley & Sons, Inc.

Heyworth, A. (1978) Submerged forests around the British Isles: their dating and relevance as indicators of Post-glacial land and sea level changes, in Fletcher, J. (ed.) *Dendrochronology in Europe*, British Archaeological Reports, Int. Series 51, 279-88.

Hillaire-Marcel, C. & Fairbridge, R. W. (1978) Isostasy and eustasy of Hudson Bay, *Geology* 6, 117-22.

Hillaire-Marcell, C. & Occhietti, S. (1977) Fréquence des datations au ^{14}C de faunes marines post-glaciaires de l'est du Canada et variations paléo-climatiques, *Palaeogeogr., Palaeoclimatol., Palaeoecol.* 21, 17-54.

Jardine, W. G. (1975) Chronology of Holocene marine transgression and regression in south-western Scotland, *Boreas* 4, 173-96.

Jelgersma, S. (1961) Holocene Sea Level Changes in the Netherlands, *Meded. Geol. Sticht.* serie C.VI 7, 1-100.

Jelgersma, S. (1979) Sea-level changes in the North Sea basin, in Oele, E., Schuttenhelm, R. T. E. & Wiggers, A. J. (eds) *The Quaternary History of the North Sea. Acta Univ. Ups. Symp. Univ. Ups. Annum Quingentesimum Celebrantis* 2, 233-48. Uppsala.

Kidson, C. & Heyworth, A. (1973) The Flandrian Sea-Level Rise in the Bristol Channel, *Proc. Ussher Soc.* 2, 565-84.

— (1978) Holocene eustatic sea level change, *Nature* 273, 748-50.

— (1979) Sea 'level', in Suguio, K. (ed.) *Coastal evolution in the Quaternary* 1-28, São Paulo.

Mörner, N-A. (1969) The Late Quaternary History of the Kattegatt Sea and the Swedish West Coast, *Sver. geol. Unders.* serie C. 640, 1-487.

— (1973) Climatic cycles during the last 35,000 years, *J. Interdiscipl. Cycle Res.* 4, 189-92.

— (1976a) Eustasy and Geoid changes, *J. Geol.* 84, 123-51.

— (1976b) Eustatic changes during the last 8,000 years in view of radiocarbon calibration and new information from the Kattegatt region and other north-western European coastal areas, *Palaeogeogr., Palaeoclimatol., Palaeoecol.* 19, 63-85.

— (1977) Palaeoclimatic records from South Scandinavia, global correlations, origin and cyclicity, in Shoji Horie (ed.) *Paleolimnology of Lake Biwa and the Japanese Pleistocene* 4, 499-528.

— (1979) South Scandinavian sea level records: a test of regional eustasy, regional palaeoenvironmental changes and paleogeoid changes, in Suguio, K. (ed.) *Coastal Evolution in the Quaternary* 77-103, São Paulo.

— (1980) The northwest European 'sea-level laboratory' and regional Holocene eustasy, *Palaeogeogr., Palaeoclimatol., Palaeoecol.* 29, 281-300.

Mörner, N-A. & Wallin, B. (1976) A 10,000 year temperature record from Gotland, Sweden, *Palaeogeogr., Palaeoclimatol., Palaeoecol.* 21, 113-38.

Morrison, I. A. (1976) Comparative stratigraphy and radiocarbon chronology of Holocene marine changes on the western seaboard of Europe, in Davidson, D. A. & Shackley, M. L. (eds) *Geoarchaeology*, 159-75. London: Duckworth.

van de Plassche, O. (1980) Holocene water level changes in the Rhine-Meuse delta as a function of changes in relative sea level, local tidal range and river gradient, *Geologie Mijnb.* 59, 343-51.

Schumm, S. A. & Lichty, R. W. (1965) Time, space and causality in geomorphology, *Am. J. Sci.* 263, 110-19.

Shennan, I. (1979) Statistical evaluation of sea-level data, *Sea Level Information Bull. of IGCP Project No.61*, 1, 6-11.

— (1980a) *Flandrian sea-level changes in the Fenland.* Unpublished Ph.D. Thesis, University of Durham.

— (1980b) The nature, extent and timing of marine deposits in the English Fenland during the Flandrian Age, in Königsson, L-K. & Paabo, K. (eds) *Florilegium Florinis Dedicatum. Striae* 14, 177-81.

— (1982) Interpretation of Flandrian sea-level data from the Fenland, *Proc. Geol. Ass.* 83, in press.

Streif, M. (1979) Cyclic formation of coastal deposits and their indications of vertical sea-level changes, *Oceanis* 5, 303-6.

Tooley, M. J. (1974) Sea-level changes during the last 9000 years in northwest England, *Geogr. J.* 140, 18-42.

— (1978) *Sea-Level Changes. North-West England during the Flandrian Stage.* Oxford: Clarendon Press.

— (1982) Sea-level changes in northern England, *Proc. Geol. Ass.* 83, in press.

Some British later prehistoric insect faunas and their climatic implications

Recent studies have shown that during Neolithic times a suite of beetle species was living in Britian many of whose members are today either extinct in this country or have had their ranges drastically reduced, sometimes down to a single locality. The fauna of which these species were a part seems to have been generally distributed in Britain during the Neolithic and in places persisted well into the Bronze Age, though it was clearly becoming broken up into relict populations. A few examples from this fauna are given below: *Rhysodes sulcatus* (F.) recorded from Shustoke, Warwickshire with a radiocarbon date of 4830±100 years BP (2880±100 bc) (Kelly & Osborne 1964), from the 'Baker' Neolithic site, Somerset Levels (Girling 1980) and from Thorne Moor, Yorkshire with a radiocarbon date 3090±90 BP (1140±90 bc) (Buckland 1979); *Isorhipis melasoides* (Lap.) from the Somerset 'Baker' site (*op. cit.*), Thorne Moor (*op. cit.*) and Misterton Carr, Lincolnshire, radiocarbon dated 4330±90 years BP (2380±90 bc) (Osborne, in prep.); *Pycnomerus terebrans* (Ol.), pollen zone VIIb, Church Stretton (Osborne 1972); *Prostomis mandibularis* (F.), recorded only from Thorne Moor so far (*op. cit.*).

These species represent a small but typical sample of a fauna which was apparently widespread in Britain between 5000 and 3000 years ago. All four are absent from Britain today and a number more could be quoted if space permitted, as well as a further group now so rare here as to be virtually extinct. The great majority of these insects are now to be found living on the continent considerably further south and a facile assumption might be made that they were all victims of a climatic deterioration. An examination of their ecology, however, shows that they are all dependent on a certain type of habitat, dense deciduous woodland, in which dead trees are allowed to decay where they fall.

This biotope was widespread in Britain until the advent of Neolithic agriculture. Destruction of forest for farming was at first localised but has continued at an accelerating rate to the present day when, of the original forest environment, almost nothing is left. Even the small patches of deciduous woodland still remaining have had a discontinuous history and still continue to suffer (as a beetle habitat) from 'tidying up' and 'clean forestry'. It is as likely, therefore, that the disappearance of the old forest fauna of pre-Neolithic time is due to destruction of its habitat by man as it is to deteriorating climate. In reality it is probable that a combination of these factors was responsible but which had the greater effect, or whether they contributed equally, is very difficult to say. Certainly a token remnant of this fauna may be found wherever patches of woodland have survived for a very long time. The New Forest

(Hampshire), Windsor Forest (Berkshire) and Moccas Park (Herefordshire) are classic examples. Furthermore, amongst those species which have become extinct in Britain or have become extremely localised, not all have moved south. A small number have gone north, either within these islands or, having become extinct here, are now found in Scandinavia and northern Europe (Osborne 1976). The climatic evidence from this period, therefore, is not unequivocal and will not be used in this paper.

During the Late Bronze Age, however, a new group of beetles started to attain prominence, encouraged, no doubt, by man's activities. This group was made up of species which inhabit open grassland. Some of these are grass root feeders such as the small chafer beetles and the larvae of some of the Elaterids, colloquially known as 'wireworms'; some live on the leaves of low plants like many of the *Chrysomelidae* and *Curculionidae* whilst many live in the droppings of large grazing animals. As the distribution of the members of this group should not have been adversely affected by the destruction of the forest habitat, nor, probably, by man's other activities until the advent of organo-chlorine pesticides and 'improved' grassland, they would seem to be a much better subject for the investigation of climatic effects than the woodland fauna whose habitat was being attacked at just the critical time. In the present paper, therefore, it is the author's intention to deal with evidence of past climates derived only from faunas of open grazing land and to leave aside the more complicated issues raised by the forest faunas recorded from Neolithic and Bronze Age times. Unfortunately few sites of this description have been entomologically investigated so far. Of these three will be described here.

Wilsford, Wilts. The first Bronze Age insect fauna to be investigated in detail was that from Wilsford, Wiltshire (Osborne 1969), from a cylindrical shaft which had been dug into the chalk about 1 mile from Stonehenge, excavated in 1960–2 (Ashbee 1963). At the bottom of the shaft, about 100 ft below the surface, beneath layers containing Roman, Iron Age and Bronze Age artefacts, was an accumulation of comminuted wood and other vegetable material, from which a radiocarbon date of 3330 ± 100 years BP (1380 ± 100 bc) was obtained. This matrix contained very numerous beetle remains in an excellent state of preservation.

The shaft, about six feet in diameter, had been plumbed and the digging corrected when necessary to maintain verticality. It stopped when a fault in the chalk which admitted water was reached. These facts, and the presence in the bottom of pieces of rope and fragments of wooden tubs seemed strongly suggestive to the author (who admittedly claims little knowledge of archaeology) that the purpose of the shaft was a well. This idea received support from the fact that a very large proportion of the insect fauna consisted of dung beetles, which might be expected to congregate around a well at which animals were watered.

A very extensive beetle fauna was recovered representing a minimum of 2600 individuals belonging to around 125 taxa. All the species recognised were typical of open country with no suggestion of trees in the vicinity. Only the furniture beetle, *Anobium punctatum* (Deg.), was found; this insect lives in dead wood and more often than not is found living in the dry, well-seasoned timber of man-made structures or furniture. If the hole was indeed a well some apparatus must have been present at the top to keep the animals from falling in and for hauling up buckets of water. As this would have been made from timber it would easily account for the presence of *Anobium*.

Apart from the anomalous *Melolontha hippocastani* (F.) which, in this country, has moved north, the entire assemblage could be found in southern England today, with the exception of those species described more fully below.

Typical of the 'southern English' character of this fauna are *Omaloplia ruricola* (F.), a chafer whose larvae live on grass roots, and the weevil *Liparus coronatus* (Goeze) whose food plant is *Heracleum*. These two species are rarely found further north in Britain than the counties bordering the channel. The dung beetles *Aphodius villosus* (Gyll.), *Onthophagus vacca* (L.) and *O. coenobita* (Hbst.) are most often seen in the southern part of England, below a line joining the estuaries of the Thames and the Severn, although they are not unknown from further north than this.

More indicative still of the southern English or continental European character of the Wilsford beetles is the presence of two further species of the genus *Onthophagus*. The first of these, *O. nutans* (F.) may be seen in old British collections, sometimes bearing labels of localities in the southern counties, and nineteenth-century dates. No examples appear to have been taken during the present century, however, and it is now regarded as extinct in Britain. The other species, *O. fracticornis* (Preyss.) seems to have had an even more precarious position in the British fauna. Although Delabie pointed out that collections of *O. fracticornis* contained two distinct sizes of beetle, and proposed the name *O. anomymus* for the larger, his ideas were not generally accepted until Landin (1959) showed, by means of constant morphological differences, particularly of the aedeagus, that two species were in fact present under the name *fracticornis* and that this name should apply henceforth to the larger insect, and that the smaller should be called *similis* Scriba. Today in Britain *O. similis* is relatively common in the southern half of England but an investigation by Allen (1967) of all the British material to which he had access revealed only seven specimens of the true *fracticornis*, none with any locality data. This is the reverse of the position at Wilsford 3000 years ago, when *fracticornis* was abundant and *similis* not recorded at all.

Finally, a number of examples of *Aphodius quadriguttatus* (Hbst.) were recovered. This species is not on the present-day British list but is known on the continent, becoming more common towards the south. *A. quadriguttatus* is yet another inhabitant of the dung of large grazing mammals and it is hard to ascribe its disappearance from this country in the last 3000 years to anything man may have done.

Bidford-on-Avon, Warwicks. A site of slightly later date is that at Bidford-on-Avon, Warwickshire (Osborne, in prep.). Under nine feet of reddish alluvial clay an organic silt layer occurred, grey at the top and black towards the bottom. The black silt, around two feet in thickness, contained many mollusc shells (see Shotton 1972), seeds and beetles. Three radiocarbon dates were obtained from this horizon, one at the base of 3006±117 years BP (1056±117 bc), one from the topmost layer of 2890±100 years BP (940±100 bc), and one in the middle of 2880±100 years BP (930±100 bc). Apart from an aquatic element the beetles were indicative of open grassland, though not quite so unanimously as those from Wilsford. Again a fauna with a marked southern English aspect was found. *Liparus coronatus,* whose modern English distribution is virtually confined to Kent, was again recorded and also *Onthophagus nutans,* mentioned above; another species of grassland chafer, *Hoplia philanthus* (Fuess.) was also identified. This insect, too, is much more southern in its occurrence in this country today.

The most exotic beetle from Bidford, however, was another dung beetle, *Onthophagus taurus* (Sch.). This very striking species is on the British list on the strength of a few examples taken early in the nineteenth century. It is possible that the species was truly indigenous at that time, or perhaps particularly favourable conditions for immigration allowed colonists to arrive from the continent, their progeny surviving a few years before dying out. On the other hand specimens may have been brought in from the continent to embellish a gentleman collector's 'cabinet' and labelled with English localities to make them more impressive, a practice not unknown amongst nineteenth-century collectors (see Allan 1943). Whatever the source of these old examples nothing has been seen of the species in this country for 150 years, even though it is very easily recognised, the male possessing two long thin horns on the head. At present it is found commonly in Spain and southern France, becoming less common further north.

Kinfauns, Perth. A third site is included here despite its rather imprecise dating. This was a bed of dark organic silt about 40 cm thick lying beneath 110 cm of topsoil and grey, stoney clay. The silt was sampled in three sub-equal layers, of which the lowest was radiocarbon-dated at 5180±100 years BP (3230±100 bc). This horizon contained a beetle fauna consisting of a mixture of aquatic and woodland forms. Unfortunately no dates are available for the two higher samples but obviously they post-date the layer dated 5180 BP and there was no reason to suspect a hiatus in deposition. The suite of woodland beetles found in the lowest sample gives way in the upper two to an assemblage primarily of open ground so that it appears that forest clearance was in progress probably between 5000 and 4000 years ago. The important points about this deposit are, first, that the head of a large *Onthophagus,* unhappily unidentifiable, but nevertheless bearing a strong southern English connotation, was recovered, and second, that the site, Kinfauns, is in Scotland near Perth.

Discussion

These three sites, therefore, all contain beetle species which today live further to the south. As it does not appear that man's activities can be held to account for these distribution changes, the most likely factor seems to be a deterioration in the climate.

A more subjective argument is based on numbers of individuals of the genus *Onthophagus* and their ratio to the numbers of individuals belonging to *Aphodius*. Fabre (1918), writing about the area in which he lived says, of the members of the genus *Onthophagus*, 'They come in crowds and stay a long time working under the spread table. . . . Turn over the heap [of dung] with your foot. You will be surprised at the swarming population . . .'. Fabre was writing in the south of France near Avignon, around latitude 44°N. It is fairly safe to say that, with the exception of *O. ovatus* (L.) members of the genus *Onthophagus* do not occur today in this sort of profusion in Britain. In thirty years as an avid collector of beetles the author has encountered only two individuals! A subjective assessment of old records and collections and the personal comments of other collectors suggests that in the very south of England examples of *Onthophagus* species may be found in ones and twos, even in tens, but hardly 'swarming'. The genus *Aphodius* contains many species, most of which also inhabit dung and these can be found in very large numbers in cattle and sheep droppings as far north as the Scottish Highlands. Somewhere, going southwards, must be a zone in which numbers of *Onthophagus* individuals rival those of *Aphodius* but this does not appear to be in Britain. At Wilsford, however, *Onthophagus* specimens were abundant. *O. fracticornis*, now represented by a mere seven 'British' examples, even these open to doubt, produced remains of nearly three hundred beetles. This sort of abundance seems much more comparable with the numbers described by Fabre and, with the addition of the other members of the genus, approaches the numbers of *Aphodius* species from the same deposit. Even considerably further north at Bidford-on-Avon, where today even to see an *Onthophagus* would seem mildly surprising, the genus must have been fairly common to become represented in the small samples taken.

Taken altogether, these effects – the occurrence of species in Britain which have since become extinct here, the records from the Midlands and even from Scotland of beetles which are either rare and restricted to the very southern part of England or no longer to be found here at all, and the enormous abundance of *Onthophagus* species at Wilsford, in numbers only matched much further south today – seem, in the absence of any obvious man-made factor such as habitat destruction, to point inevitably to a warmer climate during the Bronze Age than today. Clearly, though, work on many more sites is needed before the beetle evidence can be regarded as more than tentative.

Although it is not possible to prove the absence of a species by the lack of its occurrence in the fossil record, sufficient of this negative evidence must, if not contradicted, add up at least to a strong probability. Thus, after the Bronze Age the genus *Onthophagus* is rarely encountered in faunal lists and seems to have sunk to its present-day state of rarity.

In a number of post-Bronze Age sites investigated by the author the genus is practically unrepresented, despite the presence of *Aphodius* species and other indicators of dung. These sites include the Iron Age deposit at Fisherwick,

Staffordshire, radiocarbon-dated to 2130±100 years BP (180±100bc; Osborne 1980), and a number of Roman sites, examples being Alcester, Warwickshire (Osborne 1971a), Fishbourne, Sussex (Osborne 1971b) and Whitton, Glamorgan (Osborne 1981). Later still are the Saxon well at Portchester, Hampshire (Osborne, in press) and a number of sixteenth-century pits at Winchester (Osborne, in press). Although all these deposits are in the southern half of England, some almost as far south as it is possible to get in this country, and between them cover quite closely the time between the end of the Bronze Age and the present day, *Onthophagus* was recorded from only one site, a single example from Winchester. Although these absences cannot be taken to show that the genus disappeared from our fauna at this time, particularly as most species recorded from the Bronze Age were still extant in the nineteenth century, they certainly suggest a marked decline in abundance, even though conditions were probably increasingly favourable to beetles whose habitat is dung in open grassland. Here again, it appears that the climate is the most likely factor to have produced these effects, with optimum temperatures for this particular group of beetles having been reached between 4000 and 3000 years ago and not having been attained since.

Conclusion

The insect evidence for Bronze Age climates in Britain is admittedly slender so far but what there is seems consistent. Based entirely on beetles of open grassland, whose habitat, unlike that of the forest faunas of slightly earlier times, has not been drastically reduced by man's activities, and for the most part on a single genus, *Onthophagus*, the evidence suggests a period between four and three thousand years BP when summer temperatures were higher than those of the present day, declining to today's levels in Iron Age times and probably remaining more or less constant until the 'Little Ice Age', for which there is no insect evidence yet available.

REFERENCES

Allan, P. B. M. (1943) *Talking of Moths*. Newtown: Montgomery Press.

Allen, A. A. (1967) A review of the status of certain Scarabaeoidea (Col.) in the British Fauna with the addition to our list of *Onthophagus similis* Scriba, *Ent. Rec.* 79, 201-6, 220-4, 257-62, 284-90.

Ashbee, P. (1963) The Wilsford Shaft, *Antiquity* 37, 166-20.

Buckland, P. C. (1979) *Thorne Moors: a palaeoecological study of a Bronze Age site*. University of Birmingham, Geography Dept., Occasional publication no. 8.

Fabre, J. H. C. (1918) *The Sacred Beetle and Others*. (Trans. A. Teixeira de Mattos.) London: Hodder and Stoughton.

Girling, M. A. (1980) The fossil insect assemblage from the Baker site, *Somerset Levels Papers* 6, 36-42.

Kelly, M. R. & Osborne, P. J. (1964) Two floras and faunas from the alluvium at Shustoke, Warwickshire, *Proc. Linn. Soc. Lond.* 176, 37-65.

Landin, B.-O. (1959) Notes on *Onthophagus fracticornis* (Preyss.) and *O. similis* (Scriba) (Col. Scarab.), *Opusc. ent.* 24, 214-24.

Osborne, P. J. (1969) An insect fauna of late Bronze Age date from Wilsford, Wiltshire, *J. Anim. Ecol.* 38, 555-66.

Osborne, P.J. (1971a) An insect fauna from the Roman site at Alcester, Warwickshire, *Britannia* 2, 156-65.
— (1971b) The insect fauna from the Roman harbour, in Cunliffe, B. W., *Excavations at Fishbourne 1961-1969*. Soc. of Antiquaries Research Report 27, 393-6.
— (1972) Insect faunas of Late Devensian and Flandrian age from Church Stretton, Shropshire, *Phil. Trans. R. Soc.* ser. B, 262, no.852, 327-67.
— (1976) Evidence from the insects of climatic variation during the Flandrian period, *World Archaeology* 8, 150-8.
— (1979) Insect Remains, in Smith, C. (ed.) *Fisherwick. The Reconstruction of an Iron Age Landscape*. British Archaeological Reports 61, 85-7.
— (1981) The insect fauna, in Jarrett, M. G. & Wrathmell, S. *Whitton: An Iron Age and Roman farmstead in south Glamorgan*. Cardiff: University of Wales Press.
— (in press) in Cunliffe, B. W. (ed.) *Excavations at Portchester Castle* Vol.v, Soc. of Antiquaries Research Report.
— (in press) Insect faunas from Winchester, *Winchester Studies* 10.
Shotton, F. W. (1972) A comparison of modern and Bronze Age mollusc faunas from the Warwickshire-Worcestershire Avon, *Proc. Coventry and Distr. Nat. Hist. and Sci. Soc.* 4, no.6, 173-82.

The potential of dendrochronology for the study of climate change

At present there is only one tree-ring study that provides quantitative estimates of the climate of the later prehistoric period and this is from California (LaMarche 1974). Most of this paper is therefore based on extrapolation from work in progress at present. We want to show both the potential and the limitations of tree-rings as a proxy climate record for the period 2000 BC to AD 1000.

The rationale behind dendroclimatology

It can be demonstrated that trees from large areas (e.g. the British Isles) show the same patterns of wide and narrow rings in the same years. This is the basis of dendrochronology as a dating tool. The agreement between patterns is termed cross-dating and this can be demonstrated both in living trees and in timbers from the prehistoric period. The only way this can occur is as a result of a ubiquitous external influence. The only external influence that has a sufficiently widespread and consistent influence on tree growth is climate. Localised effects such as insect damage and woodland management practices could have a consistent effect on the trees of a single woodland but could not affect a whole region consistently for hundreds or thousands of years.

The nature of the climate's influence

Having demonstrated by means of cross-dating that climate influences tree growth, can we quantify this influence? As with so much of palaeoecology the problem is not amenable to experimental study. It is extremely difficult and costly to subject whole mature trees to controlled environmental conditions. We must rely on natural past variations in climate and on past growth as recorded in the tree-rings. By sampling at sites that are at the environmental limits of a species one may find trees that are influenced by a simple set of climate variables. For example radial growth of trees at the lower forest border in semi-desert areas is limited primarily by lack of water and those at the latitudinal or altitudinal tree-line are limited predominantly by growing season temperature. In these areas the relationship can be deduced theoretically and tested fairly simply. In other areas of less extreme climate, cross-dating between trees may still be strong and yet no simple set of climatic variables appears to limit growth directly. To study these more complex relationships more sophisticated methods are required. The starting point is a time series of tree-ring width measurements (or perhaps some other measure of wood variability such as density, cell size or isotopic ratios (Schweingruber 1981, Eck-

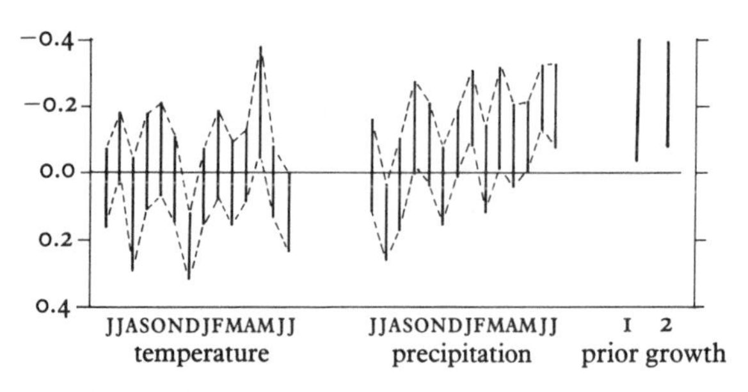

Figure 1. Example of a response function from a single site (Enniscorthy 1869–1969). Significant elements are where both ends of the 95% confidence bars are above or below the zero line.

stein 1981, Long 1981)) and time series of instrumental records of climate. In most areas the only long and complete climate records are those of temperature and precipitation; these thus form the basis of the climate data used. As it is likely that temperature and rainfall could have different effects at different times of the year it is usual to use monthly records and to extend these from the previous summer through autumn and winter to the spring and early summer of the growing season. In the examples described below, records of the 14 months from June of the previous year to July of the current year are used. Using both temperature and rainfall records this gives 28 records of climate for each record of ring-width. The ring-widths of each tree from a site are first standardised. This process is both to remove growth trends and to reduce all trees to the same mean ring-width index value of 1.0 before forming a mean time series that represents all the trees of that site. The standardisation is normally accomplished by fitting a straight line, or curve, to the ring-width series from each tree and then deriving the annual indices by dividing each ring-width by the value of the fitted curve at that year. The indices from between 10 and 40 trees from an individual site are averaged to form the final time series representing tree growth at that site. In order to reduce the number of climate variables and render the regression calculation more efficient, principal components are extracted from the 28 climatic variables. Those high-order components representing little variance are discarded before the matrix of principal components (eigenvectors) is entered into a stepwise multiple regression with the site ring width index series. This regression procedure selects a subset of principal components as predictors of ring index, on the basis that those regression coefficients with an F ratio less than unity are omitted from the regression. The regression coefficients thus determined are multiplied by the eigenvectors of the climate data to produce the response function which expresses the climate – growth response directly in terms of the original temperature and precipitation variables. In addition to the principal components of climate data, three years' prior growth values are included in the stepwise multiple regression to allow for autoregression in the tree-ring series.

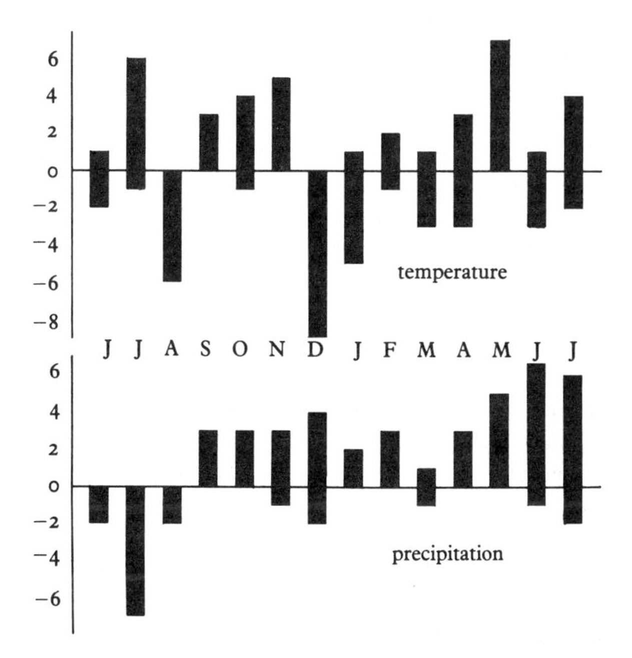

Figure 2. Summary response function for 16 oak sites in the British Isles. Histogram bars give the counts of significant elements for each month out of a total of 16.

This response function, developed by Fritts *et al.* (1971) is explained fully by Fritts (1976). The response function may be presented graphically to describe the effects of changes in climate on tree growth. Figure 1 shows a typical response function from an oak woodland in the British Isles. The site is a small patch of woodland on a steep river bank at Enniscorthy in south-eastern Ireland (Pilcher and Baillie, 1981). The horizontal axis gives the individual months of the 14-month 'growth year'. The vertical axis gives the values of the response function elements. The 95 per cent confidence limits on the coefficients are given by vertical lines. Where both limits fall to one or the other side of the zero line then that element is significantly different from zero ($p<0.05$). In the example July, January, March, May, June and July are significant for precipitation. Significant elements can be positive or negative: that is, an increase in the climate variable can be associated with either an increase or decrease in the ring width. Figure 2 shows a summary of 18 response functions from the British Isles. All are from oak (some *Quercus robur*, some *Q. petraea* and some probably hybrids). The vertical axis gives the number (out of 18) of individual response functions that have a significant positive or negative element for that month.

Some general points emerge from this summary. Warm autumns and cold winters are associated with good growth in the following year, all else being equal, and warm conditions at the start of the growing season in May are associated with good growth. At other times the apparent effect of temperature is more variable and presumably more dependent on site location and aspect. The rainfall response is simpler, showing a negative association between growth and previous summer rainfall and a consistently positive relationship for most months up to the end of the growing season. It must be stressed here that the response function provides a method of calculating tree growth from climate – it is not a relationship from which climate can be predicted or deduced. The most important conclusion to be drawn from the British Isles response functions is that the relationship between tree growth and climate is too complex for a single site to be used for reconstructing climate.

Multi-site reconstructions

In order to reconstruct climate it is necessary to use the record of many trees at a range of sites. Such a multi-site grid of tree-ring records may be used to reconstruct point climate records (Conkey 1981), regional climate records (see below) or gridded climate records (Fritts 1976). The most dramatic examples are the atmospheric pressure reconstructions for North America (Fritts *et al.* 1979). These reconstructions are based on a grid of 96 tree-ring stations and a grid of instrumental pressure records, and cover the period 1602 to the present. The relationship is established by canonical regression and the resulting 'transfer function' then used to extend the pressure record back beyond the limits of instrumental measurements. Since the regression model is an empirical one it is necessary to make an independent check on the reconstruction using independent data. This is an aspect of the climate reconstruction work that has received much attention recently (Gordon 1981).

To demonstrate the workings of the calibration and verification process we present here an example from the British Isles. This is the first published reconstruction of climate based on British Isles tree-rings. It is a preliminary result based on a small group of sites and a short period of years. It is planned to use a larger group of sites and a longer period in the near future. In this case five oak chronologies were used. Four were from ring-widths: Rostrevor, N. Ireland (Pilcher 1976), Lockwood, South-west Scotland (Baillie 1977a), Cannock, Central England (Hughes, unpublished data) and Maentwrog, North Wales (Milsom 1979). The fifth was a maximum density chronology from the same trees as the Maentwrog ring-width chronology (Milsom 1979). These were used to reconstruct the mean temperature for the period May, June, July for Central England. In order to calibrate the tree-rings, the tree-ring chronologies were regressed, after extracting their principal components, on the mean May–June–July temperature of Manley's (1974) Central England series for the period 1861–1963. The regression was offered, for each of the five chronologies, values for years $t-1$, t, $t+1$, $t+2$ and $t+3$, where t is the year whose climate is to be calculated. Thus 25 possible predictors were offered to the regression. Only ten were selected by the stepwise multiple regression method used (Guiot 1979). For the calibration period the regression equation accounted for 31.7 per cent of the variance of the May–June–July mean

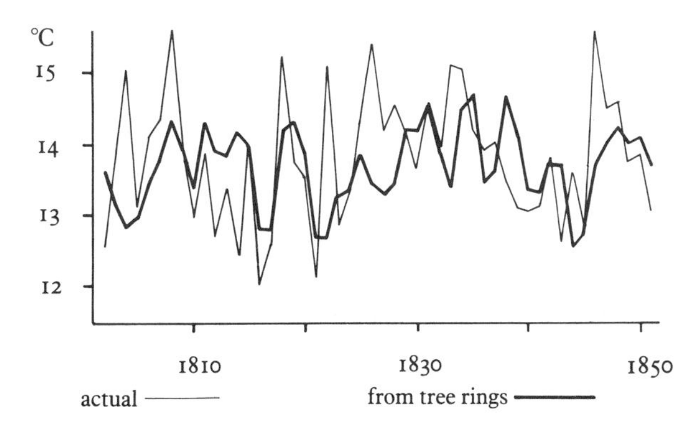

Figure 3. Reconstruction of central England mean May/June/July temperature. The calibration period was 1861–1963, thus the actual temperature values and the tree-ring derived values shown here are from an independent period and were not used in the calibration.

temperature. The equation was then used to calculate mean May–June–July temperature from the tree-ring series for the period 1802–51. The results were compared with the actual temperatures for these years reported by Manley (op. cit.). This provides an independent test of the calibration. The predicted and actual temperatures for this 50-year verification period are shown in figure 3. There was a correlation coefficient of 0.509 ($p<0.01$) for this 50-year period, giving an estimate of variance accounted for of 25.9 per cent. Visually, the reconstruction compares well with the actual data in the medium term, although it does not record faithfully those years where June was unusually warm and July not so (e.g. 1804, 1822 and to a lesser extent 1846). In general, the reconstruction has a smaller amplitude and changes more slowly than the actual data. Even so, this preliminary reconstruction based on a very small tree-ring data set shows that there is a real potential for the use of oak tree-rings as a proxy record of climate in the British Isles.

Prehistoric dendrochronology

Assuming an attempt is to be made to extend these methods into the prehistoric period we must examine the potential sources of material. There are no living trees in Europe that extend back into the prehistoric period so we must rely on timbers preserved from the past. The three main sources are archaeological sites, bogs and lakes, and river gravels. Archaeological sites have several advantages. The approximate age-range is known in most cases from the archaeological evidence and there is a reasonable chance of getting a number of samples of the same period. On the other hand, the number of archaeological sites that yield suitable timber is very small. It is only in exceptional conditions where the site was naturally waterlogged or was inundated that organic materials are well enough preserved from the prehistoric period. Examples of archaeological sites that have yielded dendrochronologically datable timbers are the early medieval settlement at Dublin (Baillie 1977b) and a number of

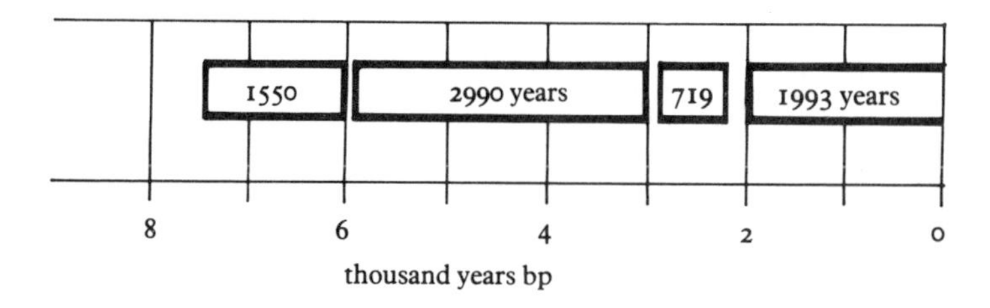

Figure 4. Summary of long tree-ring chronologies from Ireland produced by members of the Palaeoecology Centre, Queen's University, Belfast. Several short chronologies with few trees older than 7,500 years are not included.

water-mills such as Drumard in Northern Ireland (Baillie 1975) and Tamworth in central England (Baillie 1980). In Germany a chronology has been developed from archaeological material back to 739 BC (Hollstein 1980).

The second source of timber is from bogs and lakes. These are trees that have lived either on land that has subsequently been covered by lake or bog or that lived on the bog surface. As will be seen later their existence is very much determined by water levels in the bog and hence in a general but sometimes very indirect way to climate. Pine and oak are the commonest species to be found preserved in bogs, and dendrochronological studies have been carried out on both (e.g. Munaut 1966, Pilcher *et al.* 1977). Alder (*Alnus* sp.), while common in peat deposits, seldom has sufficient annual rings and yew (*Taxus baccata*) which has been found with greater than 400 annual rings (Clonsast Bog, Portarlington, Ireland) has such a contorted annual ring structure as to be useless for dendrochronology. As pine became rare in most of the British Isles at some time around 3950 BP (2000 bc), with the exception of some refuges in Scotland (Godwin 1975) and perhaps in Central Ireland, the only remaining material for dendrochronology in the later prehistoric period is oak.

Most of the oak trunks from bogs come to light only during drainage operations, river dredging, fenland reclamation or similar work, and are pulled out by machine. Hence there is no record of their stratigraphic position. Even where stratification remains it is seldom possible to place individual trees in more than the most crude sequence. In contrast to archaeological material there is usually little external indication of either the absolute or relative ages of bog oaks. In the early work on bog oak at the Belfast Palaeoecology Laboratory, a large number of radiocarbon dates were measured on individual timbers to ascertain the age-range of the bog oaks available to us (Smith *et al.* 1972). Given the large age-range spanned by the timbers it seemed counter-productive to concentrate on building chronologies back from the present. Rather, sequences were constructed as the available material allowed, these sequences then being 'floating' (i.e. not fixed to a calendrical scale). The present position is that the greater part of the last 7000 years is covered by chronologies, but the part tied to the present day extends only to 12 BC. Figure 4 shows the relationship of the various floating sequences established from bogs in the north of Ireland with the floating sections positioned according to radiocarbon dates. Included is the longest continuous tree-ring chronology from Europe of 2990 years, stretching from approximately 3950–950 BC (Pilcher *et al.* 1977). This long floating chronology has been used for radiocarbon calibration studies (Pearson *et al.* 1977) and some of the shorter floating sequences are at present the subject of calibration studies. The age-range given above is in calendar years and is based on this calibration work.

The third source of sub-fossil material is river gravels. These trees differ from those in bogs in that they were growing elsewhere from the site of deposition and were brought to their present location by erosive action of the river. From the point of view of the dendrochronologist the river gravel oaks are similar to the bog oaks in that they are generally unstratified and of unknown age. Numerous floating chronologies have been constructed from river gravels in Germany and these are summarised in Becker and Delorme (1978). Attempts are at present under way to cross-date the German and Irish sequences in the hope of bridging some of the gaps in both series.

Limitations of prehistoric chronologies for climate reconstruction

The chronologies available for the later prehistoric period clearly fall short of an ideal for dendroclimatology. We will examine the limitations of the available material.

1) *The prehistoric chronologies are mostly multi-site chronologies.* The growing conditions at one site may have been different from those at another site in the same chronology. Changes in the chronology at the transition from one site to another may reflect site conditions rather than climatic change. Similarities between modern chronologies from a range of aspects, soils and locations within the British Isles suggest that this need not be a serious limitation (Pilcher and Gray, in press), given a sufficiently large replication of sites and trees for any one year.

2) *Time stability.* Because these chronologies are potentially very long it is possible that conditions will have changed within an individual site. For example successive generations of trees growing on a bog surface may have been affected by the evolution of the bog surface.

3) *Lack of modern analogues.* The components of the Irish sub-fossil chronologies were trees of wetlands. Most of the living oaks studied are from steep rocky slopes (e.g. Rostrevor: Pilcher 1976; Maentwrog: Leggett *et al.* 1978). In Ireland there are no living fenland oak woods that can be used as analogues and such woodlands are rare elsewhere. Thus it is not clear what modern site chronologies should be used as a calibration for the sub-fossil oaks. This is probably the single most serious limitation on the use of sub-fossil chronologies for climatic reconstruction.

4) *Inadequacy of the climate record for calibration.* It is possible that the prehistoric climate fell outside the range covered by the year-to-year variations during the time of recent instrumental recording. The calibration using modern tree-rings and modern instrumental records might not be applicable to

some more extreme conditions in the past. Other proxy data suggest that this should not be a serious problem in the later prehistoric period.

5) *Small number of chronologies.* There are at present, and can only ever be, relatively few prehistoric chronologies because there is only a limited amount of material preserved.

Possibilities for climatic reconstruction in later prehistory

From the limitations above it might seem futile to try to extend dendroclimatology into the later prehistoric period. However the existing and potential tree-ring chronologies have one great virtue and that is their length. This means that we can greatly improve the reliability of reconstructions by averaging over a period of years, say 10 or 20 years. Such is the lack of any quantitative estimates of climatic conditions in prehistory that even 100-year mean estimates would be of value to archaeologists. LaMarche (1974) using upper tree-line bristlecone pines from California has inferred temperature in 100-year blocks and has shown that this record agrees well with evidence of glacier advance and retreat. In Europe it will not be possible to use a single chronology in this way, but similar information may be possible from several chronologies in the way demonstrated for modern trees above.

Qualitative palaeoclimate estimates from tree-rings

1) *Tree frequency.* It has been clear from the work in Ireland and in Germany that at certain times large numbers of trees are preserved and at other times few or none. In the case of bogs an increase in numbers suggests dryness of the bog, allowing trees to colonise a greater part of the bog surface, and therefore presumably a decrease in rainfall whereas an increase in trees preserved in river gravels suggests increased erosion caused by an increase in rainfall. As can be seen in figure 4, gaps occur in the Irish bog oak sequences at approximately 200 BC and 950 BC suggesting that these could be times of increased wetness.

2) *Isotope studies on tree-rings.* So far there has been no consistent story to emerge from the work on stable and unstable isotopes in wood. There have been claims of a clear climate signal in the stable isotope ratios and counter claims of no climate signal at all (reviewed by Long 1981). Similarly, work on the interpretation of variations in natural radiocarbon content of wood has seen claims for and against a climatic interpretation (Suess 1980). It would certainly greatly increase the value of the long tree-ring chronologies if one or more of these techniques yields palaeoclimate information. Perhaps the best we can hope for is that the isotope information will be valuable as another variable to be added into a calibration and reconstruction equation, in the same way that wood density was used in the pilot study reported above.

Conclusions

Tree-rings have the potential of offering limited quantitative estimates of climatic conditions in the later prehistoric period, probably mean values for decades or longer periods. It may also be possible to produce some less direct estimates of past conditions such as relative continentality or oceanicity of the climate or perhaps length of growing season. As these values have direct agricultural implications they could in turn be related to prehistoric agricultural practices. What is not at present possible is the estimation of annual values of temperature or rainfall nor will it be possible to produce estimates for more than one or two locations in Europe.

REFERENCES

Baillie, M. G. L. (1975) A horizontal mill of the eighth century AD at Drumard, Co. Derry, *Ulster J. Archaeol.* 38, 25-32.

— (1977a) An oak chronology for south central Scotland, *Tree-Ring Bulletin* 37, 33-44.

— (1977b) Dublin medieval dendrochronology, *Tree-Ring Bulletin* 37, 13-19.

— (1980) Dendrochronology – The Irish view, *Current Archaeol.* 73, 61-3.

Becker, B. & Delorme, A. (1978) Oak chronologies for central Europe and their extension from Medieval to prehistoric times, in Fletcher, J. (ed.) *Dendrochronology in Europe*, British Archaeological Reports, International series 51, 59-64.

Conkey, L. (1981) Temperature reconstructions in the north eastern United States, in Hughes *et al.* (eds) *Climate from Tree-Rings*. Cambridge: University Press.

Eckstein, D. (1981) Global tree-ring data base: needs and prospects in Europe, in Hughes *et al.* (eds) *Climate from Tree-Rings*. Cambridge: University Press.

Fritts, H. C. (1976) *Tree-Rings and Climate*. London: Academic Press.

Fritts, H. C., Blasing, T. J., Hayden, B. P. & Kutzbach, J. E. (1971) Multivariate techniques for specifying tree-growth and climate relationships and for reconstructing anomalies in palaeoclimate, *J. Appl. Meteorol.* 10(5), 845-64.

Fritts, H. C., Lofgren, G. R. & Gordon, G. A. (1979) Variations in climate since 1602 as reconstructed from tree-rings, *Quaternary Research* 12, 18-46.

Godwin, H. (1975) History of the natural forests in Britain: establishment, dominance and destruction, *Phil. Trans. R. Soc. Lond. B.* 271, 45-67.

Gordon, G. A. (1981) Verification of dendroclimatic reconstructions, in Hughes *et al.* (eds) *Climate from Tree-Rings*. Cambridge: University Press.

Guiot, J. (1979) Spectral multivariate regression in dendroclimatology. *Institut d'Astronomie et de Géophysique, Université Catholique de Louvain-la-Neuve, Contribution* 21.

Hollstein, E. (1980) *Mitteleuropäische Eichenchronologie*. Mainz am Rhein: Philipp von Zabern.

LaMarche, V. C. (1974) Paleoclimatic inferences from long tree-ring records, *Science* 183, 1043-8.

Leggett, P., Hughes, M. K. & Hibbert, F. A. (1978) A modern oak chronology from North Wales and its interpretation, in Fletcher, J. (ed.) *Dendrochronology in Europe*, British Archaeological Reports, International Series 51, 187-94.

Long, A. (1981) The study of isotopic parameters, in Hughes *et al.* (eds) *Climate from Tree-Rings*. Cambridge: University Press.

Manley, G. (1974) Central England temperatures: monthly means 1659 to 1973, *Quarterly J. R. Met. Soc.* 100, 389-405.

Milsom, S. J. (1979) *Within- and between-tree variation in certain properties of annual rings of sessile oak* (Quercus petraea) *as a source of dendrochronological information*, PhD thesis, Liverpool Polytechnic.

Munaut, A. V. (1966) Recherches dendrochronologiques sur *Pinus silvestris*, II. Première application des méthodes dendrochronologiques à l'études de pins sylvestres sub-fossiles (Terneuzen, Pays-Bas), *Agricultura* 14, Ser. 2, 316-89.

Pilcher, J. R. (1976) A statistical oak chronology from the north of Ireland, *Tree-Ring Bulletin* 36, 21-7.

Pilcher, J. R., Hillam, J., Baillie, M. G. L. & Pearson, G. W. (1977) A long sub-fossil oak tree-ring chronology from the north of Ireland, *New Phytologist* 79, 713-29.

Pilcher, J. R. & Baillie, M. G. L. (1981) Six modern oak chronologies from Ireland, *Tree-Ring Bulletin* 40, 23-34.

Pilcher, J. R. & Gray, B. (in press) The relationship between oak tree growth and climate in Britain, *J. Ecol.*

Schweingruber, F. H. (1981) Measurement of densitometric properties of wood, in Hughes *et al.* (eds) *Climate from Tree-Rings*. Cambridge: University Press.

Smith, A. G., Baillie, M. G. L., Hillam, J., Pilcher, J. R. & Pearson, G. W. (1972) Dendrochronological work in progress in Belfast: the prospects for an Irish post-glacial tree-ring sequence, *Proc. 8th Int. Conf. on Radiocarbon Dating* 1, 492-5.

Suess, H. (1980) Radiocarbon geophysics, *Endeavour*, New Series 4, 28-32.

Vegetation history and climatic changes in central and southern Europe

The aim of this paper is to demonstrate problems and difficulties that arise with the attempt to explain changes in vegetation that happened between 8000 and 2000 BP (6050 and 50 bc) by means of climatic change. This will be done with the help of selected examples which are considered to be important for the current and for future work. (For more detailed and comprehensive information see Firbas (1949, 1952), Frenzel (1977), Kral (1979), Oeschger *et al.* (1980) and Sawyer (1966).)

History of vegetation has to be based on a very detailed knowledge of plant fossils, the ecology of plants and the relationship between pollen rain and vegetation. With the help of that knowledge, the vegetation of the past can be reconstructed. At the latest after dating the events in the development of the vegetation it is necessary to ask the reasons for the changes. Finally, all the results from single sites have to be correlated in order to study historical processes on a regional and eventually on a global scale.

The history of vegetation has been highly influenced by the development of the climate. The history of vegetation, however, cannot be considered to be merely a response to climatic changes. It is much more the result of a very complicated complex of processes of a differing nature.

First, plant species differ in their requirement as regards climate and soils. The fossil remains therefore should be identified as far as possible, preferably to species level.

Secondly, plant species differ in respect of their migratory abilities. Migration processes caused by the amelioration of the climate after the end of the last glaciation play an important role in central and southern Europe. The plants came back at different times, at different speeds, using different routes. The position, size and number of the glacial refuges and the ecological abilities of the different plant species must be considered.

Thirdly, human activity with some influence on the vegetation started in Neolithic times, but with time it increased in intensity and finally led to the largely destroyed environment existing in Europe since the Middle Ages or Roman times, or even earlier. Periods of human activity may or may not have coincided with periods of climatic changes and may have influenced the vegetation as much as climatic changes can or actually have done.

Outline of the history of vegetation

The beginning of forest history, as considered here, dates back to the end of the last glacial period. Around the Alps and north of them, the absence of trees is easily explained by arctic climate conditions. In southern Europe, however, the absence of forests during glacial periods was due to arid climate conditions. A steppe or semi-desert climate did not allow forest vegetation to exist except in locally favourable places (Beug 1977).

In central Europe north of the Alps, no glacial tree refuges existed and the Alps played a role as a barrier against migrating species that wanted to go directly to central Europe from their glacial refuges in the south. Nevertheless, tree species that are more thermophilous than *Pinus* and *Betula* were already present in small quantities at some parts of the north-eastern border of the Alps in Late Glacial times. From here, they started to colonise the more northern parts of Europe during or at the end of the Pre-boreal. During the Boreal and Atlantic there were mixed oak forests, and pine forests became extinct in the western part of central Europe. Spruce immigrated from the south-east forming a mixed conifer forest belt in the mountains. Spruce started, for instance, from south-eastern Bavaria at about 9000 BP (7050 bc) and reached the Harz mountains 500 km away about 3000 years later. In the Black Forest area, spruce appeared in late Sub-boreal times but never reached the Vosges mountains independently. East Prussia, however, was reached by the spruce in the early Atlantic by a quite different migration route.

The last species to migrate were *Fagus*, *Abies* and *Carpinus*. *Fagus*, for instance, appeared with more than 5 per cent in the pollen diagrams in south-eastern Bavaria about 6500–6000 BP (4550–4050 bc). During the Atlantic, *Fagus* was still restricted in its distribution to the northern forelands of the Alps and some of the adjacent mountains as a non-dominant forest tree. During the late Atlantic, *Fagus* spread gradually all over central Europe. The 5 per cent value in the pollen diagrams was reached in the Harz mountains about 3600 BP (1650 bc) and in parts of the extreme north of Germany later than 2000 BP (50 bc).

The Alps were situated nearer to glacial refuges and therefore mixed oak forests were able to replace pine forests as early as Late Glacial times in parts of the southern border of that region. In addition, the southern parts of the Alps were reached much earlier by such trees which were late invaders north of the Alps. Spruce became an important forest tree in the south-eastern Alps during the Late Glacial, and fir during the Pre-boreal in the southern Swiss Alps. From those starting-points, the tree species migrated along the marginal parts of the Alps, along the valleys and even across the Alps. The large area of early pine forests was reduced and the remaining parts in the more continental central Alps invaded to a high degree by spruce. Outside the central Alps, a rich horizontal forest zonation was built up. In some areas, it took until nearly 2000 BP (50 bc) to finish that zonation.

From this very short summary it is not difficult to see that during the period 8000–2000 BP (6050–50 bc) many important vegetational changes must have occurred in various parts of central Europe and the Alps.

It was in various parts of southern Europe that central European tree species survived the last glacial period. So one may think that migration processes

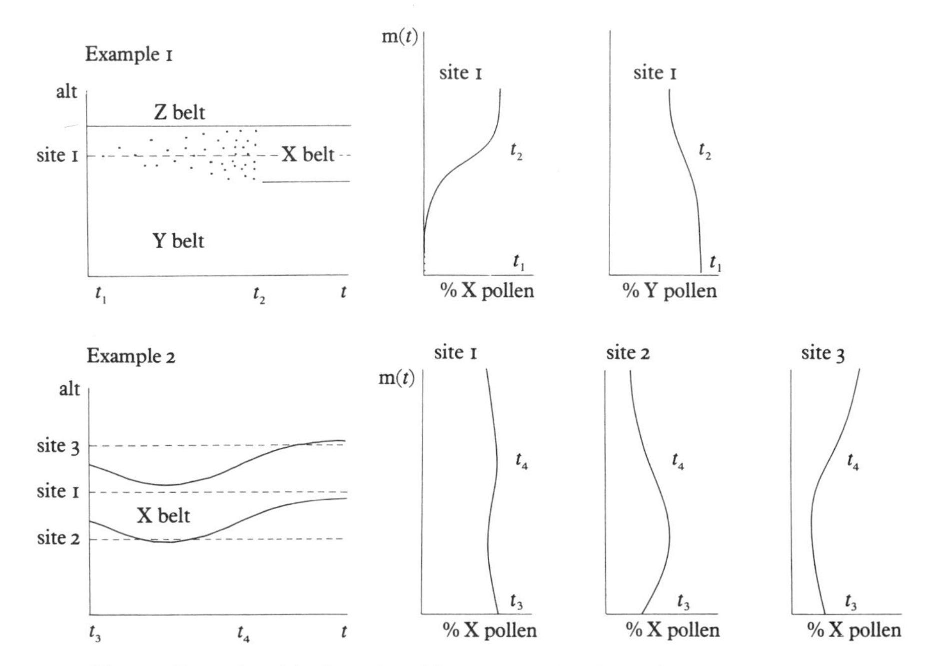

Figure 1. Examples of the formation of forest belts and their reaction to climatic changes. For explanation see text.

came to a standstill very early here and all later changes might be referred to climatic change. For some regions this may be true. In southern Europe, however, there is a great diversity in the floristic composition and in vegetation units, changing from west to east, from north to south and from sea-level to the mountains. Only a few landscapes have been investigated sufficiently thoroughly so far and no brief outline can be given for the whole area.

Methods

There is no doubt that most of the more important migration processes were released by the amelioration of the climate after the maximum of the last glacial period or during the course of that event. Those processes, set in motion more than 13,000 years ago in southern Europe, lasted till historical times. They were influenced by all the factors mentioned above including climate. What chance do we have of separating changes in vegetation which would have taken place without further changes of the climate from those which are due to climatic events in the later course of the Postglacial?

There are four principal ways to get information for the period and area concerned:

1) to study fluctuations in the vertical and horizontal zonation of forests;

2) to study fluctuations in the Alpine timberline;

3) to study changes in the occurrence of single plant species or plant communities, the distribution of which depends on well-known climatic data;

4) to study peat bog growth and peat bog stratigraphy.

Fluctuations in forest belts and the Alpine timberline are preferred here for they show the reaction of a larger part of the vegetation. First of all some simple examples will be given to explain possible interpretations and misinterpretations (figure 1).

Example 1 shows how a mountainous forest belt with the dominating tree species *X* may have formed in the upper part of the belt of tree species *Y*. *X* appeared at a certain altitude at time t_1 and became more and more frequent. At time t_2, that process became highly intensified with the result that *X* ended up forming its own forest belt.

In a pollen diagram from site 1, single *X*-type pollen grains are to be found at t_1, then forming a slowly increasing curve. At t_2, there is a more or less steep rise in the curve indicating that *X* is now becoming dominant. The time difference between t_1 and t_2 can be more than 2500 years. All trees coming to dominance show this particular behaviour but at different times, so that coming to dominance cannot be generally attributed to a climatic event at that particular moment.

Tree species *Y* necessarily shows a decline in the pollen diagram but this need not be considered the result of a climate deterioration even though *Y* may be a more thermophilous plant than species *X*. Before t_1, tree *Y* was able to occupy higher elevations by the simple reason that no other tree could act as a rival. Between t_1 and t_2, the situation may have changed without any influence from climatic change (or at least without any immediate influence) but rather by migration and competition phenomena only.

Example 2 explains how the *X* belt would react under the influence of a cold period after which the climate becomes warmer than before.

Site 1 would remain all the time within the *X* belt and there would be little change in the *X* curve. Site 1 is therefore considered not to be very sensitive during that time. Site 2, however, would be occupied by the *X* belt during the maximum of the cold phase. The pollen curve demonstrates that site 2 is in a very sensitive position. The *X* curve for site 3, situated at a higher elevation, would probably show little of the cold period. After t_4, however, the area of site 3 clearly becomes sensitive.

Consequently, forest belt formations and movements have to be studied at different elevations within a small area of the mountainous region in order to avoid serious misinterpretations. Absolute data are necessary in order to get secure connections between the sequences from different elevations.

Timberline fluctuations have been studied intensively in the Alps. Studies of that kind have often been combined with research work on the movement of glaciers. In pollen diagrams coming from sites at the timberline, the ratio of arboreal plants (AP) and non-arboreal plants (NAP) is used. A cold phase will lower the timberline by killing the uppermost trees and that in turn will cause an increase in NAP. A warm period will cause changes in the opposite direction. It has been demonstrated by ecological studies that timberline fluctuations in the Alps depend on changes of summer temperatures. If summers become

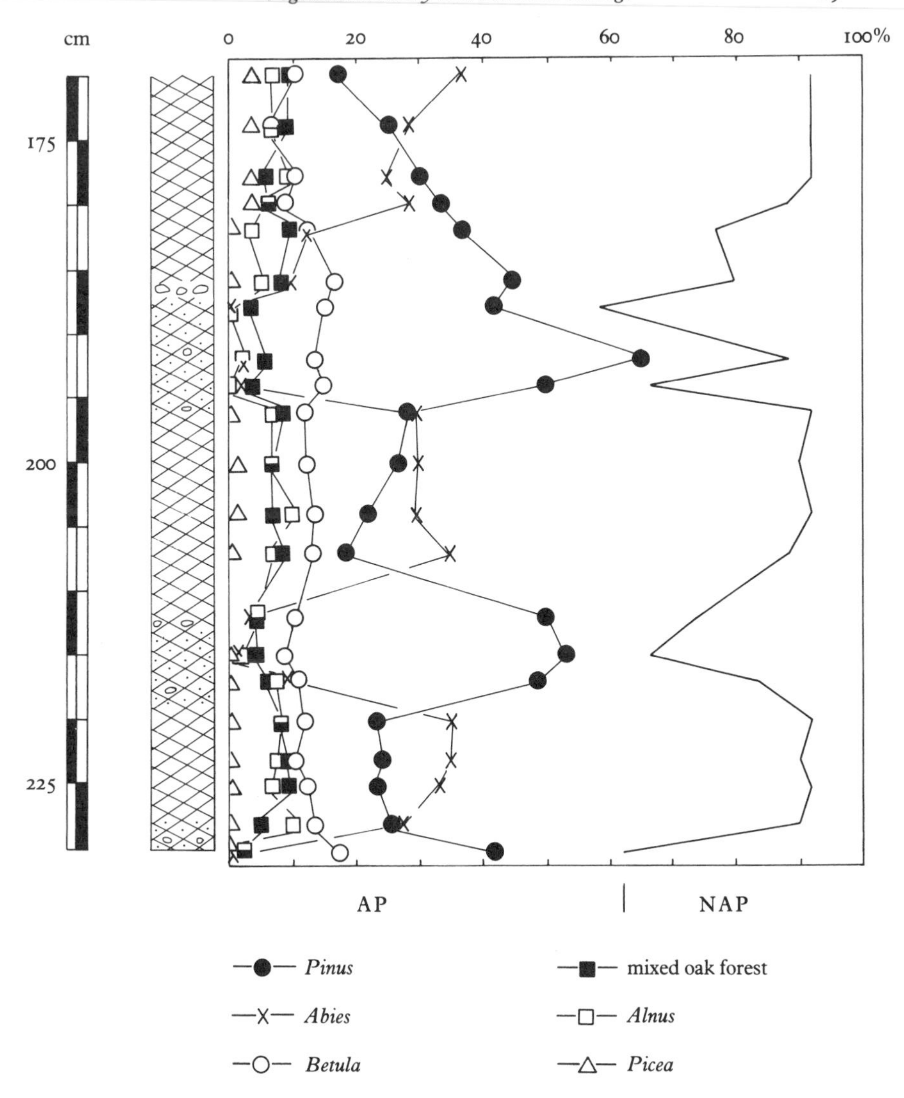

Figure 2. Pian di Signano, Tessin, Switzerland, 1540 m a.s.l. A section of the pollen diagram containing the Misox oscillations (after Zoller 1960).

colder, or shorter than three months, spruce and pine cannot produce ripe needles any more and will die in the winter by lethal rates of transpiration through their unripe needles (Lange and Schulze 1966).

Climatic changes in the Alps as detected by palynological studies

In the Swiss Alps, there are two regions which were investigated early on for their vegetational history in a very modern way. In 1952, Welten published his studies about the Simmental (northern Swiss Alps), comprising 19 sites from 560–2320 m above sea-level. In 1960, Zoller published his first study about the southern Swiss Alps, the Insubricum, ranging from the southern foothills northward to the Gotthard region. Zoller investigated five sites coming from altitudes between 350 and 1925 m above sea-level. I will start with the results from the Insubricum.

The site Pian di Signano in the Misox valley, Tessin, 1540 m above sea-level, gave very good evidence for three cold periods with a low timberline. Large peaks of the *Pinus* curve, combined with remarkably increased NAP values and developed in more minerogenous sediments, interrupt the dominance of fir (figure 2). Those Misox oscillations were dated to about 7400–6000 BP (5450–4050 bc) and the depression of the upper limit of fir forests was estimated to be about 200–250 m. Pian di Signano is a very good example of a sensitive locality at that time under the given forest zonation. Another site at 1235 m above sea-level did not show such influence, and the fir dominance existed through the time of the Misox oscillations without interruptions or fluctuations. Knowing the principal trends in forest history and the formation of forest belts, it should be possible to select regions and altitudes that were generally sensitive during a particular period of interest.

The sequence from Cadagno Fuori, 1925 m above sea-level, displays four periods or complexes with a low timberline:

at the bottom, either a pioneer phase or part of a cold period during the Boreal;

the complex of three Misox oscillations;

an oscillation now dated to between 5200 and 4000 BP (3250–2050 bc), called the Piora oscillation;

a late period connected with human influence, e.g. a forest clearance at the timberline (*Alpweiderodung*) which began in the late Middle Ages.

In his further studies, Zoller described the history of vegetation for the region of Göschenen about 40 km north-east of St Gotthard (Zoller *et al.* 1966). Here the Piora oscillation was found again as well as the cold phases Göschenen 1 and 2, which were dated to the time between 2830–2270 BP and 1600–1390 BP (880–320 bc and ad 350–560).

Nowadays there is an abundance of further records for climatic changes traced by pollen analytical work in Switzerland. The whole record has been critically compiled by Burga (1979), comprising almost 50 cases. In a certain number of cases, however, the evidence for climatic change is weak or not dated radiometrically. Nevertheless, there is a good concentration around the oscillations of Misox, Piora and Göschenen 1 and 2 as well as for some periods before 8000 BP (6050 bc) as far as the Postglacial is concerned.

If one studies publications containing primary research, it is obvious that many authors are cautious about referring changes in pollen diagrams to climatic change. They are even reluctant to translate changes in vegetation actually caused by the influence of climate into temperature and precipitation terms.

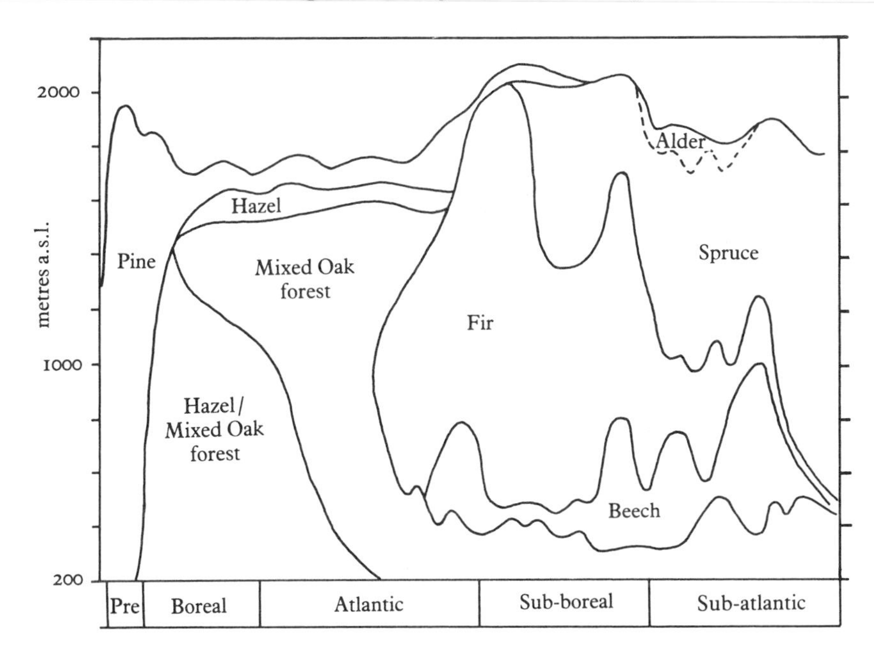

Figure 3. Time-altitude diagram for the post-glacial history of forest belts in the Simmental, northern Swiss Alps (after Welten 1952, altered).

Welten's results come from sites on the northern side of the Swiss Alps (Welten 1952). The Simmental is part of the Bernese Oberland and Bernese Mittelland. Welten explained his results concerned with the development of vegetation and climate in the final chapter of his book with a time-altitude diagram for the development of forest belts (figure 3). In this way, it can be demonstrated for the Simmental:

that the timberline formed by pine had risen to a very high level already during the Pre-boreal;

that pine forests (except those near the timberline) were rapidly replaced by hazel and mixed oak forests, while the timberline decreased from almost 2000 m to about 1700 m above sea-level;

that from the middle part of the Boreal to the late Atlantic, the timberline remained in a comparatively low position, showing a few smaller fluctuations only and that it then climbed up to its highest postglacial position at the beginning of the Sub-boreal;

how fir occupied a wide range in the horizontal scale but immediately became threatened by the spruce from above and the beech from below;

that there is almost no evidence for the Piora oscillation;

how the timberline and the upper limit of fir forests decreased during Göschenen 1.

To my mind, Welten's work at the Simmental published as early as 1952 is a model of what has to be done in regions with a rich horizontal forest zonation

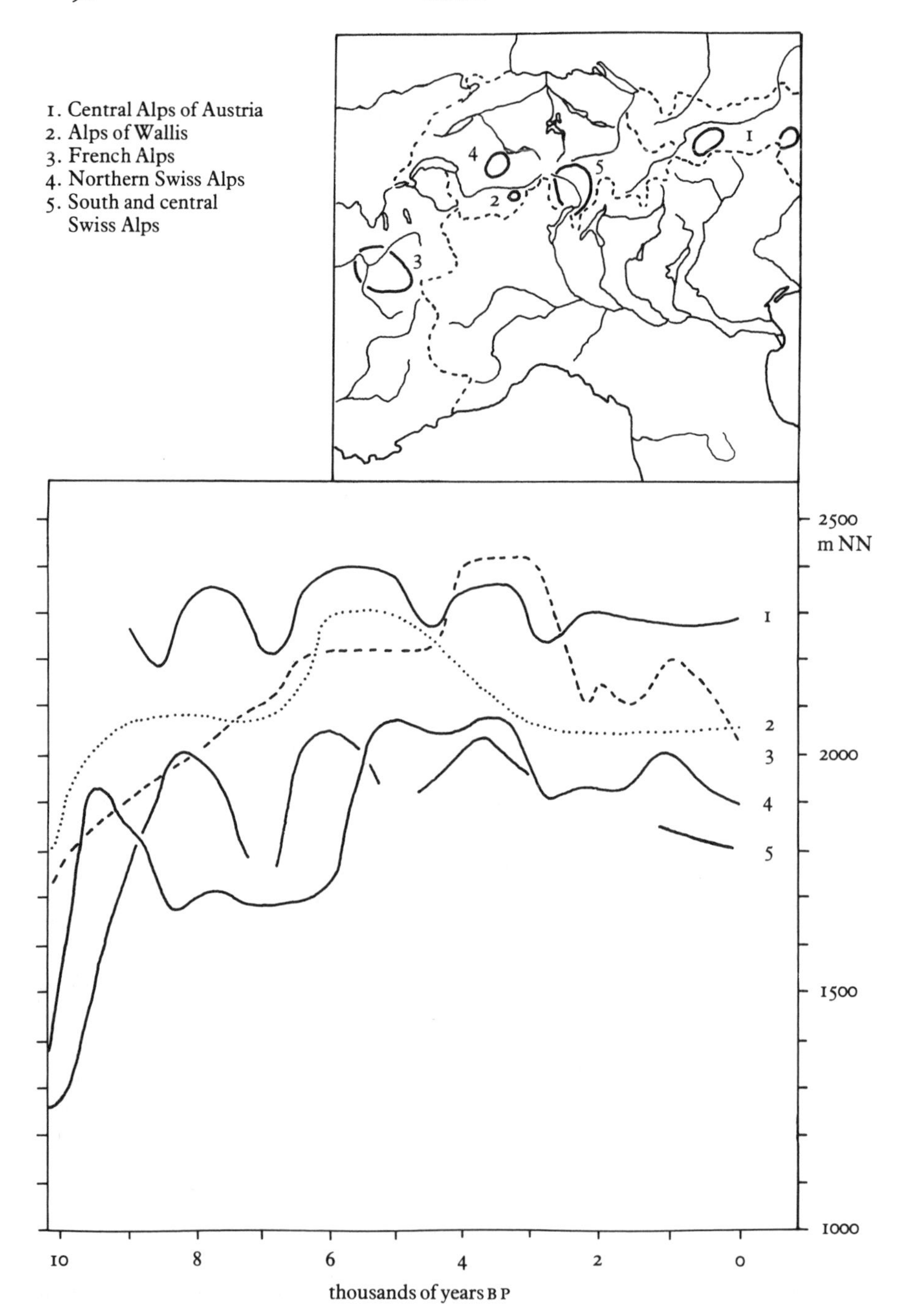

Figure 4. Timberline fluctuations in the Alps of Switzerland, France and central Austria (after Markgraf 1974, altered, and Wegmüller 1977).

before speaking about climate oscillations derivable from changes in the vegetation.

The third region I want to speak about belongs to the central Alps of Austria. During the last twenty-five years, Bortenschlager, Patzelt and co-workers have carried out intensive research on the history of vegetation and glaciers in that region. The most interesting pollen analytical results were obtained from peat bogs situated at about 2300 m above sea-level in the Venediger Group and in the Ötztal Alps (Bortenschlager 1970; Bortenschlager and Patzelt 1969; Patzelt 1974, 1977, 1980 and references cited there). From here, the following cold phases have been described:

Venediger oscillation from 8700–8000 BP (6750–5950 bc) as a group of three cold phases;

Frosnitz oscillation from 6600–6000 BP (4650–3950 bc). Frosnitz may be synchronous with the last of the Misox oscillations but their identity has not yet been convincingly demonstrated;

Rotmoos oscillation from 5300–4400 BP (3350–2450 bc) described as two cold periods following each other closely. There is good comparability with the Piora oscillation;

Löbben oscillation from 3500–3100 BP (1550–1150 bc) without a good counterpart in the Swiss Alps;

later oscillations corresponding with Göschenen 1 and 2.

For most of the oscillations there is good agreement between the examples from the Swiss Alps and those from the central Austrian Alps. It will be a future task to get more information about the meaning of these oscillations for forest history in the lowlands, in the middle and lower elevations of the mountains and inside the Alpine chain itself. As to the amplitude of the timberline fluctuations, it has been suggested for the central Austrian Alps that, during the favourable periods of the Postglacial, the timberline was not situated more than 100–200 m above the present day potential position.

Are these results valid for all other parts of the Alps and their surroundings? In 1974, Markgraf summarised the data available for the Alps (figure 4). Her figure has been completed here for the French Alps after Wegmüller 1977. The curves have in common the steep rise of the timberline in the earliest Postglacial and a remarkable decrease somewhat after 3000 BP (1050 bc), but that is a fact that has long been known. The striking differences of the curves need explaining, and the information derived from the timberline should be checked in adjacent areas to separate events of general meaning from Alpine peculiarities or even from peculiarities of certain parts of the Alps. The amplitude of the timberline fluctuations is of special interest and needs further work. In the central Alps, the amplitudes appear to be the smallest ones: it has been pointed out (Patzelt 1980) that no event was more intensive than the 1850 advance of the glaciers (figure 5).

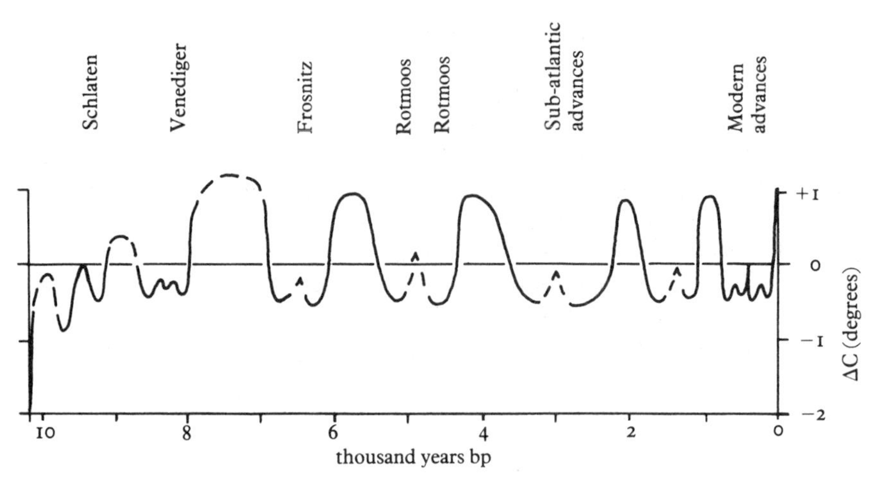

Figure 5. Post-glacial summer temperatures in the Alps as obtained from fluctuations of the timberline and the snowline. ΔC = deviation from the modern long-term average (after Patzelt 1980).

Peat bog growth and climate

There is the often discussed problem of recurrence surfaces in lowland peat bogs (see for instance Overbeck 1975) and the rarely considered relationship between the growth of peat bogs in mountainous areas and climatic changes. I shall restrict my remarks to the latter question.

For the peat bogs of the Harz mountains situated in altitudes between 700 and 900 m above sea-level, five periods were originally suggested during which a humid climate caused the formation of new peat bogs and increased the horizontal and vertical growth of those already existing (Willutzki 1962). Those five periods were dated to the end of the Late Glacial, the early Atlantic, the middle part of the Sub-boreal (about 3600 BP (1650 bc)), the beginning of the Sub-atlantic (about 2600 BP (650 bc)) and the time around 450 BP (ad 1500).

We have checked these data by investigations on more than fifteen peat bogs. The majority of them started their growth during the Pre-boreal or at the end of the Younger Dryas. In all cases, the peat bogs started from small or medium-sized areas. Within one peat bog there are several such centres which were formed at different times during the Postglacial. Those centres increased in size, they joined up and in most cases the bogs grew up almost to their present size not later than during the Sub-boreal, that is, not later than 3000 years ago. In the largest peat bog we have investigated, we found one centre formed in the Younger Dryas, eighteen centres from the Pre-boreal, eleven from the Boreal, ten from the early and four from the late Atlantic, and three from the early Sub-boreal; after that no further ones. In that case, the present-day size was also reached at about 3000 BP (1050 bc). The appearance and number of such centres did not support the suggested five periods of increased

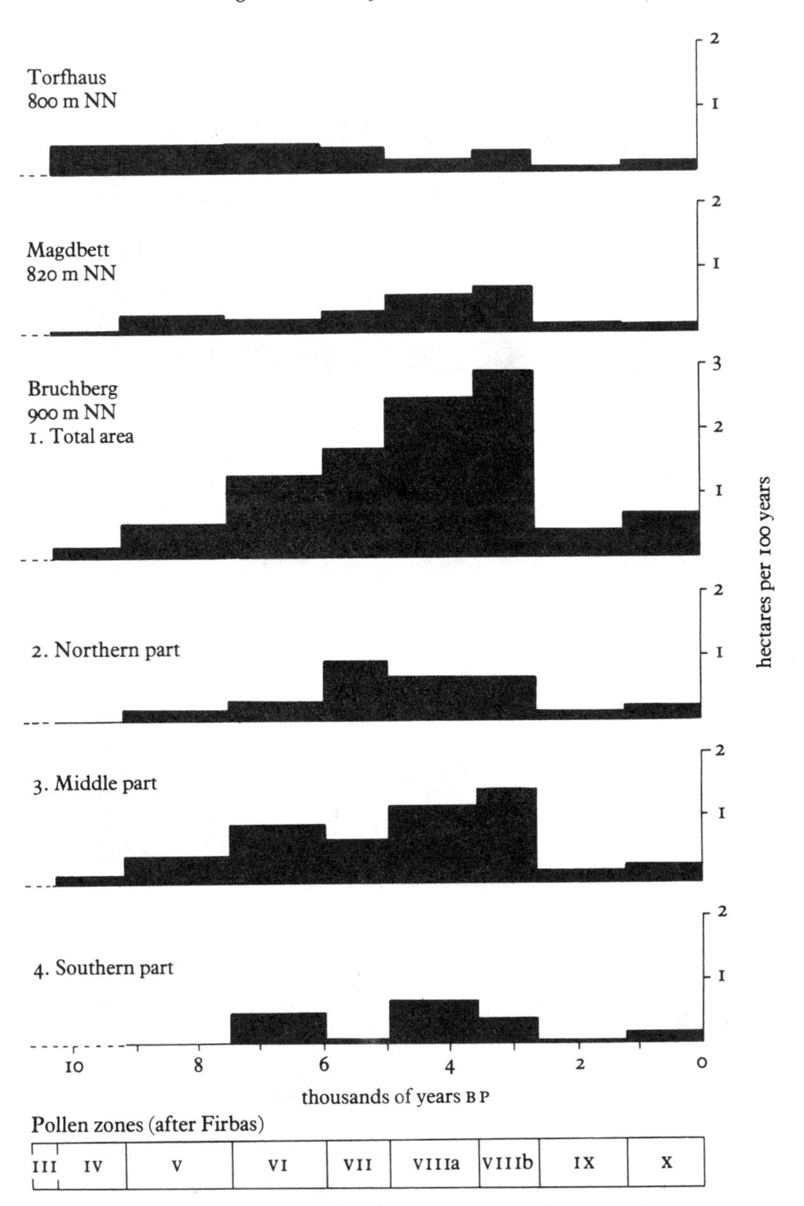

Figure 6. Horizontal growth of peat bogs in the Harz Mountains (ha per 100 years) (after Beug and Henrion, unpublished).

humidity and peat bog growth. So we checked the rates for the horizontal growth of some of the peat bogs (figure 6). The rates have been calculated for the forest zones III–X (after Firbas) and are in hectares per 100 years.

The first peat bog (Torfhaus) shows higher rates in the early, and lower ones in the later Postglacial. The second bog (Magdbett) gives a somewhat inverse

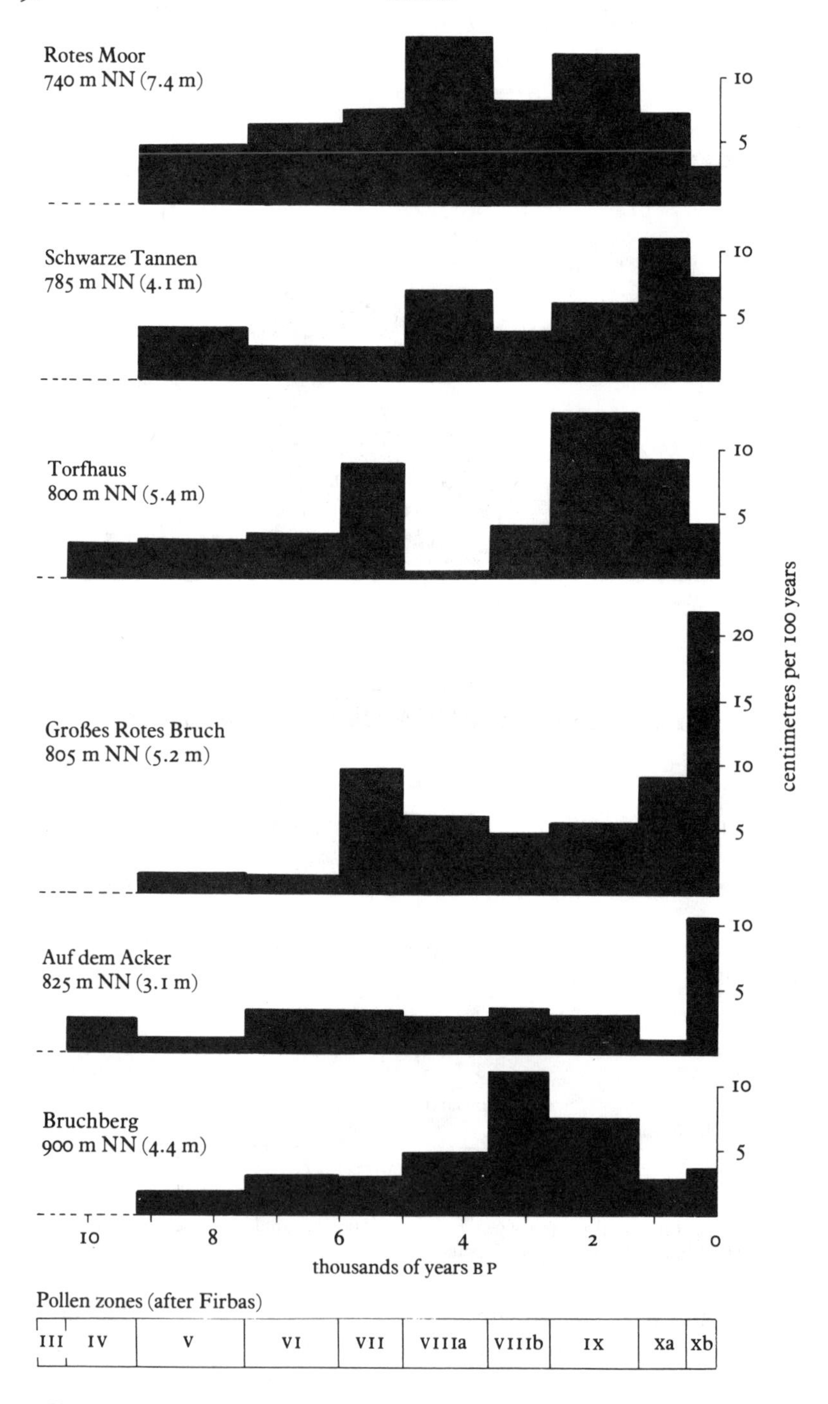

Figure 7. Vertical growth of peat bogs in the Harz Mountains (cm per 100 years) (after Beug, unpublished).

impression and it does not show growth of any significance after the end of the Sub-boreal. The third peat bog (Bruchberg) consists of three parts which developed independently and became connected into one unit in late Sub-boreal times. Until the end of the Sub-boreal, increased rates of horizontal growth are clearly to be seen; they are followed by an abrupt decrease if the whole area of the bog is considered. That abrupt decrease is to be seen in all of the three parts of the peat bog and in the Magdbett peat bog as well. I would not like to explain these data by supposing there was an increase in continentality after the end of the Sub-boreal, but would rather suggest that in mountainous areas, peat bog growth seems to be limited to boundaries given by the local topography which were apparently reached by the peat bogs generally not later than the end of the Sub-boreal. As to the three parts of the Bruchberg peat bog, one can say that their history and growth-rates are quite individual.

The last possibility of finding a relationship between peat bog growth and climatic change was by studying the vertical growth of different bogs (figure 7). The values are given for six peat bogs in cm per 100 years.Individual behaviour of the peat bogs can clearly be concluded from figure 7. The growth of the peat bogs in the Harz mountains is apparently controlled to a high degree by local factors such as hydrology and subsurface topography. Changes in humidity and temperature have had no chance of influencing the growth so much that it becomes discernible.

Examples from southern Europe

In southern Europe, the components of Mediterranean vegetation depend for their distribution on summer aridity and mild winter temperatures. In the eu-mediterranean zone, the summer is the unfavourable season and the typical plants of that zone show evergreen leaves. Deciduous plants form the next forest belt (the sub-mediterranean zone) and here the climate shows colder winters and more humid summers. I have selected examples from Dalmatia and Greece.

On the Dalmatian coast of Jugoslavia, deciduous sub-mediterranean oak forests with some Mediterranean species existed from 9000 BP (7050 bc) or even earlier to 7600 BP (5650 bc) (see Beug 1967 and references cited there). During that period, no evidence for migration processes or climatic changes are to be found. At 7600 BP (5650 bc), deciduous oaks lost part of their importance in the coastal area and became replaced by *Juniperus* and *Phillyrea* (figure 8, zone A and B). That situation lasted till 6300 BP (4350 bc) and during that time, the evergreen oak *Quercus ilex* immigrated and began to spread over the region. At about 6300 BP (4350 bc), that tree came to dominance. *Quercus ilex* forests grew there from 6300 to about 2200 BP (4350–250 bc) when the natural forests were destroyed by human influence.

Part of the history of the forests can easily be explained by migration processes. From 9000 to 7600 BP (7050–5650 bc), forests existed in balance with environmental factors. The climate was either colder in winter or more humid in summer than today. At about 7600 BP (5650 bc), the climate must

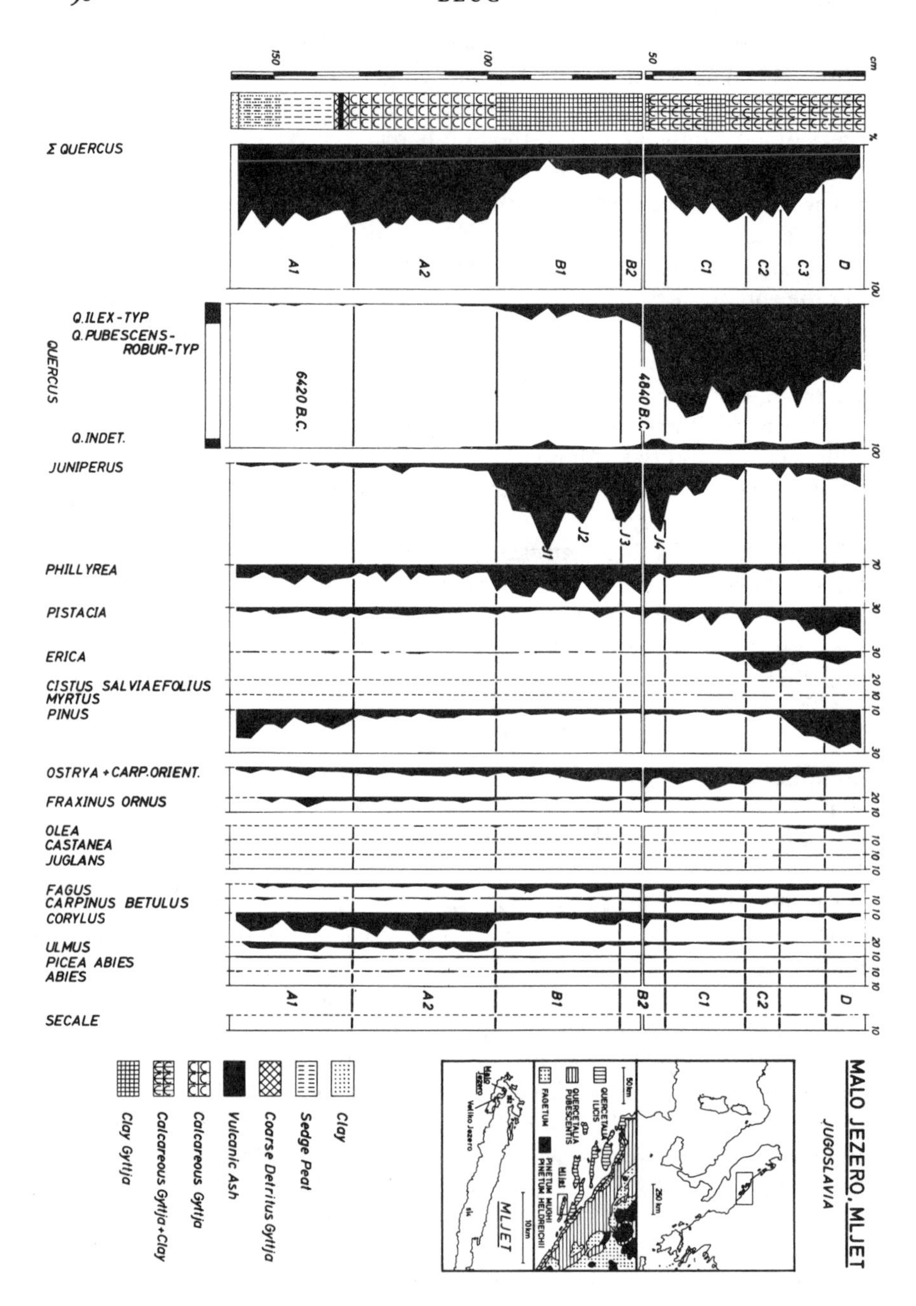

Figure 8. Pollen diagram of Malo Jezero, Mljet, Yugoslavia (after Beug 1967; reproduced by permission of Elsevier Scientific Publishing Company).

have changed to the real eu-mediterranean conditions which caused the immigration of *Quercus ilex*. The beginning of *Quercus ilex* forests, however, is not necessarily to be connected with a climatic event at that time. After 6300 BP (4350 bc), nothing in the forest history can be explained by changes in the climate. The hectic picture of numerous cold and warm periods as detected from the Alps cannot be reproduced here. On the other hand, the very simple course of the development of the vegetation may partly be due to the geomorphological situation. Islands and a small coastal mainland area are immediately followed by steep slopes. Possible changes of the climate after 7600 BP (5650 bc) might have affected the boundary between eu- and sub-mediterranean forests situated on those mountain slopes. By climatic oscillations, small strips of the slopes could have been won or lost by one of the two zones and such changes may have remained invisible in the pollen rain.

Further inland, there is an unbroken dominance, from the beginning of the record at about 7000 BP (5050 bc), of sub-mediterranean deciduous oak forests (Brande 1973). Changes which could be due to climate were not found. Human influence began a few centuries BC and at once caused a great change in the highly stabilised situation of the preceding 5000 years.

From Greece, we have an increasing number of investigations coming mainly from areas in which forests show a majority of deciduous trees (for the most important results see Athanasiadis 1975, Bottema 1974, Turner and Greig 1975, Wijmstra 1969).

Forest development started at about 10,600 BP (8650 bc), that is, at the beginning of the Postglacial. The dominating late glacial steppe communities were gradually replaced by dry and still open deciduous oak forests with some *Pistacia*. The period between 10,600 and 8200 BP (8650–6250 bc) can be characterised by a still dry climate with increasing temperatures. For the time after 8200 BP (6250 bc), an increase in precipitation is assumed, for closed deciduous or mixed oak forests now completely occupied the lower and middle altitudes.

At 6500 BP (4550 bc) there was an expansion of *Carpinus orientalis* which is a member of the sub-mediterranean forests, and an assumed slight decrease in temperature after 4000 BP (2050 bc). Apart from that, the forest history shows a great monotony at that altitude and no more suggestions of climate changes can be found.

In Dalmatia, sub-mediterranean forests date back to at least 9000 BP (7050 bc). In Greece, they seem to be 1000 years younger at least. For climatic history in Greece the transitional period with dry open forests is important. That period connected the late glacial steppe climate with the postglacial forest climate. If such a period did exist in Dalmatia, it finished earlier than 9000 BP (7050 bc). The change to a wetter climate in Greece after 8200 BP (6250 bc) has no counterpart in Dalmatia and the change from a sub-mediterranean to a eu-mediterranean climate in Dalmatia at 7600 BP (5650 bc) no counterpart in Greece. Possibly, that period of transitional climate was shorter and/or finished earlier the further west the region in question is situated. That would agree well with results from southern Spain where *Quercus ilex* forests date back precisely to the beginning of the Postglacial or even to Late Glacial times (Florschütz *et al.* 1971).

Concluding remarks

Postglacial vegetational history is used for explaining the way in which our present vegetation came into existence, for stratigraphical purposes, for reconstructing the environment of the past and for tracing human influence. The existing record in Europe is good but not yet sufficient to carry out these tasks.

A picture of climatic development can be drawn in broad terms by the coincidence of indications of similar tendencies from differing sources, as has been done by, among others, Zoller (1967): at 9000–8500 BP (7050–6550 bc) a trend from a cool-dry to a warmer and moister climate, at 5000 BP (3050 bc) to a cooler and at 3000–2800 BP (1050–850 bc) to a cooler and moister climate. There is a great need, however, for a more detailed picture.

Such a detailed picture can be obtained by making use of phenomena in the distribution of plants that are highly sensitive to climatic changes. The timberline is one of them, but it can be used only in the higher mountains. Other phenomena are the distribution of those plant species whose ecological demands and abilities are well known and which are or have been at their limits of distribution in Middle Europe in the past. So the occurrence of *Ulmus, Viscum, Hedera, Ilex, Cladium, Vitis,* several water plants and factors like the sensibility of *Fagus* to late frost have been used. The possibility of misinterpretation exists because of the meagreness of the record and the small amplitude of the fluctuations in relation to statistical error. To avoid such problems means repeating many previous studies and investing much more time and manpower in new basic research than has been done before. By sifting the data – not always the same old data again but newly obtained data – for possible climatic influence, we will most probably obtain many results of regional validity for single landscapes, as seems to be the case with certain results coming from Alpine timberline fluctuations (see figure 4). To find such regional characteristics in vegetational history which can be explained in climatic terms, however, should be the aim for vegetational history studies during the next decades.

REFERENCES

In order to avoid an excessive number of references, papers listed below may serve as a source for citations of additional relevant publications.

Athanasiadis, N. (1975) Zur postglazialen Vegetationsentwicklung von Litochoro Katerinis und Pertouli Trikalon (Griechenland), *Flora* 164, 99-132.

Beug, H.-J. (1967) On the forest history of the Dalmatian coast, *Rev. Palaeobotany and Palynology* 2, 271-9.

— (1977) Waldgrenzen und Waldbestand in Europa während des Eiszeitalters. *Göttinger Universitätsreden* 61, Vandenhoeck & Ruprecht, Göttingen.

Bortenschlager, S. (1970) Waldgrenz- und Klimaschwankungen im pollenanalytischen Bild des Gurgeler Rotmooses, *Mittl. Ostalp.-din. Ges. f. Vegetkde.* 11, 19-26.

Bortenschlager, S. & Patzelt, G. (1969) Wärmezeitliche Klima- und Gletscherschwankungen im Pollenprofil eines hochgelegenen Moores (2270 m) der Venedigergruppe, *Eiszeitalter u. Gegenwart* 20, 116-22.

Bottema, S. (1974) *Late Quaternary Vegetation History of Northwestern Greece*. Thesis, Univ. of Groningen, Groningen: V.R.B. Offsetdrukkerij.

Brande, A. (1973) Untersuchungen zur postglazialen Vegetationsgeschichte im Gebiet der Neretva-Niederungen (Dalmatien, Herzegowina), *Flora* 162, 1-44.

Burga, C. A. (1979) Postglaziale Klimaschwankungen in Pollendiagrammen der Schweiz, *Vierteljahrsschrift d. Naturforschenden Ges. i. Zürich* 1979, 265-83.

Firbas, F. (1949) *Spät- und nacheiszeitliche Waldgeschichte Mitteleuropas nördlich der Alpen, 1. Bd. Allgemeine Waldgeschichte*. Jena: Verlag G. Fischer.

— (1952) *Spät- und nacheiszeitliche Waldgeschichte Mitteleuropas nördlich der Alpen, 2. Bd. Waldgeschichte der einzelnen Landschaften*. Jena: Verlag G. Fischer.

Florschütz, F., Menéndez Amor, J. & Wijmstra, T. A. (1971) Palynology of a thick Quaternary succession in southern Spain, *Palaeogeogr., Palaeoclimat., Palaeoecol.* 10, 233-64.

Frenzel, F. (ed.) (1977) *Dendrochronologie und Postglaziale Klimaschwankungen in Europa*. Wiesbaden: F. Steiner Verlag GmbH.

Kral, F. (1979) *Spät- und postglaziale Waldgeschichte der Alpen auf grund der bisherigen Pollenanalysen*. Wien: Österr. Agrarverlag.

Lange, O. W. & Schulze, E.-D. (1966) Untersuchungen über die Dickenentwicklung der kutikularen Zellwandschichten bei Fichtennadeln, *Fortwiss. Zbl.* 85, 27-38.

Markgraf, V. (1974) Paleoclimatic evidences derived from timberline fluctuations, in *Colloques Internationaux du C.N.R.S.* no.219, *Les méthodes quantitatives d'étude des variations du climat au cours du Pléistocène*, 67-83.

Oeschger, H., Messerli, B. & Svilar, M., eds (1980) *Das Klima*. Berlin, Heidelberg, New York: Springer Verlag.

Overbeck, F. (1975) *Botanisch-geologische Moorkunde*. Neumünster: Karl Wachholtz Verlag.

Patzelt, G. (1974) Holocene variations of glaciers in the Alps, in *Colloques Internationaux du C.N.R.S.* no.219, *Les méthodes quantitatives d'étude des variations du climat au cours du Pléistocène*, 51-9.

— (1977) Der zeitliche Ablauf und das Ausmaß postglazialer Klimaschwankungen in den Alpen, in Frenzel, F. (ed.) *Dendrochronologie und postglaziale Klimaschwankungen in Europa*. Wiesbaden: F. Steiner Verlag GmbH.

— (1980) Neue Ergebnisse der Spät- und Postglazialforschung in Tirol, *Österr. Geogr. Ges. Jahresber.* 76/77, 11-18.

Sawyer, J. S., ed. (1966) *World climate from 8000 to 0 B.C.* London: Royal Meteorological Society.

Turner, J. & Greig, J. R. A. (1975) Some Holocene pollen diagrams from Greece, *Rev. Palaeobotany and Palynology* 20, 171-204.

Wegmüller, S. (1977) Pollenanalytische Untersuchungen zur spät- und postglazialen Vegetationsgeschichte der französischen Alpen (Dauphiné), Bern: Verlag Paul Haupt.

Welten, M. (1952) Über die spät- und postglaziale Vegetationsgeschichte des Simmentals, *Veröff. d. Geobotan. Inst. Rübel i. Zürich*, H.26, Bern: Verlag Hans Huber.

Wijmstra, T. A. (1969) Palynology of the first 30 metres of a 120 m deep section in northern Greece, *Acta Bot. Neerl.* 18, 511-27.

Willutzki, H. (1962) Zur Waldgeschichte und Vermoorung sowie über Rekurrenzflächen im Oberharz, *Nova Acta Leopoldina* N.F. Nr. 160, Bd. 25, Leipzig: J. A. Barth Verlag.

Zoller, H. (1960) Pollenanalytische Untersuchungen zur Vegetationsgeschichte der insubrischen Schweiz, *Denkschriften d. Schweiz. Naturf. Ges.* 83, Zürich: Gebrüder Fretz AG.

— (1967) Postglaziale Klimaschwankungen und ihr Einfluß auf die Waldentwicklung Mitteleuropas einschließlich der Alpen, *Ber. Dtsch. Bot. Ges.* 80, 690-6.

Zoller, H., Schindler, C. & Röthlisberger, H. (1966) Postglaziale Gletscherstände und Klimaschwankungen im Gotthardmassiv und Vorderrheingebiet, *Verhandl. Naturf. Ges. Basel* 77, 97-164.

Peat-bog stratigraphy as a proxy climate record

In a paper entitled 'The relationship of bog stratigraphy to climatic change and archaeology' published in the *Proceedings of the Prehistoric Society* for 1946, Professor Godwin attempted to enlighten the archaeologist who 'at heart prefers the dry chalk trench to the soaking black peat face', on the potential of the peat record. Today, with the splendid series of reports coming out of the Somerset Levels Project and the apparent willingness of archaeologists to get their feet and their trowels into sites such as the waterlogged deposits of Viking York or Roman Vindolanda, we may assume that no such encouragement is necessary. The purpose of this contribution is not, however, to dwell upon the marvellous preservation of organic artefacts of worked wood, leather etc., but to explore and to demonstrate the proxy climatic records which may be derived from the stratigraphy of a particular type of peat, that formed in raised peat bogs.

Godwin (1946) is still worth reading as a clear exposition of the ecological terms and concepts and the effects of climatic change on bog vegetation and stratigraphy, even though some of his conclusions have been altered by more recent research. The methods used in such research have recently been reviewed by the present author (Barber 1976).

Peat accumulation and climate

Peat bogs are unique plant communities because of the way in which their vegetation is preserved over thousands of years through the formation of the peat itself, the partially decayed remains of the bog plants. The mechanism of peat formation is dependent upon the maintenance of a high near-surface water-table and this is achieved mainly through the peculiar structure of *Sphagnum* bog-mosses which possess a system of empty (hyaline) cells in their minute leaves, as well as the living pigmented cells which give the plants their often striking colours. A single *Sphagnum* shoot may not look like a potent agent of environmental change (see Open University 1972, pp.15–19 for a good illustration of their structure and role) but when one sees them gathered together in their millions on the surface of a growing bog their potential becomes clear. The empty cells can absorb water to the extent of many times the dry weight of the plant and the plant has a high cation exchange capacity – that is to say it can extract from the surrounding water nutrients such as potassium and magnesium, giving up hydrogen ions in exchange and thus acidifying the water which is either flowing through (in the case of valley bogs) or falling upon (in the case of raised bogs) the *Sphagnum* mat (see Moore and

Bellamy 1974, pp. 122-7 for details).

Add to these attributes of water retention and acidification the fact that *Sphagna* grow from the tip or capitulum, while the lower parts of each shoot, waterlogged and deprived of light and oxygen, die off but do not rapidly decay, and you have a system capable of self-sustainment and reinforcement. In this way, carrying its own water-table with it, masses of *Sphagnum* peat are able to grow above the local mineral ground water-table to form raised bogs – great upturned saucers of peat often several square kilometres in extent.

What this means, of course, is that such bogs are dependent upon rainfall (hence the terms ombrophilous, ombrotrophic and ombrogenous to describe their nutrition and formation), or rather, dependent upon the interaction of precipitation and evaporation at the bog surface. Although the vascular plants of bogs – *Calluna* (heather), *Eriophorum* (cotton-grasses) and a few others – can exert some control over their evapotranspiration by closing their stomata (leaf-pores), the *Sphagna* are more or less at the mercy of the climate, their only protection against drying out and the death of their capitula being afforded by their cover of heather and other plants and some fairly primitive characteristics such as close-packing of the shoots and leaves, as seen in the different 'ecological strains' of *Sphagnum imbricatum* (Green 1968), and by feedback mechanisms of the sort described by Clymo (1973). It is also apparent that different species of *Sphagna* inhabit different micro-habitats on the undulating surface of a raised bog with some found at or below water level – *S. cuspidatum* and *S. subsecundum* – and others at higher levels – *S. papillosum* and *S. rubellum* (Ratcliffe and Walker 1958). This is the basis of the reconstructions of past surface wetness conditions of raised bogs (Barber 1978, 1981) which will be described later. However, much of the earlier work on bog stratigraphy and climate concentrated on the grosser manifestations of change – that from relatively well-humified dark *Sphagnum* peat, rich in *Calluna* remains, to a relatively unhumified light-coloured *Sphagnum* peat. These changes, which are real changes of humification induced by climatic change and not by secondary humification (Godwin 1946, Aaby 1976, Barber 1978), were termed Recurrence Surfaces by Godwin, following Granlund's (1932) suggestion, and became the *idée fixe* of peat stratigraphic studies.

Recurrence surfaces: the search for fixed points

The best known and usually the most pronounced of the Recurrence Surfaces (RY's – from the Swedish *rekurrensytor*) is that known as the *Grenzhorizont* – the Boundary Horizon of Weber (1900). This is RYIII in Granlund's scheme of five RY's: RYI at 750 BP (AD 1200), RYII at 1550 BP (AD 400), RYIII at 2550 BP (600 BC), RYIV at 3150 BP (1200 BC) and RYV at 4250 BP (2300 BC). Others have been recognised at various dates – Nilsson (1935) put forward nine RY's between 5450 BP (3500 BC) and the present. Lundqvist (1962) settles for seven – the five above and RYVI at 4850 BP (2900 bc) and RYVII at 5650 BP (3700 bc) – before going on to discuss radiocarbon datings of them which his Stockholm laboratory had then just performed and which, like Overbeck's (1957) work and that of Schneekloth (1965), showed a variety of dates for what they identified as the same RY – differences of several hundred years for the same RY in one bog or in closely adjacent bogs. This confusion of dates led to a spate of claims and the 'game' of dating RY's became a fast-growing pastime amongst those with access to a radiocarbon laboratory. And yet, before the advent of radiocarbon dating a flexible and sensible attitude to these striking stratigraphic changes had been promulgated by Godwin and Conway (1939), Godwin (1946, 1948) and Conway (1948). The latter paper is worth quoting from, although many of the concepts have been invalidated by later work. In discussing her figure 2 – 'Schematic interpretation of the stratigraphy of four British peat profiles in terms of a hypothetical 'moisture factor' – she postulates the idea of 'threshold values' for individual bogs whereby

> . . . any given stage in the course of the climatic fluctuations over a large area will give a value of the moisture factor which will vary from locality to locality according to the altitude, the general situation, and the topographic characteristics of each locality. Thus the moisture-factor curves for different localities should be roughly parallel in behaviour but not necessarily coincident. Further, unless a given climatic oscillation causes the curve for the moisture factor at a given locality to cross a threshold line, then that climatic oscillation will not be expressed by the vegetation at that locality. (p.227)

This can certainly be looked upon as an early expression of what is now generally known as Catastrophe Theory (Wagstaff 1976) and was incorporated in Godwin's 1948 paper on the Somerset Levels (p.282) and his 1954 review paper on Recurrence Surfaces (p.29). I have taken the argument a little further (Barber 1978) in suggesting that some bogs (e.g. Bolton Fell Moss near Carlisle) may be particularly sensitive to climatic fluctuations in that they lie at a climatic 'hinge-line' somewhere between areas where conditions are so wet that only the peaks of surface dryness may be reflected in an otherwise 'wet' stratigraphy (e.g. bogs in Western Ireland) whereas others, in a drier zone, may reflect only large shifts to greater surface wetness (e.g. bogs in central Germany). Obviously confirmation of this idea could only come from a very large-scale survey, but it is nevertheless surprising that Conway's idea was not reflected in subsequent literature to any great extent, though there is some recognition of it perhaps in the generally held view that climatic deterioration was first felt in western Britain.

To return to the search for 'fixed points' and the dating of Recurrence Surfaces we may note Mitchell's (1956) paper which produced evidence for a spread of dates but with concentrations of shifts to wetter conditions around 3450 BP (1500 bc), 2750 BP (800 bc) and 1450 BP (ad 500). An earlier shift of 4481 BP (2531 bc) was dated from Fallahogy (Smith and Willis 1962). Only shifts to wetter conditions can, of course, be used as fixed points, in that the change to drier, more humified peat may take place under drying or constant moisture conditions as the peat builds up above the 'wet datum' of the Recurrence Surface. Lamb (1977), as well as reproducing Mitchell's 1956 diagram of RY's, has a table (13.12) of other dates, including those of Overbeck and his co-workers (1957 – dates around 2650 BP (700 bc), 2050 BP (100 bc) and 1350 BP (ad 600). The 1960s were the heyday of this dating game and produced much valuable data. As already mentioned Lundqvist (1962), in a series of dates from Högmossen produced evidence for a time-gap between the old *Sphagnum* peat member of a recent RY (dates of 1080, 1270 and 1475 BP, ad 870, 680 and 475) and the younger *Sphagnum* regrowth (800, 1135 and 1125 BP, ad 1150, 815 and 825 respectively), an average hiatus period of 255 years. However if one takes the extremes of the standard deviations on his middle series of radiocarbon dates (from his fig.4, BP22) there is no hiatus (1135 ± 60 BP and 1270 ± 90 BP; ad 815 ± 60 and 680 ± 90) and the others are reduced to 120 and 195 years. In the absence of detailed stratigraphic information on the sample depths and sizes, and taking into account the fact that his data are derived from sample boreholes 50 metres apart (with all the problems of small-scale lateral variation that this implies – see Barber 1978, 1981), then one finds it difficult to agree with his conclusions – that RY's form only when a bog 'has arrived at a suitable stage of development' and that climate is 'certainly only of secondary importance'.

Schneekloth (1965) working on the Gifhorner Moor near Hannover also found a range of dates for the RY's stretching from 2350–1250 BP (400 bc to ad 700), some 1100 years difference, but again the work was from boreholes and may have not clearly differentiated the different bands of humified peat, though pollen-analytical correlations were used.

Godwin (1966) was in no doubt that climate was the prime cause of Recurrence Surfaces, even though the precise response to climatic change was variable from bog to bog. He gives a table of dates of a prominent RY in England and Wales where there is an archaeological connection in the form of trackways built across several of the bogs. His averaged dates of 2959 BP (1009 bc) for the dry lower surfaces, 2604 BP (654 bc) for the trackways and 2575 BP (625 bc) for the wet regrowth of the peat show conclusively that we are dealing with a phenomenon which, whatever the details of its effects on the bog plants, certainly elicited a response from man.

Turner (1965), as an adjunct to her detailed pollen-analytical work, also produced an interesting series of radiocarbon dates, encompassing the period 2954–768 BP (1004 bc to ad 1182). Working from her figure 23 it is possible to produce a number of peat accumulation rates which do undoubtedly show a remarkable increase in peat formation (and thereby a wetter bog surface), viz:

1) *Across the* RY: 63–52 cm between 1477 and 768 BP (ad 473 and 1182): Rate of 64 years/cm.
2) *Between Lower* RY (III) *and upper one in 1) above, which seems to 'include'* RY II *and* I:
   a) 82–63 cm: 19 cm between 2354 and 1477 BP (404 bc and ad 473) = 877 years = 46 years/cm.
   b) 170–82 cm: 88 cm between 2646 and 2354 BP (696 and 404 bc) = 292 years = 3.3 years/cm.

c) 170–63 cm: 107 cm between 2646 and 1777 BP
(696 bc and ad 473) = 1169 years = 10.9 years/cm.
(These figures are given in years/cm rather than mm/year, cm/century or cm/1000 years since I claim these are easier to comprehend and are meaningful in terms of pollen, macrofossil and radiocarbon date sample sizes.)

Similar figures can be easily worked out from the other diagrams in Turner's paper and I have given a number of figures from other sites (Barber 1978, 1981) varying from 62.5 years/cm to 2.75 years/cm, with an average value for 'post-Grenz' peats of around 17 years/cm, a figure not out of line with Walker's (1961, 1970) estimates of 20 years/cm.

What these figures demonstrate, of course, is that bogs are perfectly capable of growing at widely varying rates according to changing climatic conditions. Although there are certainly gaps in the accumulation of *some* bogs at the level of Recurrence Surfaces, recent research has tended towards a lesser emphasis on these grosser manifestations of change and a closer look at continuous secular variation.

Climatic shifts and curves

The move to a more explicit statement of trends may be dated to the 1964 paper of Nilsson on Ageröds mosse in southern Sweden. Whilst concluding that RY's could be recognised at 4650, 3700, 2750, 2250, 1300, 950 and 550 BP (2700 bc, 1750 bc, 800 bc, 300 bc, ad 650, ad 1000 and ad 1400), he stresses the secular nature of the record from his site and elsewhere. One may fairly conclude that the previous concentration of effort on dating RY's tended to distract attention from what is now seen as the aim of peat-stratigraphic work related to climate – the construction of climatic curves based not only on visible field stratigraphy but on analysis of the *Sphagna* in thin slices of peat, thus reconstructing the past surface wetness condition of each of a number of profiles.

The growth of peat bogs *between* RY's had, following the classic work of Osvald (1923, 1950), been thought to follow an autogenic cycle of hummock and hollow succession. Put simply, the idea was that the mosaic of plants of slightly different hydrologic requirements which inhabited the small hummocks and hollows (sometimes open pools) gave rise to a situation whereby growth on hummocks ceased due to dryness while surrounding hollows continued to grow, overtopped the moribund hummocks to become hummocks themselves, only to be 'drowned' by the former hummock, now a hollow, growing up and repeating the process. The stratigraphic evidence for this process was at best equivocal and grave doubts were raised by Walker and Walker (1961) in their examination of Irish peat sections. My own work on the Osvald theory led on from these doubts but I was fortunate enough to be directed by the late Gordon Manley and Frank Oldfield to a site, Bolton Fell Moss, Cumbria (N.G.R. NY4969) where the peat is still growing today in parts but where most of the bog is being cut for horticultural peat. This meant that the uppermost stratigraphy (one metre or so), and detailed macrofossil and pollen-analytical work on it, could be related to *independently known* climatic change. Working from representative sections chosen from ditches hundreds of metres long (thus obviating the problem of correlating borehole detail) I was able to show conclusively that no cyclic alternation of hummocks and hollows had occurred for at least 2500 years but that a clear relationship existed between *Sphagnum* species changes, peat type and humification, in 21 profiles, and climatic variation. In particular three pool levels, characterised by their macrofossils of *S. cuspidatum, S. subsecundum* and various algae, at 1000, 500 and 200 BP (ad 950, 1450 and AD 1780) could be related to Lamb's (1977) data for High Summer Wetness – which must be one of the most important parameters in bog growth – and there is a very high degree of correspondence between my Surface Wetness curve (fig. 76 in Barber 1978, 1981) and the trend of climatic variation (Lamb 1977) since the Middle Ages. The resolution of event in this sort of peat is of the order of a few decades and work is now in progress to extend the record at Bolton Fell Moss right back through the Postglacial at a similar sort of resolution on a core 10 metres in depth. At the moment the oldest phase-shift to wet conditions on this bog is dated at about 2830 BP (880 bc) (RYIII again!) and this is followed by drier or constant conditions, with humified peat of mainly *S. imbricatum* and *Calluna* forming at a rate of 34 years/cm through to around 1350 BP (ad 600); there follows a wet and/or cold period up to 1150 BP (ad 800), the next half-century is drier and/or warmer, followed by another decline between 1090 and 850 BP (ad 860 and 1100), which is followed by the well-known Medieval Optimum (no pools or wet lawns on the bog) before a catastrophic decline, with the virtual extinction of *S. imbricatum*, into the Little Ice Age relieved only by a slightly warmer/drier episode in the early 1500s. Recent work in northern England has also shown climatic deterioration at 2686 BP (736 bc) (Dickinson 1975) as well as an RY at about 1550 BP (ad 400), and in the Somerset Levels the ongoing work of Coles and his many co-workers have validated the earlier research of Godwin. Whilst in this situation one must bear in mind that the tremendous feats of prehistoric labour in building trackways would have had a variety of stimuli the trackways themselves owe their survival to rapid peat growth. Coles and Orme (1980), in summarising the work of the Project, admit the likelihood of climatic deterioration around 3350 BP (1400 bc), from 3050 BP (1100 bc) onwards (with a hiatus in trackbuilding from 2650–2350 BP (700–400 bc), when it may have been so wet that boat transport was preferable), and with the end of the 'lake-villages' at about 1950 BP (turn of the era). On the other hand there seems to be little alternative to a drier/warmer climatic period around 1550 BP (ad 400) to explain the cessation of bog growth at sites such as Shapwick Heath. This ties in with the evidence from Bolton Fell Moss, from Rusland Moss (Dickinson 1975) and from sites further away such as Clonsast where a pine stump below an RY was dated at 1585 BP (ad 365) (Mitchell 1956), but it is interesting to note that while these more northerly and westerly bogs continued to grow until the present day the Somerset bogs would appear to have been beyond resuscitation after perhaps 300 years or so of drying conditions.

Casparie (1969, 1972) has also produced well-dated peat sequences and macrofossil analyses from the raised bog near Emmen, including a nine-stage diagram of peat growth at site Emmen-17 from 3840 to 2050 BP (1890 to 100 bc). However, he finds it difficult to see a climatic 'signal' in this section owing to its proximity to a lake formed by the coalescent growth of the raised bogs in the locality. This lake overflowed around 2550 BP (600 bc) – perhaps due to increasing wetness though Casparie sees only the 'alteration of the original balance' at about 3880 BP (1930 bc) as being due to climatic change.

Aaby's work on Danish bogs is a good example of the recent approach of careful stratigraphic work, which he was fortunate enough to have backed up by large numbers (55 on one profile at Draved Mose) of radiocarbon dates (Aaby and Tauber 1974, Aaby 1976). Using humification values, *Sphagnum* leaf counts and other methods on Draved Mose and other sites he found shifts to phases of wetter peat formation, over a period of 5500 years, had occurred with a statistically tested periodicity of 260 years. Some of these shifts – e.g. at 5060 BP (3110 BC) – seem rather insignificant but if one notes points at which shifts occur close together from at least three bog profiles one comes out with the following (calibrated radiocarbon) dates of major change: 450, 900, 1500, 1700, 2550, 3450 and 3950 BP (AD 1500*, AD 1050, AD 450*, AD 250, 600* BC, 1500* BC and 2000* BC). The asterisks mark RY I - V – we appear to have come full-circle! It is interesting to note that Aaby predicts, but does not find, a shift at 200 BP (AD 1780), precisely the date of the last phase-shift at Bolton Fell Moss. It seems likely that there would be less apparent variance in the earlier dates (pre-2450 BP (500 BC)) quoted in the literature if all were calibrated on the same scale.

Finally in this section the excellent work of van Geel and his collaborators, on Dutch bogs, must be reviewed. Van Geel has worked in the sort of detail that no-one had dared contemplate – analysing contiguous 1-cm samples throughout a profile and analysing every possible fossil: pollen, spores, *Sphagna*, fungi etc., and giving a Type Number to everything that could not be identified but which may later turn out to be important.

To date his team have catalogued 320 Types, many of which have been given a name because of the large reference collection and expertise of his institution, the Hugo de Vries Laboratory of the University of Amsterdam. The resulting diagrams (e.g. van Geel 1977, figs 2–5) are a mine of detailed information and from them he has produced curves of local moist conditions and fluctuations of oceanic climate (van Geel 1977, figs 6 and 8). Based upon correlations of diverse indicators such as *Corylus* pollen curve fluctuations, the presence of zygospores of *Mougeotia* (indicating shallow pools in spring), *Sphagnum* and many other macrofossils, etc. (for details see van Geel 1977, pp.13–22) he presents two curves of local moist conditions from the late Atlantic period through to the Sub-atlantic (no peat surviving from 1650 BP (ad 300) onwards). These show a distinct deterioration at 2850 BP (900 bc) (and a further even more oceanic phase beginning at 1850 BP (ad 100)), a fluctuating unstable climate in the early Sub-boreal 4850–3950 BP (2900–2000 bc) and a fluctuating but generally deteriorating climate thereafter, with especially moist conditions c. 3450 BP (1500 bc) at the beginning of the decline to the Sub-atlantic. This sort of admirable approach is also exemplified in a more recent paper (van Geel, Bohncke and Dee 1981) wherein relatively wet or dry phases are noted (and graphed – fig.7) at various times between 9650 and 6150 BP (7700 and 4200 bc), demonstrating that with care peat stratigraphic studies can indicate climatic conditions in the earlier Postglacial.

What we can conclude from the peat-stratigraphic data relevant to the later prehistoric period is that:

1) There was probably a climatic deterioration c. 3950–3850 BP (2000–1900 bc) even if it was only of a minor nature.

2) A more pronounced decline followed c. 3450–3350 BP (1500–1400 bc).

3) A catastrophic decline to a cooler and/or wetter climate around 2850–2550 BP (900–600 bc); taking into account the 'sensitivity' of individual bogs the earlier date may be more generally applicable.

4) Some evidence for further decline around 2050 BP (100 bc).

The warmer and/or drier episodes are more difficult to characterise owing to the *caveat* mentioned earlier – that most raised bogs will, by the build-up of peat above a recurrence surface, tend towards drier peat formation in either a constant or drying climate. New techniques of stable isotope analysis (next section) may allow us to solve this problem.

I do not think one should worry too much about the variation of dates of deterioration from different bogs. Indeed it would be preferable for archaeologists to look for the *nearest available* peat-stratigraphic evidence in that peat bogs in a particular area should surely reflect the *local* conditions of surface wetness which will presumably be more relevant to agricultural conditions of that area.

Future research

From the evidence of peat stratigraphy, evidence with a long history and of undoubted veracity, we can now be fairly sure of the course of climatic change in later prehistory in north-west Europe, as outlined in this chapter – though it would be premature to draw any kind of definitive climatic curve without more work, from more localities, along the lines of the more recent research described above. In particular there is a need for more continuous data from north-west Scotland, Ireland and Wales to compare these more oceanic areas with the work from Cumbria, Denmark and the Netherlands. Ideally such work should be done from peat sections but the recent work of Moore (1977) and of Boatman and Tomlinson (1977) show that closely-spaced cores (one metre or less apart) from living bog surfaces, at Claish Moss and Brishie Bog respectively, can also be used. There is a real need for radiocarbon dates from such profiles. Such work could also be usefully extended to the east and south of the areas mentioned – Tolonen's work (1971) is an example of such studies from a more north-easterly area. In Overbeck (1975), for example, fig.225 on p.589 is a map of the constituents of the upper light peat which are shown diagrammatically and one is struck immediately by the presence of a 'border region' to the north and west of Hannover; on the 'oceanic' side of this border *Sphagnum imbricatum* is present, towards the continental interior it is replaced by *S. magellanicum* and *Sphagna* of the *Acutifolia* group. There is surely scope for further palaeoclimatic reconstructions from this peatland area, though, of course, much is known already as is clear from Overbeck's massive study (1975).

Another promising line of development may be the application of stable isotope studies to peat – an extension of the well-known oxygen isotope work of Dansgaard *et al.* (1975) on ice cores from Greenland and of Schiegl's (1972) work on deuterium content of peats. In May 1981 Carl Brenninkmeijer of the Rijksuniversiteit, Groningen, and the present author visited Bolton Fell Moss and took two cores from the present living surface to the base of the bog at 10 metres depth. Building on the author's previous demonstration of the clear climatic control of ombrotrophic peat formation at this site (Barber 1978, 1981) it is hoped to produce a complete radiocarbon-dated postglacial curve of deuterium/hydrogen and O^{16}/O^{18} ratios by a newly worked-out method (Brenninkmeijer, personal communication). With macrofossil and pollen analysis to go with the stable isotope measurements, and the high resolution of these cores (c. 10 years/cm), the exciting potential of this work is clear.

REFERENCES

Aaby, B. (1976) Cyclic climatic variations in climate over the past 5,500 yr. reflected in raised bogs, *Nature* 263, 281-4.

Aaby, B. & Tauber, H. (1974) Rates of peat formation in relation to degree of humification and local environment, as shown by studies of a raised bog in Denmark, *Boreas* 4, 1-17.

Barber, K. E. (1976) History of Vegetation, in Chapman, S. B. (ed.) *Methods in Plant Ecology*, 5-83. Blackwells Scientific Publications, Oxford.

— (1978) *A palaeoecological test of the theory of cyclic peat bog regeneration.* University of Southampton Ph.D. thesis: 2 volumes.

— (1981) *Peat Stratigraphy and Climatic Change.* Rotterdam: Balkema.

Boatman, D. J. & Tomlinson, R. W. (1977) The Silver Flowe II. Features of the vegetation and stratigraphy of Brishie Bog, and their bearing on pool formation, *J. Ecol.* 65, 531-46.

Casparie, W. A. (1969) Bult- und Schlenkenbildung in Hochmoortorf (zur Frage des Moorwachstums-Mechanismus), *Vegetatio, Acta Geobotanica* 19, 146-80.

— (1972) *Bog Development in Southeastern Drenthe* (The Netherlands). The Hague: Junk.

Clymo, R. S. (1973) The growth of *Sphagnum*: some effects of environment, *J. Ecol.* 61, 849-70.

Coles, J. M. & Orme, B. J. (1980) *Prehistory of the Somerset Levels.* Cambridge: Somerset Levels Project.

Conway, V. M. (1948) Von Post's work on climatic rhythms, *New Phytol.* 47, 220-37.

Dansgaard, W., Johnsen, S. J., Reem, N., Gundestrup, N., Clausen, H. B. & Hammer, C. U. (1975) Climatic changes, Norsemen and modern man, *Nature* 255, 24-8.

Dickinson, W. (1975) Recurrence surfaces in Rusland Moss, Cumbria (formerly North Lancashire), *J. Ecol.* 63, 913-35.

Godwin, H. (1946) The relationship of bog stratigraphy to climatic change and archaeology, *Proc. Prehist. Soc.* 12, 1-11.

— (1948) Studies of the post-glacial history of British vegetation. X: Correlation between climate, forest composition, prehistoric agriculture and peat stratigraphy in Sub-Boreal and Sub-Atlantic peats of the Somerset Levels, *Phil. Trans. R. Soc.* B, 233; 275-86.

— (1954) Recurrence Surfaces, *Danm. Geol. Unders.* II, R 80, 22-30.

— (1966) Introductory address, in Sawyer, T. S. (ed.) *World Climate 8000-0 BC*. London: Royal Met. Soc.

Godwin, H. & Conway, V. M. (1939) The ecology of a raised bog near Tregaron, Cardiganshire, *J. Ecol.* 27, 315-59.

Granlund, E. (1932) De svenska Högmossarnas geologi, *Sver. geol. Unders.* C 26, 1-193.

Green, B. H. (1968) Factors influencing the spatial and temporal distribution of *Sphagnum imbricatum* Hornsch ex Russ. in the British Isles, *J. Ecol.* 56, 47-58.

Lamb, H. H. (1977) *Climate: Present, Past and Future. 2: Climatic History and the Future*. London: Methuen.

Lundqvist, B. (1962) Geological Radiocarbon Datings from the Stockholm station, *Sver. Geol. Unders.* C 589, 3-23.

Mitchell, G. F. (1956) Post-Boreal pollen diagrams from Irish raised-bogs, *Proc. R. Irish Acad.* 57B, 185-251.

Moore, P. D. (1977) Stratigraphy and pollen analysis of Claish Moss, north-west Scotland: significance for the origin of surface pools and forest history, *J. Ecol.* 65, 375-98.

Moore, P. D. & Bellamy, D. J. (1974) *Peatlands*. London: Elek.

Nilsson, T. (1964) Standardpollendiagramme und C^{14} Datierungen aus dem Agerods mosse in Mittleren Schonen, *Lunds Univ. Arsskr.* N.F. (2) 59: 7, 1-52.

Open University (1972) *Changing Environments*. S2-3 Block 4 Environment.

Osvald, H. (1923) Die Vegetation des Hochmoores Komosse, *Svensk. Växtsoc. Sallsk. Handl.* 1.

— (1950) The raised bog Komosse. *7th Internat. Bot. Congress, Excursion Guide AIIb2*. Stockholm.

Overbeck, F. (1975) *Botanisch-geologische Moorkunde*. Neumunster: Wachholtz.

Overbeck, F., Munnich, K. O., Aletsee, L. & Averdieck, F. R. (1957) Das Alter des 'Grenzhorizonts' norddeutscher Hochmoore nach Radiocarbon Datierungen, *Flora* 145, 37-71.

Ratcliffe, D. A. & Walker, D. (1958) The Silver Flowe, Galloway, Scotland, *J. Ecol.* 46, 407-45.

Schiegl, W. E. (1972) Deuterium content of peat as a palaeoclimatic recorder, *Science* 175, 512-13.

Schneekloth, H. (1965) Die Rekurrenzflache im Grossen Moor bei Gifhorn – eine Zeitgleiche Bildung?, *Geol. Jb.* 83, 477-96.

Smith, A. G. & Willis, E. H. (1961-2) Radiocarbon dating of the Fallahogy Landnam phase, *Ulster J. Archaeol.* 24-5, 16-24.

Tolonen, K. (1971) On the regeneration of North European Bogs. I Klaukkalan Isosuo in S Finland, *Acta Agralia Fennica* 123, 143-66.

Turner, J. (1965) A contribution to the history of forest clearance, *Proc. R. Soc.* B 161, 343-92.

Van Geel, B. (1977) *A palaeoecological study of Holocene peat bog sections* etc. University of Amsterdam Ph.D. thesis (also published in *Rev. Palaeobot. & Palynol.* 25, 1-120, 1978).

Van Geel, B., Bohncke, S. J. P. & Dee, H. (1981) A palaeoecological study of an Upper Late-Glacial and Holocene sequence from 'De Borchert', The Netherlands, *Rev. Palaeobot. & Palynol.* 31, 367-448.

Wagstaff, J. M. (1976) Some thoughts about geography and Catastrophe Theory, *Area* 8, 316-20.

Walker, D. (1961) Peat Stratigraphy and Bog Regeneration, *Proc. Linn. Soc.* 172, 299-33.

— (1970) Direction and rate in some British Post-glacial hydroseres, in Walker, D. & West, R. G. (eds) *Studies in the Vegetational History of the British Isles,* 117-39. Cambridge: University Press.

Walker, D. & Walker, P. M. (1961) Stratigraphic evidence of regeneration in some Irish bogs, *J. Ecol.* 49, 169-85.

Weber, C. A. (1900) Über die Moore, mit besondere Berücksichtigung der zwischen Unterweser und Unterelbe liegenden, *Jahresbericht der Männer von Morgenstern* 3, 3-23.

Pedogenesis during the later prehistoric period in Britain

Soils are complex natural bodies evolving in response to the interaction of environmental factors. The soil-forming factors are climate, organisms (including man), parent material, relief and the passage of time. Five important trends in soil development during the postglacial period in the British Isles can be seen: 1) podzolisation, 2) clay movement, 3) gleying, 4) peat formation and 5) erosion. The causal factors relating to these trends have been the subject of considerable debate. The soil classification used in this paper is that of Avery (1980).

1) *Podzolisation.* The horizon sequence of a podzol shows that iron, aluminium and organic matter have been removed from the top of the mineral soil (E horizon) and, at least partially, deposited in the B. How the compounds are mobilised in the E and then immobilised in the B has been the focus of considerable research, much of which has been summarised by Petersen (1976) and reviewed more recently by De Coninck (1980).

All podzols are acid and the podzolisation process includes leaching of all basic compounds, such as carbonates, and most adsorbed mono and divalent metal ions from the soil. The time required to leach decreases with the buffer capacity of the soil, so podzols are primarily formed on light-textured parent materials.

Formation of water-soluble complexes is a pre-requisite for podzolisation and these are produced during decomposition of plant residues in the soil and are also present in leaf leachates of certain species. As long as the soil has a fairly high *p*H and high content of adsorbed divalent cations (mainly Ca), podzolisation will not take place.

Soils which are susceptible are sandy with little Ca, Al or Fe and become acid easily. In such soils water-soluble organic compounds take up only small amounts of Al and Fe in the place where they are formed and, in humid climates, will leach downwards taking up more Al and Fe. They probably only remain soluble while they have enough negatively charged functional groups, and uptake of Al and Fe presumably leads to neutralisation of this charge; after a certain amount of metal has been taken up, precipitation occurs because of the reduced charge. Precipitation of organic compounds in the B is incomplete and a fraction of the organic matter may be leached entirely out of the profile, removing some metals as well. The organic compounds dissolved in the leaching water may be subject to biological attack. Petersen (1976) considers this is not responsible for the regular precipitation pattern observed in podzols, but Ball (1975) has suggested that Fe and Al are progressively deposited in the

Bh or Bs horizons because microbial and fungal activities destroy the organic part of the complex.

It may well be that a cool climate favours some of the causes of podzolisation, e.g. accumulation of mor-type humus through reduced breakdown of organic matter and possibly also vegetation that is likely to promote podzolisation. However, many podzols in the tropics have thick bleached horizons, so high temperature itself does not prevent or impede podzolisation.

Stagnopodzols may develop where the formation of an iron pan leads to waterlogging in the E horizon and subsequent peat formation. Alternatively a change in climate or land use may lead to the formation of a compact surface accumulation of organic remains which cause mobilisation of Fe under wet, acid conditions and development of an iron pan in what was originally an acid brown earth or brown podzolic soil.

2) *Clay movement.* The development of a B horizon enriched in clay occurs through washing of particles suspended in the soil solution into the lower parts of the soil. In well-developed argillic horizons clayskins may be seen with a hand lens, or even the naked eye. Following removal of calcium carbonate, bases are leached from exchange positions resulting in increased acidity. As the depth of leached soil increases and the flocculating effect of Ca ions is reduced, gradual movement of clay particles begins. These are washed from the A and Eb horizons into the Bt, where clay particles are deposited on and lie parallel to ped faces. The Bt develops strong medium prismatic or blocky structure, in contrast with the weaker blocky structure of the Eb and A horizons. The clay particles are washed down pores and cracks in the soil, particularly after a period of summer drying when shrinkage cracks are most evident; consequently the continental climate of mainland Europe encourages formation of these soils, but they are relatively weakly developed in Britain.

3) *Gleying.* Gleying occurs when water saturates a soil, filling all the pore spaces and driving out the air. Any remaining oxygen is soon used by the microbial population and anaerobic conditions are established. At the same time the soil water contains the decomposition products of organic matter and in the presence of these, and the reducing conditions brought about by the absence of oxygen, iron compounds are chemically reduced from the ferric to the ferrous state, in which iron is very much more soluble and is removed from the soil, leaving behind the colourless minerals. This gives gley soils their characteristic grey colour, with yellow, brown or red mottles if seasonal oxidation occurs preferentially, for example in root channels. Surface water gley soils have grey and/or ochreous mottles owing to anaerobic conditions of waterlogging caused by slow permeability of the soil, high rainfall, lateral flushes or some combination of these. Ground-water gley soils have grey colours and/or ochreous mottles owing to anaerobic conditions of waterlogging caused by a high ground-water table.

4) *Peat formation.* Peat is formed through accumulation, under anaerobic conditions, of slightly humified but recognisable plant remains and is therefore encouraged in conditions of very poor soil drainage. In moorland areas leach-

ing of soils led to increased acidity and development of mor humus at the soil surface, followed by formation of less humified peat as soil drainage deteriorated; consequently moor peat is acid. Fen peat accumulates under the influence of calcareous ground-water and largely consists of the remains of aquatic plants such as reed and sedge; it is neutral or mildly alkaline. Raised bogs occur in sites where an acid peat sustained from the nutrient supplies of the rainwater overlies a peat formed in a declivity of the landscape.

5) *Erosion*. Soil particles can move by three processes: they may be blown away, washed away or the whole soil may slide or slump down a hill-side. Wind erosion can in a short time remove as much material as a more prolonged period of water erosion but water running over the soil surface is a more frequent cause of erosion in most parts of the world. Removal of trees and other natural vegetation interrupts the biogeochemical cycling of elements required for vegetative growth and results in profound changes in the soil (including loss of organic matter and bases), making it more prone to erosion, by reduction in structural stability and lack of permanent root system to bind the soil together.

Cultivation leads to soil movement even on the slightest slope, and further damage to soil structure may be caused by animals trampling and puddling the ground, thus increasing the probability of erosion. The material removed may accumulate to considerable depths in adjacent valleys, as shown in Martin Bell's paper (this volume).

Postglacial soil development in the British Isles

The history of soil development in the British Isles has been discussed in detail by Limbrey (1975) and Evans (1975) and summarised by Bridges (1978) and more recently by Simmons and Tooley (1981). It is becoming increasingly clear that the main trends occurred at vastly different times in various areas.

Estimates of time required for soil processes to occur vary considerably; for instance at least 3000 years were required for the formation of a podzol Ah horizon in southern Norway (Matthews 1980); 250 years for a podzol to develop from acid brown earth in Denmark (Andersen 1979) and less than 100 years for a podzol to develop on coastal sand dunes in Australia (Paton *et al.* 1976). Other examples are given by Ellis (1980), Jauhiainen (1972a) and Ugolini (1966). The Australian example, in particular, suggests that the speed of pedological processes, especially in disturbed systems, may have been underestimated.

At about 7500 BP (5550 bc) Britain was finally isolated from Europe and during the stable period from 7500 to 5000 BP (5550–3050 bc) much of the British Isles was covered with mixed deciduous forest, dominated by oak, and had a relatively warm and oceanic climate. It has been suggested that brown soils predominated (e.g. Bridges 1978), although there are examples of podzolisation without man's influence during this period (e.g. Valentine 1973). The forest may not have closed where soils had the lowest base reserves and climate was most severe (Limbrey 1975) and these areas succumbed soonest to soil degradation and have provided evidence of Mesolithic activity, for example in the Pennines and on Dartmoor. It is generally accepted that Mesolithic man, at least locally, drastically modified his environment, probably mainly through the use of fire to increase the grazing and browsing potential of the forest and thereby increase numbers of herbivores. In particular, the pollen analytical work of Dimbleby (e.g. Dimbleby 1962) and Simmons (1964, 1969) has shown forest clearance associated with Mesolithic activity and pointed to the existence of podzols in some areas by this time, and possible instigation of soil erosion, particularly on coarse-textured parent materials.

Some clay eluviation occurred during this period, such as in the profile developed in the loess of Pegwell Bay, Kent (Weir *et al.* 1971) as in loess areas in Germany (Kwaad and Mücher 1977). Blanket bog formation increased at the onset of the Atlantic period. Mesolithic flints are frequently found at the base of the Pennine and Dartmoor peats, associated with remains of birch, which may have failed owing to grazing pressure or fire. Peat formation could have resulted from opening of the forest, not necessarily linked with a climatic change (Limbrey 1975).

Substantial forest clearance coincides with the elm decline, possibly connected with established and expanding communities. There was still a general forest cover, varying in constitution, over the British Isles, and the height of the tree-line is not known. Peat formation led to development of mires in the lowlands and, also, fens and bogs, and soil erosion occurred in the uplands, with widespread downwash of soils in the Lake District (Pennington 1975). Clay movement seems to have occurred in soils as a direct result of forest clearance and agriculture (Evans 1975), possibly initiated in the Mesolithic and intensified in the Neolithic (Limbrey 1975), leading to a certain amount of hill wash. Although a favourable climate for clay eluviation is one having a wet and dry season, evidence for the change to a more continental climate is elusive. Limbrey (1975) has suggested that the possible dry summers of the Sub-boreal may have contributed to the eluvial horizons of the argillic brown soils but implies that their initiation resulted from the activities of Neolithic cultivators, as stated by Evans (1975), or even Mesolithic man. In the Ardennes in Luxembourg and Belgium, soils with an argillic horizon are thought to have developed during the Sub-boreal and it is suggested that the clay migration and swelling and shrinking phenomena must have occurred in a climate drier and possibly warmer than today (Langohr and Van Vliet 1979), although it appears that formation came to an end because of human interference in the Sub-atlantic period, as in the loess areas of Dutch south Limburg, not because of climatic change (Kwaad and Mücher 1977).

The area of podzols continued to expand during the Neolithic period with the depletion and decline of more marginal soils, associated with increased forest clearance.

Vegetation at the start of the Bronze Age was largely forest but much reduced in some places, particularly at high altitude. The Chalk Downs had been cleared by the beginning of the Bronze Age and large-scale clearance of uplands, such as Dartmoor, led to permanent replacement of woodland by heath and bog communities, although at lowland and valley sites clearance was restricted to grassy enclosures (temporary) in the forest. Dimbleby (1962) pointed to rapid pedogenesis in the Bronze Age with the example of a thin iron pan podzol from an unbleached soil on the North York Moors during this period. Decline in soil fertility coincided with soil erosion and Tinsley (1981) suggests this is the direct consequence of the introduction of metal technology (i.e. more efficient tools).

Environmental deterioration was particularly marked in marginal upland woodlands, where exploitation probably reached a peak in the Bronze Age, but as climate worsened towards the end of the Sub-boreal and upland settlement retreated, woodland failed to regenerate and heath and bog spread over the grazing lands. In contrast, much of lowland Britain, apart from the chalk, was subject to only temporary clearance during the Bronze Age.

In the Iron Age the climate was much wetter and there was considerably less forest in many parts of the country (Turner 1981); further soil deterioration, including gleying and peat formation, occurred. Mixed farming was carried out on light calcareous soils in south-east England and mainly pastoral farming in the North and West. The timing of forest clearance (no doubt aided by the availability of more sophisticated iron tools) varied from region to region but was intensified on Dartmoor, although Iron Age occupation was concentrated on the edge, with continued peat development (Simmons 1964), as on Exmoor. Podzolisation of soils and the spread of heath also continued.

It has been suggested, however, that in many moorland areas soils reached their present form late in their land-use history (Limbrey 1975, Bridges 1978); the intensification of podzol horizon differentiation, the build-up of peat and the formation of thin iron pans correlate with changes in vegetation possibly consequent on intense grazing of the uplands by sheep (Limbrey 1975). Certainly in south Wales ericaceous vegetation associated with the development of organic horizons can be dated to the Middle Ages, but in other areas such as Dartmoor, the basic outline of soil distribution appears to have been established by the beginning of the Iron Age.

Soil studies at archaeological sites

Archaeological excavations may provide the opportunity to study soils which have been sealed. The buried soil itself gives evidence of the stage of soil development reached at the time of burial and comparison with modern soil profiles can indicate subsequent pedogenesis. Evidence of the past landscape derived from pedological studies is considerably strengthened when linked with pollen or molluscan analysis, examination of macroscopic plant remains, etc. Post-burial changes, particularly resulting from variations in the soil drainage régime, are often found, even in well-sealed profiles, but these do not preclude the drawing of valid conclusions about the history of the land. Examples of archaeological soil studies at later prehistoric sites carried out by the author are described below.

1) *Trefignath, Anglesey*. A Neolithic burial chamber of segmented cist type

has recently been excavated by Dr C. Smith at Trefignath, Anglesey. The site is 1½ miles south-south-east of Holyhead and the soils have been mapped by Roberts (1958) as low base status brown earths of the Rocky Gaerwen series, developed on glacial drift derived from pre-Cambrian schists of the Mona complex. Surface soil *p*H is usually around 5, the soils are low in phosphorus and potassium and well-drained. The normal phase can carry arable crops or pasture and agriculturally these are the most important soils on Anglesey (Roberts 1958). These soils were also important in prehistoric times when the most densely populated areas were on light to medium-textured soils (Grimes 1945). The rocky phase is shallow, with frequent rock outcrops, so farms and fields are smaller (Ball 1963).

Natural soil profiles were compared with buried soils beneath the mound (Keeley 1977a, 1979). Pollen analysis of buried soil profiles and a peat core taken from a nearby bog was carried out by James Greig (University of Birmingham). The buried soils showed evidence of post-depositional iron and manganese movement.

Pollen analysis of samples from the bog indicated the presence of trees, particularly oak (and alder carr round the peat bog), in the early Neolithic although the environment was essentially open and very grassy (Greig, pers. comm. 1981). Soil pollen from the period immediately preceding construction of the earliest burial chamber and cairn (charcoal on the old ground surface has been dated to 5050 ± 70 BP (3100 ± 70 bc)) showed more trees were present than in later periods but substantial clearance had occurred by this time. The next phase showed little change in the soil pollen record, although more cereal pollen occurred, and the buried soil appeared to have an undisturbed Ah horizon, consistent with a soil under grassland. By the final phase of building there was much less tree pollen and the buried soil appeared to have been disturbed prior to mound construction.

To summarise, therefore, buried soils showed marked similarities with modern soils and pollen analysis confirmed that the monument was built in an environment of open grassland with occasional trees, not unlike the present landscape.

2) *Gwernvale, Powys.* During 1977 and 1978 excavations of a Neolithic Severn-Cotswold chambered tomb were carried out by Mr B. Britnell at Gwernvale, Crickhowell, Powys. The site is on the north side of the Usk valley, to the west of Crickhowell, on a kame terrace of sand and gravel. The buried soil was a freely drained brown earth showing considerable disturbance but no direct evidence for cultivation, such as plough marks (Keeley 1978, 1980). The Ap horizon contained carbonised plant remains and one sample produced examples of a very primitive form of emmer wheat, two grains of six-rowed hulled barley and wild edibles including hazelnut, blackberry and rosehip (Hillman, pers. comm. 1981). Pollen preservation was very poor (mean soil *p*H was 7.2 in distilled water).

The evidence indicated that emmer was cultivated locally and habitation was nearby. The modern soils are under grass but are essentially similar to the

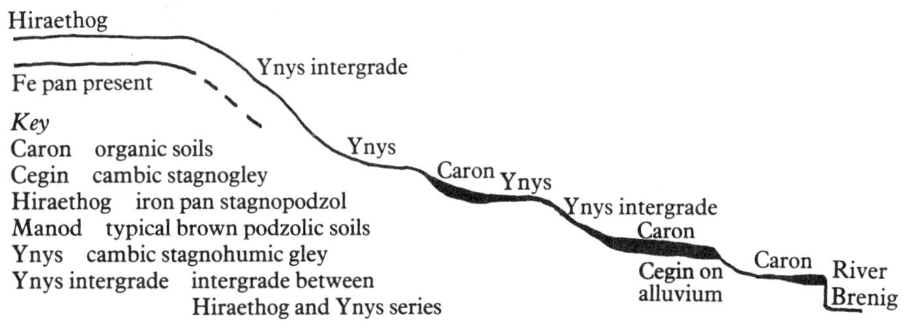

Figure 1. Catenary soil sequence, Brenig valley, Denbigh Moors.

buried soils, which would have been suitable for cultivation – possibly droughty in dry years but better than the valley soils, which are still prone to flooding today.

3) *Brenig Valley, Clwyd.* A programme of archaeological excavations was carried out, in advance of flooding for a reservoir, in the Brenig Valley (Denbigh moors) beginning in 1973 (Lynch *et al.* 1974) and completed in 1974 (Lynch 1975; summary, Lynch 1977). In addition to vegetation surveys of the general moorland area (Bonner 1971) and monuments (Palmer 1974), a survey of modern and buried soils was carried out (Keeley 1977b). The focus of the excavations was a major group of Early Bronze Age burial mounds, including seven large barrows, two ring cairns and a platform cairn.

Soils in the area are developed on drift derived from Silurian shales and siltstones and the main series have been described by Ball (1960) and Rudeforth (1970). Distribution is related to topography and drainage in a catenary fashion, as shown in figure 1.

Pollen analysis was carried out on samples from buried soils and turves from the mounds (Hibbert 1977), in addition to studies of peat deposits (results not yet available). The state of pollen preservation varied but in general about 10 per cent of the total dry land pollen was from trees and it therefore appeared that there was no extensive development of forest in the area when the monuments were constructed. The highest representation was of alder and some birch, with low values of oak, lime and elm, probably through long range transportation, for example from the Clwyd valley (Hibbert 1977). The local habitat gave high values for hazel and other herbaceous pollen; values were especially high for grasses and sedges and large quantities of heather pollen came from some sites. Cereal pollen occurred in small quantities at all sites and was abundant in the soil buried beneath one of the ring cairns, associated with Beaker occupation that was dated to 3500 ± 70 BP (1550 ± 70 bc). Peat from a later occupation of this site contained pollen indicating wetter conditions and less local agricultural activity.

Buried soils were examined beneath several of the monuments and all had been affected by post-burial Fe and Mn movement to some degree; a few were truncated. Most of the buried soils were iron pan stagnopodzols similar to the

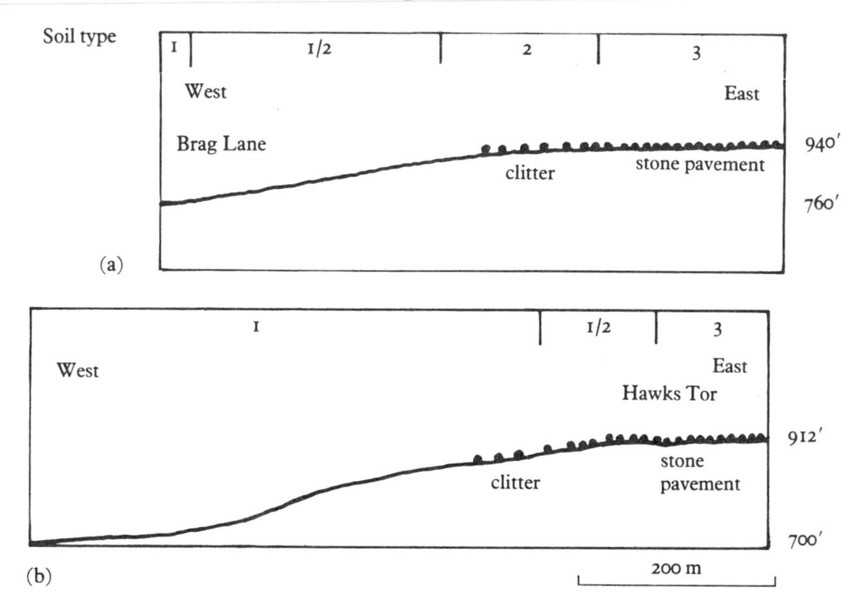

Figure 2. Sections across Shaugh Moor: (a) Saddlesborough area; (b) Hawks Tor area. Soil types: 1 brown podzolic soil; 1/2 brown podzolic/stagnopodzolic intergrade; 2 stagnopodzolic; 3 stagnohumic gley soil.

modern Hiraethog series, although peaty surface horizons were less developed and the soils appeared to be generally better drained than at present.

It appears, therefore, that the environment of the Denbigh Moors at the time of erection of the monuments was an open landscape of grass / sedge moor with hazel locally abundant on the steeper, better drained soils. Alder was present in waterlogged sites around the main watercourses and birch was generally distributed. Some local cereal cultivation occurred but the main emphasis was no doubt on pastoral farming in this area. The soils were essentially similar to those of today, although somewhat better drained, and pollen evidence indicates increasing wetness, presumably coinciding with deterioration in climate towards the end of the Sub-boreal.

4) *Shaugh Moor, Dartmoor, Devon.* Since early 1976 the DoE Central Excavation Unit has been involved in extensive archaeological surveys and excavation of prehistoric monuments and field systems in the area of Shaugh Moor, on the southern edge of Dartmoor. The prehistoric land boundaries, including the Shaugh Moor system, have been discussed by Fleming (1978) and Wainwright *et al.* (1979), and Wainwright and Smith (1980) have described progress of the project to date. In 1976 a general environmental survey was carried out (Keeley 1976), including a vegetation survey (Wilkins 1977) and a soil survey (Keeley and Macphail 1979, 1981).

The soils of Dartmoor have been described (Clayden and Manley 1964), and surveyed in part (Clayden 1964, Harrod *et al.* 1976). Simmons (1962) showed that in much of the area of Moretonhampstead (typical brown podzolic) and

Hexworthy (iron pan stagnopodzols) soils were formerly forested. In the Shaugh Moor area soil distribution was related to slope in a catenary fashion, similar to other moorland areas of Devon (Harrod *et al.* 1976), as shown in figure 2. Brown podzolic soils occurred at lower altitudes, being 'improved' at the lowest elevations of the moor, while stagnohumic gleys and stagnopodzols occurred on plateaux tops, which had a relatively low density of prehistoric settlement. No substantial accumulation of soil was found upslope of prehistoric field boundaries, implying that the fields were used for pastoral rather than arable farming. Soil build-up was noted in the lower part of some huts and behind enclosure walls, which could have resulted from cultivation or disturbance by animals and man and subsequent erosion. It has been suggested that the high density of Bronze Age settlement in the Shaugh Moor area may have been due to tin working (Price 1979).

Buried and unburied soils associated with an enclosure and hut circles were examined (Keeley and Macphail 1979) and found to show considerable variation, with both stagnopodzol and related gley types present, all formed in granite head. The settlement may have been founded by 3450 BP (1500 bc); by 3150 BP (1200 bc) it was probably enclosed by a stone wall, and long-term use of the houses was a feature of the site. Some settlement of unknown intensity persisted until about 2550 BP (600 bc) (Wainwright and Smith 1980).

There was no real difference in degree of degradation between the buried soils and those in the surrounding area, except for slightly more intensive eluviation of the Eag horizon in soils with a contemporary peat cover. Soil variation appeared to be natural and often related to differences in parent material. Some soils contained weakly formed palaeoargillic horizons and fragipans relating to earlier phases of soil formation – probably brown earth types prior to degradation and the change to a moorland environment.

Buried soils were examined below the Saddlesborough reave – a low linear mound of turf-covered stone with occasional projecting orthostats. The first phase of construction is dated to around 3540 ± 80 BP (1590 ± 80 bc); the second to around 3340 ± 90 BP (1390 ± 90 bc). The buried soil below the upper part of the reave was a humic iron pan stagnopodzol, further downslope a stagnohumic gley with a mor humus surface was found and below the lower section of the reave the buried soil was a stagnohumic gley with about 15 cm of peat at its surface. Preliminary results of soil pollen analysis indicate an open grassland environment at the time the boundary was constructed (Balaam, pers. comm. 1981). Degraded stagnohumic podzols were found below the Wotter reave and a soil with a peaty top was also found beneath another boundary forming part of the parallel reave system.

Pollen analysis of peat deposits from several sites in the area has been carried out by S. Beckett (Smith *et al.*, forthcoming). After the elm decline (about 5000 BP (3050 bc)) the environment was open with scattered woodland. There was some woodland regeneration after the Neolithic, as found by Simmons (1964). In the Bronze Age there was greatly increased clearance activity and predominantly pastoral farming. The main development of heath occurred after the Bronze Age.

Evidence from Shaugh Moor fits in well with the picture of early soil degradation on coarse parent materials and conforms to the suggestion of Staines (1972), that the basic outline of soil distribution found today on Dartmoor was established by the beginning of the Iron Age.

Summary and conclusions

During the Mesolithic period, on coarse parent materials where the forest cover was thinner or, at the highest altitudes, may not have closed at all, man's activities led to soil degradation including podzolisation, peat formation and soil erosion. In lowland areas in southern parts of the country where loess was present in the soils, clay eluviation occurred, probably because these areas were exploited by Mesolithic people, as in the loess belts of Europe (Cornwall 1958).

At the beginning of the Neolithic period clay movement intensified, mainly as a result of forest clearance and agriculture but possibly enhanced by a climate in which summers were drier than in preceding or subsequent periods. Peat formation and podzolisation continued during this period and some soil erosion occurred, particularly in parts of the uplands. By the beginning of the Bronze Age the Chalk Downs had been cleared and heath and bog communities, with their associated podzolised, gleyed and peaty soils, had permanently replaced woodland in some upland areas. Soil and pollen studies at Trefignath indicate an open grassland environment with occasional trees in this part of Anglesey during the Neolithic period; studies at Gwernvale provide evidence of local cereal cultivation in that part of south Wales. Both sites are on light-textured soils.

The Bronze Age was a period of maximum exploitation of uplands resulting in rapid pedogenesis, decline in soil fertility and soil erosion. Woodland failed to regenerate in these areas, particularly where parent materials were coarse-textured, and heath and bog spread over the grazing lands. Over much of lowland Britain, apart from the chalk, however, pedogenesis was not greatly influenced by man during the Bronze Age. Examples from the Denbigh Moors and Dartmoor confirm the extent of soil degradation in these upland areas.

The climate was much wetter in the Iron Age and extensive forest clearance was carried out, with associated soil deterioration and the spread of heath.

It is difficult to link changes in soils during the later prehistoric period directly to climatic change and pedogenesis must therefore be considered in terms of all the soil-forming factors.

REFERENCES

Andersen, S. T. (1979) Brown earth and podzol: soil genesis illuminated by microfossil analysis, *Boreas* 8, 59-73.

Avery, B. W. (1980) *Soil Classification for England and Wales (Higher Categories)*. Soil Survey Technical Monograph No. 14. Harpenden: Soil Survey of England and Wales.

Ball, D. F. (1960) *The Soils and Land Use of the District around Rhyl and Denbigh.* Memoirs of the Soil Survey of England and Wales. London: HMSO.
— (1963) *The Soils and Land Use of the District around Bangor and Beaumaris.* Memoirs of the Soil Survey of England and Wales. London: HMSO.
— (1975) Processes of soil degradation: a pedological point of view, in Evans, J. G., Limbrey, S. & Cleere, H. (eds) *The Effect of Man on the Landscape: the Highland Zone.* CBA Research Report 11, 20-7.
Bonner, I. R. (1970) In Colvin and Moggridge: Brenig Reservoir Scheme: Landscape Report (for the Dee and Clwyd River Authority), May 1971.
Bridges, E. M. (1978) Interaction of soil and mankind in Britain. *J. Soil Science* 29, 125-39.
Clayden, B. (1964) *Soils of the Middle Teign Valley District of Devon.* Harpenden: Soil Survey of England and Wales Bulletin 1.
Clayden, B. & Manley, D. J. R. (1964) The Soils of the Dartmoor Granite, in Simmons, I. G. (ed.) *Dartmoor Essays* 117-40. Exeter: Devonshire Association.
Cornwall, I. W. (1958) *Soils for the Archaeologist.* London: Phoenix.
De Coninck, F. (1980) Major mechanisms in formation of spodic horizons, *Geoderma* 24, 101-28.
Dimbleby, G. W. (1962) *The development of British heathlands and their soils.* Oxford Forestry Memoirs No.23. Oxford: Clarendon Press.
Ellis, S. (1980) Physical and chemical characteristics of a podzolic soil formed in neoglacial till, Okstindan, Northern Norway, *Arctic and Alpine Research* 12, 65-72.
Evans, J. G. (1975) *The Environment of Early Man in the British Isles.* London: Elek.
Fleming, A. (1978) The prehistoric landscape of Dartmoor. Part 1: South Dartmoor, *Proc. Prehistoric Soc.* 44, 97-123.
Grimes, W. F. (1945) Early Man and the Soils of Anglesey, *Antiquity* 19, 169-74.
Harrod, T. R., Hogan, D. V. & Staines, S. J. (1976) *Soils in Devon II: Sheet SX 65 (Ivybridge).* Harpenden: Soil Survey Record 39.
Hibbert, A. (1977) Brenig excavations. Unpublished report of pollen analysis on sites 40, 41, 42, 44, 45, 47 and 51.
Jauhiainen, E. (1972a) Rate of podzolisation in a dune in Northern Finland, *Commentationes Physico-Mathematical* 43, 33-44.
— (1972b) Structure, C14 age and environment of an iron humus podzol under a peat layer, *Annales Academiae Scientiarum Fennicae* Series A III, *Geologica-Geographica* 112.
Keeley, H. C. M. (1976) Interim report on environmental work at Shaugh Moor, Devon. Ancient Monuments Laboratory Report no.2151.
— (1977a) Interim report on the soils of Trefignath, Anglesey. Ancient Monuments Laboratory Report no.2300.
— (1977b) The soils of the Brenig valley. Ancient Monuments Laboratory Report no.2342.
— (1978) Interim soil report for the site of Gwernvale chambered tomb, Crickhowell, Powys. Ancient Monuments Laboratory Report no.2670.
— (1979) Interim report (II) on the soils of Trefignath, Anglesey. Ancient Monuments Laboratory Report no.2716.
— (1980) Soils associated with Gwernvale chambered tomb, Crickhowell, Powys. Ancient Monuments Laboratory Report no.3105.
Keeley, H. C. M. & Macphail, R. I. (1979) The soils of Shaugh Moor, Devon. Ancient Monuments Laboratory Report no.2925.
— (1981) A soil survey of part of Shaugh Moor, Devon, in Smith, K., Coppen, J., Wainwright, G. J. & Beckett, S., *Proc. Prehistoric Soc.*, forthcoming.

Kwaad, F. J. P. M. & Mücher, H. J. (1977) The evolution of soils and slope deposits in the Luxembourg Ardennes near Wiltz, *Geoderma* 17, 1-37.

Langohr, R. & Van Vliet, B. (1979) Clay migration in well to moderately well drained acid brown soils of the Belgian Ardennes: morphology and clay content determination, *Pedologie* 29, 367-85.

Limbrey, S. (1975) *Soil Science and Archaeology*. London: Academic Press.

Lynch, F., Waddell, J., Allen, D. & Grealey, S. (1974) Brenig Valley excavations 1973: Interim report, *Trans. Denbighshire Historical Soc.* 23, 9-64.

Lynch, F. (1975) Brenig Valley excavations 1974: Interim report, *Trans. Denbighshire Historical Soc.* 24, 1-25.

— (1977) Brenig, *Current Archaeology* 55, 230-40.

Matthews, J. A. (1980) Some problems and implications of C14 dates from a podzol buried beneath an end moraine at Haugabreen, Southern Norway, *Geografiska Annaler* 62A, 185-208.

Palmer, J. (1974) *An investigation of the vegetation of the Brenig valley with special reference to the vegetation of some archaeological monuments in the valley*. Unpublished M.Sc. Thesis, University College of North Wales, Bangor.

Paton, T. R., Mitchell, P. B., Adamson, D., Buchanan, R. A., Fox, M. D. & Browman, G. (1976) Speed of podzolisation, *Nature* 260, 601-2.

Pennington, W. (1975) The effect of Neolithic Man on the environment in north west England: the use of absolute pollen diagrams, in Evans, J. G., Limbrey, S. & Cleere, H. (eds) *The Effect of Man on the Landscape: the Highland Zone*. CBA Research Report 11, 74-86.

Petersen, L. (1976) *Podzols and Podzolisation*. Copenhagen: D. S. R. Forlag.

Price, D. G. (1979) The Moorland Plym – a Reassessment, *Trans. Devonshire Association for the Advancement of Science* 111, 125-37.

Roberts, E. (1958) *The County of Anglesey: Soils and Agriculture*. Memoirs of the Soil Survey of Great Britain. London: HMSO.

Rudeforth, C. C. (1970) *Soils of North Cardiganshire*. Harpenden: Memoirs of the Soil Survey of England and Wales.

Simmons, I. G. (1962) An outline of the vegetation history of Dartmoor, *Trans. Devonshire Association* 92, 555-74.

— (1964) Pollen diagrams from Dartmoor, *New Phytologist* 63, 165-80.

— (1969) Environment and early man on Dartmoor, Devon, England, *Proc. Prehistoric Soc.* 35, 203-19.

Simmons, I. G. & Tooley, M. (1981) *The Environment in British Prehistory*. London: Duckworth.

Smith, A. G., Grigson, C., Hillman, G. & Tooley, M. J. (1981) The Neolithic, in Simmons & Tooley (1981), 125-209.

Smith, K., Coppen, J., Wainwright, G. J. & Beckett, S. (1981) *Proc. Prehist. Soc.* 47, 205-73.

Staines, S. J. (1972) *Soils and vegetation on Dartmoor*. Unpublished M.Sc. thesis, University of Bristol.

Tinsley, H. M. (1981) The Bronze Age, in Simmons & Tooley (1981), 210-49.

Turner, J. (1981) The Iron Age, in Simmons & Tooley (1981), 250-81.

Ugolini, F. C. (1966) Soils, in Mirsky, A. (ed.) *Soil development and ecological succession in a deglaciated area of Muir inlet, South-east Alaska*. Institute of Polar Studies, Report 20, 29-72, Ohio State University.

Valentine, K. W. G. (1973) *The identification, lateral variation and chronology of three buried palaeo-catenas in lowland England*. PhD thesis, University of Reading.

Wainwright, G., Fleming, A. & Smith, K. (1979) The Shaugh Moor Project: First Report, *Proc. Prehistoric Soc.* 45, 1-33.

Wainwright, G. & Smith, K. (1980) The Shaugh Moor Project: Second Report, *Proc. Prehistoric Soc.* 46, 65-122.
Weir, A. H., Catt, J. A. & Madgett, P. A. (1971) Postglacial soil formation in the loess of Pegwell Bay, Kent (England), *Geoderma* 5, 131-49.
Wilkins, P. (1977) The vegetation of Shaugh Moor, West Devon. Ancient Monuments Laboratory Report no.2278.

The effects of land-use and climate on valley sedimentation

In an archaeological context valley sediments have been quite frequently employed as sources of proxy, that is indirect, climatic data. This has come about because artifactual and even settlement evidence is increasingly being found interstratified with valley sediments. The potential for dating the sediments, relating them to river régime and run-off, and at the same time obtaining data about aspects of the prehistoric environment is obvious. The most extensive studies have so far been based on the Mediterranean where climatic change is seen as the most important influence on the pattern of postglacial valley sedimentation (Vita-Finzi 1969). Contrasting with this are the majority of writers who have considered British and north-west European evidence and have tended to give much greater emphasis to ecological change wrought by man (Butzer 1974, 1976; Dimbleby 1976). Indeed, what can only be described as an intellectual fault line separates the hypotheses advanced for the Mediterranean from those favoured in relation to the British and north-west European sediments. In common with the analogous chronological fault line in prehistoric Europe (Renfrew 1973), it derives from the employment of different sources of evidence in the two geographical areas. The basically archaeology-related sediment sequences of the Mediterranean contrast with the British sequences where the main emphasis has been on the use of pollen and molluscs to examine the relationship between sedimentological and land-use changes. With the various contrasting hypotheses and approaches which this has produced, there is an obvious need for critical reassessment of the causes of valley sedimentation changes.

Processes

Basically we will be concerned with alluvial and colluvial valley sediments. Colluvium is unsorted or poorly sorted sediment transported largely by the force of gravity, which builds up, often by gradual increments but sometimes during major erosion episodes, at the foot of a slope. This tends to come about because any process that causes the movement of particles on a slope is liable to incorporate a component of downslope movement: examples are raindrop splash action; wetting and drying, freezing and thawing, small scale solifluction movements, the movement of particles by fauna and, perhaps most important, tillage.

Alluvium, sediment laid down by running water, originates from particles picked up by erosion which might take the form of colluviation, sheet and rill erosion from the slopes or the further erosion of permanent drainage courses such as gully, bank and bed erosion. Deposition will take place, particularly during times of overbank flooding, where the amount of sediment to be transported exceeds the competence of the stream or the velocity of the water is no longer sufficient to keep the particles in motion. Particles of different sizes are laid down at different velocities with the result that alluvial sediments are sorted to some degree. Alluvial sediments are encountered wherever there is a good deal of surface run-off whereas colluvium is the main type of valley sediment on permeable bedrock such as in the dry valleys on chalk and limestone. It is, however, a mistake to make a rigid division because, as we shall see, run-off does occur even in areas of permeable bedrock, and on impermeable bedrocks the role of colluviation in contributing material for subsequent riverine transportation has probably tended to be overlooked in some archaeological work.

Climate obviously has an important effect on the pattern of valley sedimentation, particularly through the amount and distribution of precipitation but also through a variety of other factors, such as frosts, episodes of frozen ground, etc. The amount of run-off is also influenced to a major extent by the nature of the vegetation and thus the land-use régime. Vegetation has the effect of protecting the soil surface from erosion and aiding infiltration; indeed processes such as rainsplash and sheetwash are really only important on devegetated, or partly devegetated, slopes. The removal of climax vegetation is also likely to affect the structural stability of the soil (Dimbleby 1976): this may lead to surface slaking or the development of less permeable subsoil horizons all of which will lead to increased run-off and erosion. We cannot necessarily assume, however, that increased erosion will lead to greater sedimentation since that depends on the competence of the river to remove the eroded sediment. Other influences on the pattern of alluvial sedimentation are base-level changes, a particularly important factor in coastal areas where there is the possibility of sea-level changes. Modifications of base level may also occur upstream because of beaver dams, man-made dams, etc., all of which will effect the velocity of water and cause sedimentation.

Evidence of climatic factors in recent times

An increased incidence of flooding has been recorded in glaciated Alpine valleys at the time of the Little Ice Age between c. AD 1550 and 1850 (Ladurie 1972, p. 199). In Norway the Little Ice Age was accompanied by an increase in documented evidence for various forms of mass movement, such as landslides and avalanches, and an increase in flooding episodes during some of which masses of sand, gravel and stones were deposited on the fields (Grove 1972). There have not, so far as I know, yet been attempts to relate actual flood sediments to any of these historically documented events but this would clearly be a useful exercise in glaciated valleys where the climatic sequence is well known.

Geomorphologists are tending to lay increasing emphasis on the role of exceptional storms in shaping the landscape. One event that brought this home was the Lynmouth (north Devon) flood of 15 August 1952, when, after a period of heavy rain which meant that the ground was saturated, up to 225 mm of rain fell in 24 hours over Exmoor, and run-off in the steep restricted catchment of the West Lyn river carried 100,000 tonnes of boulders, as well as soil and uprooted trees, which devastated the town of Lynmouth (Newson 1975, p.7; Kidson 1953; Gifford 1953). The Lyn catchment and the devastating effects of the flood are exceptional in many ways but there are many much less spectacular examples which show that much of the work of erosion and deposition may occur during exceptional storms; for instance, Morgan's (1977) two-year study of sandy soils in Bedfordshire demonstrated that 99 per cent of erosion occurred during ten storms.

In areas of permeable bedrock there is increasing observational data which emphasises the contribution of storms to dry valley sediments. Evans and Morgan (1974) recorded the effects of a storm at Balsham, Cambridgeshire. It occurred at a time when the arable land was already hard owing to raindrop impact and resulted in rills and gullies on the slopes and the deposition of 86.6 m^3 of silt on the valley floor. Two comparable events have recently been recorded by the writer. By good fortune one occurred while we were sectioning dry valley sediments in the parish of Chalton, Hampshire. On the night of 24 March 1979, a heavy storm produced 39 mm of rain at the nearest station, the highest for any 24-hour period that year. Run-off on the valley sides of Bascomb produced shallow rills and deposited small fans of silty clay on the valley floor. The geology of this area is basically Upper Chalk but there are areas of superficial Clay-with-flints and subsoil clay loam and flint horizons which probably help to increase run-off.

My second example is at the head of a dry valley at Saltdean, East Sussex, at a point where there is a shallow superficial cover of Clay-with-flints. Erosion here first became manifest in 1976 when heavy rain occurred on arable land made hard and compact by the drought. A mass of silt was washed down the valley axis and structural damage was done to a bungalow downslope. Following this the Ministry of Agriculture made a pond and drain between the arable land and the residential area. Further small-scale erosion occurred at this point during the winter of 1980 when much silty sediment was deposited in the pond and a residue of large flints was left on the slope. It is of particular archaeological interest that this erosion occurred within the confines of what was, prior to post-war cultivation, an impressive 'Celtic' field system. Marling pits within the lynchet banks attest to earlier, probably Roman, attempts to combat the pedological and erosion problems now confronting the present farmer. Cliff sections 2 km away reveal good sequences of Romano-British colluvium.

These events are basically localised and of small scale, but Oakley (1945) has described the effects of an exceptional storm on the Chilterns when normally dry valleys carried torrential streams and great alluvial fans of flints and Reading Beds sands were deposited in places. Occasionally the seasonal streams which flow in major chalkland valleys may flood, causing considerable damage; examples are the Louth flood of 1920 caused by run-off from the

Lincolnshire Wolds (Latter 1932), and the flooding of the Till valley in Wiltshire in 1841 when heavy rain fell on still frozen subsoil (Cross 1967).

Special emphasis has been given to examples from areas of permeable bedrock because these are of direct relevance to archaeological sediments in dry valleys, which will be considered below. They also help to emphasise that it is not so much the annual amount of water to be drained that is significant but its seasonal distribution and the frequency of storms. Many of the major flooding and depositional episodes occur as a result of convectional storms which may be of a fairly localised nature and, owing to the short period of observational records, we seldom have much idea of their recurrence interval. Only really severe floods tend to be recorded. They occurred, for instance, at Lynmouth in 1607 and 1769 as well as in 1952 (Newson 1975, p.5). Because of the important effects of major storms we cannot necessarily make the tacit assumption that more erosion and deposition will occur in major secular episodes of higher rainfall; indeed, under certain circumstances, storm intensities may often be higher in areas of lower mean rainfall (Raikes 1967, p.43). There is some problem, therefore, in distinguishing the effects of short-term climatic events from major secular episodes of climatic change, a problem recently highlighted by Brunsden and Thornes (1979, p.471) in relation to the factors responsible for recent landslips.

Evidence for land-use factors in recent times

Large areas of the British lowlands and river valleys experienced their major postglacial land-use change with the clearance of climax forest for agricultural purposes in Neolithic or Bronze Age times. Analogues for the possible effects of this are the very much more recent, generally mid-nineteenth century, effects of colonial farmers on parts of the New World. Palaeolimnological studies of a small Michigan lake (Davis 1976) showed a sedimentation rate increase of ten to thirty times since the arrival of colonial farmers and this accompanied a transition from organic gyttja to clay and a dramatic increase in the ash content. Similar results come from a comparison of the sedimentation rates in neighbouring American river systems under differing land-use régimes. Wolman's (1967) work has shown relatively small-scale erosion under forest conditions but a pronounced peak c. 1850 with deforestation and arable agriculture. The sedimentation rate then tends to stabilise and decrease until the area is once again devegetated for urban development. The effects of land-use changes on erosion and sedimentation will obviously depend on a variety of local factors, not least climate and bedrock geology, but a number of attempts have been made to quantify the effects of clearance on what is described as the 'geologic norm'. In the upper Mississippi, where 42 per cent of the land is cultivated or idle, sediment production is calculated to be five times the 'geologic norm' (Leopold 1956) whilst in the mid-Atlantic states the conversion of forest to farmland is said to cause about a ten-fold increase in sedimentation (Meade 1969, p.1267).

As for colluvial sediments there are numerous studies which record a loss of organic matter content and structure accompanying the advent of agriculture and leading to increased colluviation. Icknield Series soils on the South Downs undergo a reduction in organic matter content from between 7 and 11 per cent under grass to between 2.5 and 4 per cent under arable (Hodgson 1967, p.49). In the South-West Carson and Kirkby (1972, p.217) have shown that the removal of grassland is likely to increase soil movement by something like 400 times; conversely, much reduced rates of colluviation have been demonstrated following afforestation in Luxembourg (Kwaad 1977).

Archaeological evidence: the continental background

Over large areas of the Mediterranean Vita-Finzi (1969) has identified widespread alluvial deposits which he called the Younger Fill. At many of the exposures investigated this material contained Classical sherds or overlay Classical structures, and its dating to the late- or post-Roman period has been confirmed by detailed fieldwork in Greece (Bintliff 1977) and by radiocarbon determinations (Vita-Finzi 1976). A climatic as opposed to anthropogenic cause for this major alluviation episode was favoured because of the apparently synchronous nature of the deposits throughout the Mediterranean and the late date of the episode in areas which have been cleared and cultivated since early times. The suggestion was that the change might have been brought about by a temporary southward shift of the European depression tracks which might have caused a change from seasonal to perennial flow.

At present it does not seem to be possible to correlate the post-Classical onset of alluviation with a major independently attested secular climatic change. Evidence is gradually accumulating for valley alluviation in certain areas at other dates: in Hellenistic times on Sicily (Judson 1963) and around Ephesus, Turkey (Eisma 1964); in the Roman period at Elis, Greece, where there was very little post-Roman alluviation (Raphael 1973); and during the Bronze Age around the site of Phylakopi on Melos (Davidson *et al.* 1976). All this hints that the Mediterranean valley fills may not be so uniformally synchronous as the pioneering studies suggested and if there is some chronological disparity then it is possible that local land-use factors played a more significant role. Of crucial importance here is the origin of the sediment which makes up the Younger Fill. Vita-Finzi (1975) has maintained that it consists largely of material derived from the Older Fill, of Pleistocene date, but he admits elsewhere (1974) that it is difficult to ascertain to what extent erosion on the interfluves was responsible. In some areas there is evidence for fairly extensive colluviation which may have contributed to the Younger Fill. Judson's (1968) studies in central Italy have demonstrated substantial lowering of ground levels since the erection of Roman buildings and in Epirus, Greece, more recent slope erosion is indicated by significant lowering of the soil surface during the life of olive trees a few hundred years old (Hutchinson 1969).

There is also a growing literature on the valley sediments of north-western Europe. Recent floodplain silts, known as *Auelehm*, are apparently widespread in Germany; those in the provinces of Saxony and Thuringia have produced artifact evidence (Jäger 1962) indicating two main periods of deposition: one in the Late Bronze Age / Early Iron Age is only present in certain valleys, while the other, dating to the high Middle Ages, is on a much larger scale and more widespread. Jäger argued that the deposits were the result of forest clearance followed by tillage, and it may be significant that isolated mountainous areas, which seem to have been intensively settled rather later, tend to produce later deposits. *Auelehm* deposits in north-west Germany, particularly the Weser and its tributaries, have been reviewed by Mensching (1951, 1958) who showed that much of the alluvium was reworked loess. Its date seems to vary from one valley to another: in some areas it contains Bronze Age, or other prehistoric material, but over much of the Weser it is argued that prehistoric clearances were not of a sufficient scale and most of the deposits resulted from large-scale clearances in the high Middle Ages.

Rather later erosion and sedimentation episodes are represented in eastern France and south-western Germany (Vogt 1953) where cartographic evidence shows they resulted from extensions of agriculture onto particularly susceptible bedrocks in the eighteenth and nineteenth centuries. Intensive studies in the Luxembourg Ardennes have produced evidence for soil erosion and, largely colluvial, valley sediments. As regards the conditions under which colluviation occurred, palynological evidence suggests it followed cultivation, and micromorphological phenomena are present which are interpreted as the result of a breakdown of soil structure consequent upon cultivation (Kwaad and Mücher 1977). One instance of accelerated erosion occurred c. AD 800 and other deposits are known on palynological evidence to have accumulated in the last 500 years (Riezbos and Slotboom 1974, Kwaad 1977). Just over the French border in the Chalk country of Champagne recent investigations of the La Tène cemeteries have led to the identification of colluvial and alluvial valley sediments. Evidence has been found for significant pedological change and soil erosion since the Iron Age (Flouest and Stead 1979, p. 10).

The Holocene valley sediments of north-western Europe make an interesting comparison with the Mediterranean and British sediments. Even so they have been largely overlooked in making comparison between the two latter areas, except by Butzer (1976). Several of the west European studies mentioned have produced evidence of major sedimentation during the Middle Ages and this might be contemporary with the later phases of Mediterranean sedimentation. However, the majority of studies known to the writer (Bell 1981b) have placed rather greater emphasis on land-use than on climate as a causative factor.

Archaeological evidence: British alluvial sequences

Potter (1976) has identified a number of sites, such as Braughing in Hertfordshire and Watercrook in Cumbria (Potter 1979), where there is evidence for late- or post-Roman flooding and alluviation. This list has subsequently been added to by Gater (1979) and both writers have turned for an explanation to the Mediterranean hypothesis of climatic change. The synchroneity on which this

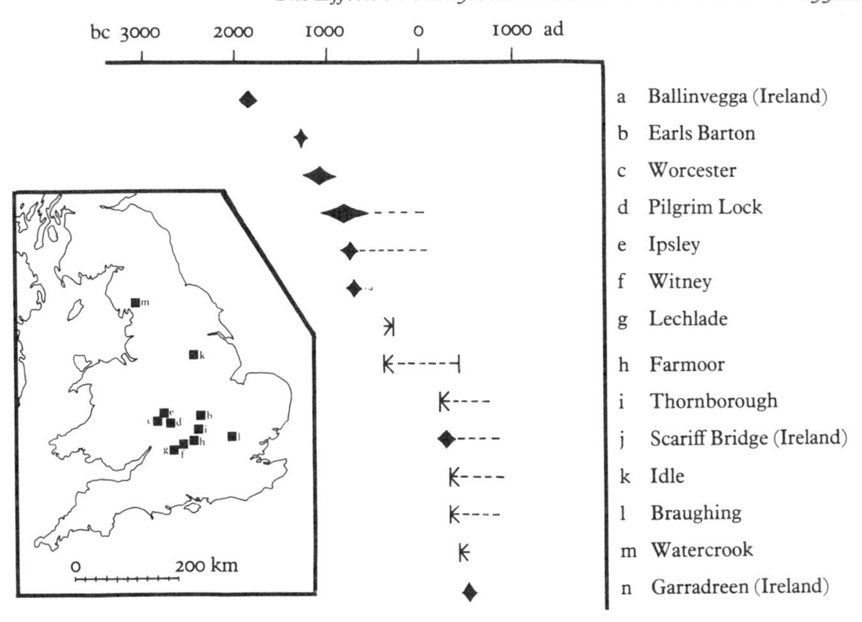

Occupation horizon above alluvium

Possible period of alluviation

Occupation horizon below alluvium

Radiocarbon-dated layer below alluvium

Figure 1. An attempt to plot the approximate dates at which the deposition of recent mineral-rich floodplain alluvium was initiated and was occurring. The inset shows the distribution of sites. Full bibliographical references for the sites are in Bell 1981b, pp. 15-20.

hypothesis rests must, however, be examined in the context of the full sequence of postglacial alluvial sediments.

Many river valleys exhibit a basically comparable sequence of Flandrian sediments (Limbrey 1978, 1979). There is an earlier episode when the rate of sedimentation was low and its organic matter content high. Under the conditions of waterlogging that prevailed in many valleys at this time, reducing conditions obtained, giving rise to black or grey sediments. Within these there are occasional mineral-rich bands representing episodes of greater erosion. Bands of this kind occur in peat-filled channels in north-east Yorkshire where they are associated with palynological evidence for Mesolithic burning (Jones 1976), whereas similar bands in the lacustrine sequences of the Lake District may correlate with the elm decline (Pearsall *et al.* 1960).

Above the basal organic-rich silts are oxidised sediments with a much higher mineral content. On a small number of sites we have some indication of the date at which this transition occurred although it must be emphasised that many of the sediment sequences are not very closely dated and where a site or horizon is buried by alluvium we cannot necessarily assume that deposition commenced soon after the dated horizon. Despite these caveats a plot of some of the more reliable dates (figure 1) does indicate that there is little evidence for exceptional alluviation in the late Roman period. The dates cover a long timespan from 3825 BP (1875 bc) in Co. Wexford, Ireland (Mitchell 1976, p.150) through c. 2600 BP (650 bc) for three sites in the Severn/Avon valleys (Shotton 1978) to the later Iron Age at Farmoor in the Thames valley (Lambrick and Robinson 1979, p.168) and 1900±85 BP (ad 500±85) at Garradreen Td., Ireland (Culleton and Mitchell 1976).

On several sites there is independent biological evidence that the organic rich silty alluvium was laid down under woodland conditions whilst the mineral alluvium low in organic matter was deposited following forest clearance (Shillitoe 1961, Kelly and Osborne 1964). Furthermore the late Roman alluviation of the river Idle in South Humberside seems to correlate with palynological evidence from elsewhere in this area for forest clearance in Iron Age and Roman times (Samuels and Buckland 1978). It may not necessarily be that floodplain alluviation began immediately following *initial* clearance of an area since many of these deposits are rather later than we would normally hypothesise for primary clearance. More probably they relate to subsequent clearances of much larger areas in later prehistory and possibly, as Limbrey (1978, p.25) has suggested, to agricultural changes consequent upon the introduction of winter-sown crops.

Archaeological evidence: British colluvial sequences

Many of the Chalk and limestone areas carry relict landscapes and the problems which these present for interpretation are basically similar to those posed by the uplands of the Highland Zone, for example Dartmoor. Has all this evidence of prehistoric activity survived because it represents occasional incursions into land which has always been marginal, as Taylor (1972) argued? Alternatively, is it possible that a change in environmental parameters, such as climate or soils, made these areas more attractive in certain prehistoric periods? Lamb (1977, p.418) has argued along these lines in suggesting a shift away from the Chalk in the Bronze Age because of drier conditions followed by resettlement in the wetter Iron Age. Colluvial sediments provide us with opportunities to examine these and other hypotheses relating to the long-term settlement trends on the Chalk.

Major studies of dry valley sediments have been made by Kerney *et al.* (1964), at Brook, Kent, and by Evans (1966), at Pitstone, Buckinghamshire. More recently the sediments in three archaeologically well-known study areas (Kiln Combe, Eastbourne; Itford Bottom, near Lewes; Chalton, Hampshire) within the South Downs have been investigated specifically to examine the relationship between sediment sequences and land-use history. To this end one or two machine-dug trenches (figure 2) and some soil pits were put down in each study area. Alongside the major trenches an adjoining strip was hand-excavated in order to obtain dating evidence. The aspects of these

Figure 2. Dry valley sediments exposed by a trench beside the village of Chalton, Hampshire. In this instance artifact distributions indicated that the earliest colluvial deposits were of Bronze Age/Early Iron Age. (Photo: Brenda Westley)

various recent studies which are particularly pertinent to the question of climatic change are the conditions under which the sediments accumulated and their date.

Sedimentology

There is a close sedimentological similarity between chalkland valley fills and the colluvium found in lynchet banks, which implies that they may both be associated with arable activity. The conditions of bare ground created by cultivation would of course be particularly conducive to large-scale colluviation and it is also likely that tillage itself would contribute to the down-slope movement of soil. On one or two archaeological sites there is sedimentological evidence from ditch deposits, rather than valley fills, which may relate to climatic factors. A number of Bronze Age sites have produced possible evidence of aeolian sedimentation in areas like the Oxfordshire gravels and

Stonehenge where little wind blowing seems to be occurring today (Cornwall 1953). There is also evidence from the Mount Pleasant Neolithic henge ditch for a well-sorted and apparently wind-blown deposit (Evans and Jones 1979, p.210). Deposition of this began c. 3410±130 BP (1460±130 bc) (BM-664) and ceased at some time prior to the Romano-British period when it was covered by a colluvial deposit. The suggestion was that the transition from aeolian to colluvial sedimentation reflected a transition from a dry Bronze Age climate to a wetter Iron Age climate. Evans and Jones (1979, p.213) have further argued that colluvial deposits of pre-Iron Age date are virtually unknown and it is frequently stated that colluviation is predominantly a process of later prehistory (e.g. Bradley 1978, p.123).

Dating

The question of dating thus emerges as of central importance. Valley fills on the South Downs (Bell 1981a) contain very large numbers of artifacts, particularly pottery sherds, flint flakes and tools, and charcoals. The maximum number of artifacts recorded in one valley trench was 3278 and the densities varied between 72 and 214 per cubic metre. Such high densities, found also in lynchet deposits, argue persuasively for a causal link between the processes of accumulation and human activity. Many of the artifacts probably arrived along with domestic and farmyard manure and this alone implies fairly intensive land-use.

Despite the fact that the deposits have been mixed by cultivation, reasonably good artifact stratigraphy is preserved. In three sites basal charcoal layers, which probably represent clearance immediately prior to cultivation, have been radiocarbon-dated; these are Brook, 4540±105 BP (2590±105 bc) (BM-254) (Barker *et al.* 1971, p.169); Pitstone, 3910±220 BP (1960±220 bc) (HAR-327) (Evans and Valentine 1974); and Itford Bottom, 3720±120 BP (1770±120 bc) (BM-1545). Pottery distributions demonstrate that a Beaker settlement site was buried by colluvium in Kiln Combe and probably a Neolithic site at Brook (Burleigh and Kerney 1981). Pottery confirms an Early Bronze Age date for the onset of colluviation in Itford Bottom and suggests that in Chalton Trench b colluviation was initiated at sometime during the Bronze Age/Early Iron Age. A neighbouring major dry valley produced very little in the way of pre-Medieval colluvium and, in all probability, the sediments have been removed by a seasonal lavant stream. Such streams require further study because their occurrence and frequency may well help us to identify climatic factors in valley sedimentation. Once colluviation had been initiated in each of the South Down study areas it seems to have continued intermittently to an extent which correlates broadly with the number of artifacts of each period and thus presumably with the intensity of land-use.

In considering the temporal range of the reasonably well-dated colluvial sequences (figure 3) we must remember the caveats already mentioned in relation to the alluvial sequences. Seldom is the dating evidence as detailed as one would like and it is consequently necessary to employ an element of

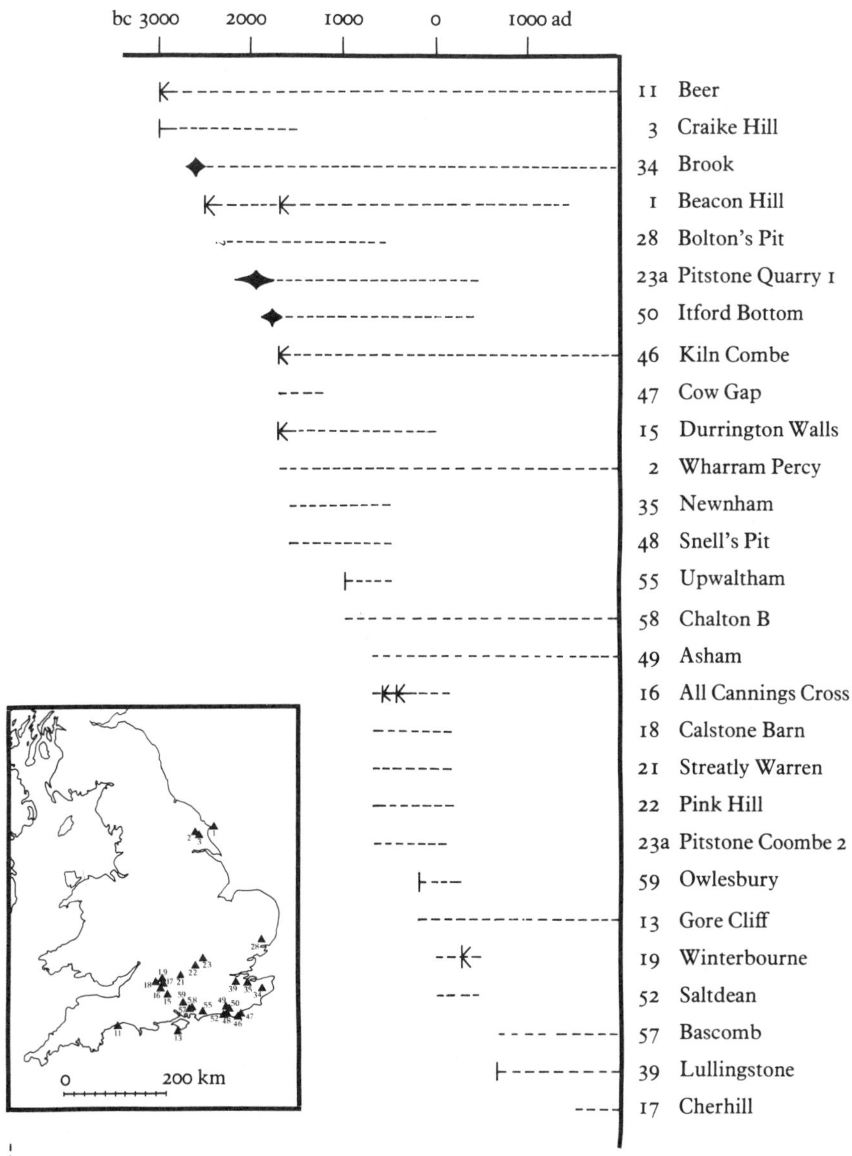

Figure 3. An attempt to plot the approximate dates at which colluviation was initiated and was occurring. The inset shows the distribution of the sites. Full bibliographical references for the sites are in Bell 1981b, appendix 1.

subjective judgement in the interpretation of certain dates. Nonetheless, the margins of uncertainty introduced by these caveats cannot negate the general conclusion that colluviation was initiated and was occurring at all periods from Neolithic to Post-Medieval. What may have led some writers to assume it is basically a later prehistoric process is possibly the contrast between non-calcareous silt loam with flints and the typically later calcareous 'hillwash' deposits with a high proportion of Chalk granules. I would suggest that both deposits are of basically similar origin and the contrast between them is probably mainly a reflection of thinning soil profiles in later prehistory leading to the erosion of a higher proportion of Chalk granules.

If we compare the spatial and temporal distribution of dated colluvial sediments (figure 3) with that of dated alluvial sediments (figure 1) some interesting contrasts begin to emerge. Colluviation seems to have begun rather earlier, possibly reflecting its more localised origin in contrast to alluvial sediments which might reflect land-use changes over a major portion of the catchment. It is also significant that many of the colluvial sequences are on the Chalk and limestone in the South-East whereas the alluvial sequences are mainly in the river valleys and clay vales of the south Midlands, so we may also be observing the more intensive exploitation of these latter areas in later prehistory.

Mollusca

Molluscan studies show that below the colluvium there are frequently truncated subsoil hollows containing faunas indicative of closed woodland conditions and presumably representing fossil tree holes. Radiocarbon-dated soil horizons dating around the time of the Neolithic survived in the Brook and Pitstone valleys and in both cases these preserved a mollusc sequence showing that woodland clearance had been followed by colluviation. In none of the South Down valleys was an original woodland soil preserved (except in subsoil hollows) implying that it had been removed during earlier erosion episodes. However, at Itford Bottom the radiocarbon-dated charcoal horizon represents an Early Bronze Age secondary clearance of isolated trees and shrubs, in an otherwise open landscape, which led to the onset of colluviation. On all these sites the fauna from the overlying colluvium is of open country ecological preferences, chiefly *Vallonia costata*, *Vallonia excentrica*, *Trichia hispida* and the *Limacidae*. Thus the fauna is restricted both in terms of the numbers of individuals and the range of species present. This implies that we are dealing with a dry, harsh and most probably arable environment. This is not, however, true of one site, Cwm Nash on the Lias Limestone in Glamorgan, where colluviation seems to have occurred under open woodland conditions perhaps as a result of heavy grazing (Evans *et al.* 1978, p.72).

Despite all this evidence for the importance of land-use factors there is some hope from recent molluscan studies that we may eventually be able to identify climatic factors in a more precise way. Kerney (1968) has shown that *Pomatias elegans*, *Lauria cylindracea* and *Ena montana* had wider and more northerly

British distributions during the climatic optimum. It has also been observed that examples of *Pomatias elegans* from this period tend to be significantly larger than modern populations on the same site (Preece 1980, p.354; Kerney *et al.* 1980, p.27). Comparisons of pre- and post-Iron Age populations of *Cepaea nemoralis* show pre-Iron Age contexts to have much higher proportions of unbanded and mid-banded forms. This is probably explained by present-day evidence suggesting that unbanded and mid-banded forms are favoured by better summers than are normal in Britain at present (Currey and Cain 1968).

Conclusions

The present-day examples have shown that climatic factors play a key role in the erosion process. Major storms are of special interest because they provide us with golden opportunities to investigate processes of landform development concentrated in time (Newson 1975). It may also be true, however, that smaller-scale, but more frequent, climatic events have greater cumulative importance and in this regard further studies of present-day erosion processes on the Chalk would be welcome. Despite the obvious importance of climatic factors little evidence has emerged from the archaeological record for major periods of increased sedimentation which may have a climatic cause. Both alluvial and colluvial sediments seem to have built up over a wide span of time and there is evidence that all the colluvial sequences studied built up slowly by gradual increments rather than in a few major catastrophic episodes. This, together with the biological evidence from the sediments themselves, suggests that in the lowland zone of the British Isles, land-use factors are the major influence on the pattern of sedimentation and that this tends to swamp and mask underlying climatic trends. What this means is that valley sediments are, and perhaps always will be, rather less than satisfactory proxy climatic indicators, at least in a postglacial lowland British context. There is an obvious need, particularly in the Mediterranean, for detailed studies of the sediments in specific small areas in relation to their land-use history. Detailed studies of this kind should also facilitate the development of a more refined chronology against which the causes of sedimentation can be critically examined. If future studies are to succeed in disentangling the roles of climate and land-use they will also need to give greater emphasis to independent interstratified biological evidence and to compare the evidence from a variety of sources and disciplines as Ladurie (1972) has urged in relation to historical studies of climatic change.

REFERENCES

Barker, H., Burleigh, R. & Meeks, N. (1971) B.M. natural radiocarbon measurements VII, *Radiocarbon* 13, 169.

Bell, M. (1981a) Valley sediments and environmental change, in Jones, M. & Dimbleby, G. W. (eds) *The Environment of Man: the Iron Age to the Anglo-Saxon period*. Oxford: British Archaeological Reports 87, 75-91.

— (1981b) *Valley sediments as evidence of prehistoric land-use: a study based on dry valleys in South East England*. London University unpublished Ph.D. thesis.

Bintliff, J. (1977) *Natural Environment and Human Settlement in Prehistoric Greece*. Oxford: British Archaeological Reports, Supplementary Series 28.
Bradley, R. (1978) *The Prehistoric Settlement of Britain*. London: Routledge and Kegan Paul.
Brunsden, D. & Thornes, J. B. (1979) Landscape sensitivity and change, *Institute of British Geographers Transactions* 4, 463-84.
Burleigh, R. & Kerney, M. P. (1981) Some chronological implications of a fossil molluscan assemblage from a Neolithic site at Brook, Kent, England, *J. Archaeological Science* 8, forthcoming.
Butzer, K. W. (1974) Accelerated soil erosion: a problem of man-land relationships, in Manners, I. & Mikesell, M. (eds) *Perspectives on Environment*. Washington: Association of American Geographers, 57-78.
— (1976) *Geomorphology from the Earth*. New York: Harper and Row.
Carson, M. A. & Kirkby, M. J. (1972) *Hillslope Form and Process*. Cambridge: University Press.
Cornwall, I. W. (1953) Soil science and archaeology with illustrations from some British Bronze Age monuments, *Proc. Prehistoric Soc.* 19, 129-47.
Cross, D. A. E. (1967) The great Till Flood of 1841, *Weather* 22, 430-3.
Culleton, E. B. & Mitchell, G. F. (1976) Soil erosion following deforestation in the early Christian period in South Wexford, *J. Soc. Antiquaries of Ireland* 106, 120-3.
Currey, J. D. & Cain, A. J. (1968) Studies on *Cepaea* IV: Climate and selection of banding morphs in *Cepaea* from the climatic optimum to the present day, *Philosophical Trans. Royal Soc. London* B 253, 483-98.
Davidson, D., Renfrew, C. & Tasker, C. (1976) Erosion and prehistory in Melos: a preliminary note, *J. Archaeological Science* 3, 219-227.
Davis, M. B. (1976) Erosion rates and land-use history in Southern Michigan, *Environmental Conservation* 3, 139-48.
Dimbleby, G. W. (1976) Climate, soil and man, *Philosophical Trans. R. Soc. London* B 275, 197-208.
Eisma, D. (1964) Stream deposition in the Mediterranean area in historical times, *Nature* 203, 1061.
Evans, J. G. (1966) Late glacial and Postglacial subaerial deposits at Pitstone, Bucks., *Proc. Geologists' Association* 77, 347-64.
Evans, J. G. & Valentine, K. W. G. (1974) Ecological changes induced by prehistoric man at Pitstone, Bucks., *J. Archaeological Science* 1, 343-51.
Evans, J. G., Leighton, D. & French, C. (1978) Habitat changes in two early Postglacial sites in Southern Britain, in Evans, J. G. & Limbrey, S. (eds) *Man's Impact on the Landscape: the Lowland Zone*. London: CBA Research Report 21, 63-75.
Evans, J. G. & Jones, H. (1979) The land Mollusca, in Wainwright, G. J., *Mount Pleasant, Dorset: Excavations 1970-71*, London: Society of Antiquaries Research Report 37, 190-213.
Evans, R. & Morgan, R. P. C. (1974) Water erosion of arable land, *Area* 6, 221-5.
Flouest, J.-L. & Stead, I. M. (1979) *Iron Age Cemeteries in Champagne: Third Interim Report*. London: British Museum Occasional Paper, 6.
Gater, J. A. (1979) *Flooding and flood deposits in Britain: some implications*. Bradford University, unpublished undergraduate dissertation, Dept. of Archaeological Science.
Gifford, J. (1953) Landslides on Exmoor caused by the storm of 15 August 1952, *Geography* 38, 9.
Grove, J. M. (1972) The incidence of landslides, avalanches and floods in Western Norway during the Little Ice Age, *Arctic and Alpine Research* 4, 131-8.

Hodgson, J. M. (1967) *Soils of the West Sussex Coastal Plain*. Harpenden: Memoir Soil Survey.

Hutchinson, J. (1969) Erosion and land-use: the influence of agriculture on the Epirus region of Greece, *Agricultural History Rev.* 17, 85-90.

Jäger, K.-D. (1962) Über Alter und Ursachen der Auelehmablagerung thüringischer Flüsse, *Praehistorische Zeitschrift* 40, 1-59.

Jones, R. L. (1976) The activities of Mesolithic man: further palaeobotanical evidence from NE Yorkshire, in Davidson, D. A. & Shackley, M. L. (eds) *Geoarchaeology*. London: Duckworth.

Judson, S. (1963) Erosion and deposition of Italian stream valleys during historic time, *Science* 140, 898-9.

— (1968) Erosion rates near Rome, Italy, *Science* 160, 1444-6.

Kelly, M. & Osborne, P. J. (1964) Two faunas and floras from the alluvium at Shustoke, Warwickshire, *Proc. Linnean Society* 176, 37-65.

Kerney, M. P. (1968) Britain's fauna of land Mollusca and its relation to the post-glacial thermal optimum, *Symposia of the Zoological Soc. London* 22, 273-91.

Kerney, M. P., Brown, E. H. & Chandler, T. J. (1964) The late glacial and post-glacial history of the chalk escarpment near Brook, Kent, *Philosophical Trans. R. Soc.* B 248, 135-204.

Kerney, M. P., Preece, R. C. & Turner, C. (1980) Molluscan and plant biostratigraphy of some late Devensian and Flandrian deposits in Kent, *Philosophical Trans. R. Soc.* B 291, 1-43.

Kidson, C. (1953) The Exmoor storm and the Lynmouth floods, *Geography* 38, 1-9.

Kwaad, F. (1977) Measurement of rainsplash erosion and the formation of colluvium beneath deciduous woodland in the Luxembourg Ardennes, *Earth Surface Processes* 2, 161-73.

Kwaad, F. J. P. M. & Mücher, H. J. (1977) The evolution of soils and slope deposits in the Luxembourg Ardennes near Wiltz, *Geoderma* 17, 1-37.

Ladurie, E. Le Roy (1972) *Times of Feast, Times of Famine: a History of Climate since the Year 1000*. London: Allen and Unwin.

Lamb, H. H. (1977) *Climate: Present, Past and Future. 2. Climatic History and the Future*. London: Methuen.

Lambrick, G. & Robinson, M. (1979) *Iron Age and Roman Riverside Settlement at Farmoor, Oxfordshire*. London: CBA Research Report 32.

Latter, P. R. (1932) Floods at Louth, *The Lincolnshire Magazine* 1:2, (Nov./Dec.), 73.

Leopold, L. B. (1956) Land-use and sediment yield, in Thomas, W. L. (ed.) *Man's Role in Changing the Face of the Earth*. Chicago: University Press, 639-47.

Limbrey, S. (1978) Changes in quality and distribution of the soils of lowland Britain, in Limbrey, S. & Evans, J. (eds) *The Effect of Man on the Landscape: the Lowland Zone*. London: CBA Research Report 21, 21-7.

— (1979) Evidence for the chronology of alluvial accumulations, Unpublished lecture at British Museum seminar on Hillwash and Archaeology, 5.3.79.

Meade, R. (1969) Errors in using modern stream load data to estimate natural rates of denudation, *Geol. Soc. Am. Bull.* 80, 1265-74.

Mensching, H. (1951) Une accumulation post-glaciaire provoquée par des défrichements, *Revue géomorphologie Dynamique* 2, 145-56.

— (1958) Soil erosion and formation of Haugh-loam in Germany, *Association International for Hydrological Science: Toronto Congress* 1, 174-8.

Mitchell, F. (1976) *The Irish Landscape*. London: Collins.

Morgan, R. P. C. (1977) *Soil erosion in the U.K., field studies in the Silsoe area, 1973-75*, National College of Agricultural Engineering, Silsoe, Occasional Paper 5.

Newson, M. D. (1975) *Flooding and Flood Hazard in the U.K.* Oxford: University Press.

Oakley, K. P. (1945) Some geological effects of a cloudburst in the Chilterns, *Records of Bucks.* 14, 265-80.

Pearsall, W. H., Gay, J. & Newbould, J. (1960) Postglacial sediment as a record of regional soil drifts, *J. Soil Science* 11, 68-76.

Potter, T. W. (1976) Valleys and settlement: some new evidence, *World Archaeology* 8, 207-19.

— (1979) *Romans in North-West England,* Cumberland and Westmorland Antiquarian and Archaeological Society Research Series 1. Kendal: Titus Wilson.

Preece, R. C. (1980) The biostratigraphy and dating of the tufa deposit at the Mesolithic site at Blashenwell, Dorset, England, *J. Archaeological Science* 7, 345-62.

Raikes, R. (1967) *Water, Weather and Prehistory.* London: John Baker.

Raphael, C. N. (1973) Late Quaternary changes in coastal Elis, Greece, *Geographical Rev.* 63, 73-89.

Renfrew, C. (1973) *Before Civilization.* London: Cape.

Riezebos, P. & Slotboom, R. T. (1974) Palynology in the study of present day hillslope development, *Geologie en Mijnbouw* 53, 436-45.

Samuels, J. & Buckland, P. C. (1978) A Romano-British settlement at Sandtoft, South Humberside, *Yorkshire Archaeological J.* 50, 65-75.

Shillitoe, J. S. (1961) Borings in the first terrace and alluvium of the River Tame at Tamworth, *Proc. Coventry Natural History and Scientific Soc.* 3:4, 133-8.

Shotton, F. W. (1978) Archaeological inferences from the study of alluvium in the Lower Severn/Avon valleys, in Limbrey, S. & Evans, J. G. (eds) *The Effect of Man on the Landscape: the Lowland Zone.* London: CBA Research Report 21, 27-32.

Taylor, C. C. (1972) The study of settlement patterns in pre-Saxon Britain, in Ucko, P. J., Tringham, R. & Dimbleby, G. W. (eds) *Man, Settlement and Urbanism.* London: Duckworth, 109-13.

Vita-Finzi, C. (1969) *The Mediterranean Valleys: Geological Changes in Historical Times.* Cambridge: University Press.

— (1974) Chronicling soil erosion, in Warren, A. & Goldsmith, F. B. (eds) *Conservation in Practice.* London: Wiley, 267-77.

— (1975) Related territories and alluvial sediments, in Higgs, E. S. (ed.) *Palaeoeconomy.* Cambridge: University Press, 225-31.

— (1976) Diachronism in Old World alluvial sequences, *Nature* 263, 218-19.

Vogt, J. (1953) Erosion des sols et techniques de culture en climat tempéré maritime de transition, *Revue de Géomorphologie Dynamique* 4, 157-83.

Wolman, M. G. (1967) A cycle of sedimentation and erosion in urban river channels, *Geografiska Annaler* 49-A, 385-95.

Climatic change, archaeology and Quaternary science in the eastern Mediterranean region

There has been a very significant shift in recent decades within the discipline of climatology away from the highly detailed, particularising approach to regional climates, with its emphasis on unique combinations of topography and surface pressure systems, and on to a far more powerful analysis in which the fundamental source of dominant surface weather systems is to be sought in large-scale airmass and circulation dynamics in the upper atmosphere. This approach rests on the fundamental link between the development and steering of surface weather and wind systems, and the general atmospheric circulation and the flow of the circumpolar vortex (the broadly latitudinal flow of dominant winds concentric around the poles) (Lamb 1978a, p.121; Lamb 1978b, p.183).

The major wind systems under analysis in this approach are such as the upper westerly system, affecting both Europe and the Mediterranean latitudes, and therefore of sufficient amplitude that the possibility exists of interpolating from indications in widely separate localities the overall climatic pattern for regions of subcontinental size. Moreover, the pattern of the dominant upper circulation features is then also inferable from discrete but consistent indications of surface weather and pressure systems on the strength of their significant distributional characteristics. Such an overall approach has been most notably applied by Professor Hubert Lamb in his extensive publications on climatic history.

These considerations encourage the modelling of climate for past eras in the east Mediterranean, even when it apparently relies excessively on data from selected areas within that wider region, or is visibly propped up by reference to data available for adjacent regions (such as temperate Europe or north Africa). Underlying this attempt therefore, and those incorporated into it from published work by previous scholars, is that concept fundamental to Lamb's *oeuvre*, that major climatic fluctuations (secular changes of climate), in one region of the globe are believed to be correlated with predictable fluctuations in contiguous regions, because of the strong interdependence of the major features of the Earth's climate and the large scale on which the underlying circulation features operate. A second major concept in Lamb's approach that is invaluable for palaeoclimatic reconstructions is the building of models for changing secular climatic patterns on the basis of analogous recent short-term fluctuations, with allowance being made for degree and duration.

The foregoing points are especially relevant to the study of climatic change in the east Mediterranean. For almost all of this region, the availability of wild

1. Latitudinal displacement of present-day circulation (westerlies, equatorial rains)
2. Changes in strength of 'zonal flow' – frequency of 'blocking' of circulation
3. Out-of-phase north vs south hemisphere circulation (shift in average position of intertropical convergence zone = ITCZ)
4. Unusual exchanges between normally remote weather systems (e.g. westerly and equatorial precipitation)

Figure 1.

game and plants, the successful maturing of cultivated cereals and tree fruits, and of pasture for domestic animals, all are dependent on the winter-season incursion of upper westerly steered cyclonic stormtracks from the west and northwest, coupled with the parallel retreat of the summer-dominant subtropical arid pressure systems (predominantly high pressure) towards the equator. These displaced troughs in the upper westerlies also bring rain to winter-season northern Europe, just as the expanded Azores subtropical anticyclone is responsible for prolonged periods of warm, dry weather in northwest European summers.

Essentially there would seem good reason for establishing a palaeoclimatic model linking unusually wet and cold winters in northern Europe with a similar tendency in southern (Mediterranean) Europe and the Levant, and a corresponding correlation between Mediterranean winter rainfall decline and a decrease in Europe north of the Alps. This *Model One* (figure 1) envisages a simple northward or southward displacement of present-day circulation patterns. It is one of the key climatic changes isolated by Lamb (1977, p.400; Lamb and Dickson 1975, p.142; Lamb 1978b, p.184).

A complicating factor arises if we consider another source of precipitation, that of the equatorial rains (primarily the monsoons). At present such rain affects only the southernmost area of the Middle East, and even there only where relief is significant. But if, as seems likely, there have been periods in the past, especially that of the supposed climax of warmth and ice-melt during the Atlantic era (c. 7450–5450 BP (5500–3500 bc)), when the circumpolar vortex of broadly latitudinal climatic zones contracted towards the poles, then it would be appropriate for the monsoon/equatorial rains not only to have an effective influence further north in the east Mediterranean and Saharan Africa, but to operate there also irrespective of local relief. This is an important corollary of Model One.

Model Two relates to the strength of the zonal circulation of the upper atmosphere. It has been argued (cf. Lamb 1977, 1979), that the vigour of the Earth's circulation is correlated with the existence of marked contrasts between low latitude heat surplus and high latitude heat deficit (hence the concentration of atmospheric disturbances due to mixing of cold and warm air, in middle latitudes). The efficient running of this heat engine is therefore at its maximum when both equatorial insolation and polar ice development are well balanced. During the climax of glacial eras and the maximum warming of interglacials, it is argued that one or the other tendency would gain the upper hand tending to produce a marked decline in circulation vigour. Under ideal conditions (e.g. the early decades of this century rather than in the present climatically abnormal period), there is an apparent tendency for the strong equator-polar heat contrast to create a vigorous flow of airmasses between them, that is converted by effects such as the Earth's rotation into a broadly latitudinal or 'zonal' flow. A decline in this heat exchange vigour would weaken the zonal flow (west to east in the northern hemisphere, hence the 'upper westerlies'), and encourage a strong development of meridional flow, that is north-south airmass exchanges. This disruption of the smooth passage round the hemispheres of important zonal features, such as the rain-bearing westerly winds, would be a greatly-accentuated version of lesser interruptions and deviations that are always found in these windstreams. At all times the upper westerly flow is disturbed by recurrent or semi-permanent wave-like meanders. These arise as a consequence of the relative disposition of land and ocean masses, variations in physical relief, a 'balancing' of wave disturbances in different segments of each hemisphere, and the relative distribution of regions of intense warmth and cold (e.g. ice-sheets). Under 'ideal' conditions, a powerful zonal flow is interrupted by three to four low amplitude waves per hemisphere, but under conditions of sluggish flow these can increase to five to six high amplitude waves. The meanders themselves represent diversions of airflow around relatively static pressure systems such as expanded belts of warm high pressure, or polar cold low pressure (which can be the direct cause of the sluggish flow in the first place), or physical barriers as noted above. The larger the diversions, the greater the scope for meridional exchanges in the place of westerly flow. This results in the areas concerned being subject either to the relatively static extreme climates or to mobile airmasses from unaccustomed directions and with a tendency to notable divergence from previous zonal flow character (warmer from the south, colder from the north, in the case of the northern hemisphere). These situations of highly disturbed flow are termed 'blocked', and it is an important feature of such patterns that major shifts can occur on a season-by-season, or longer-term basis, in the location of the blocking warm, subtropical or cold, polar anticyclones and hence the areas where the disturbed flow is concentrated. Severe drought may be followed by remarkable flooding in the same region, under such a régime, on a short-term basis.

The implications of this for Mediterranean latitude climates during periods of known expansion of subtropical or polar anticyclones are clear, and will be pursued in application later in this paper. But it will be obvious that a particular complication arises in the correct identification of the ultimate cause of surface effects indicating a 'blocked' circulation. They may originate from an unusual increase in equatorial warming or cooling, that is they can be indicative of either mini-glacial or climax warming phases. Winstanley has in fact demonstrated the relevance of the joint operation of our *Model One* and *Model Two* climatic patterns in an examination of climatic fluctuations in the

Middle East and north Africa between 1950 and 1970 (Winstanley 1973). He stresses that precipitation curves for localities throughout this region tend to show a similar path for the period, subject as they are to the same incursion of westerly stormtracks.

Model Three (and note that all of these models may be applicable at the same point in time) considers the possible effects of an out-of-phase relationship between the north and south hemisphere circulation. There seems to be some evidence within the Holocene and the late Pleistocene for warming and cooling tendencies to have been out-of-phase in the short term (i.e. one to several centuries) on either side of the equator, but in-phase on longer timescales (such as the one to several thousand year cycles of climatic phases defined by the classic pollen zonation of north-west Europe). A notable exception to this rule existed with the universal Little Ice Age.

A commonly-accepted practical effect of this imbalance might be a shift in the average position of the meteorological equator, that is, the dividing line between the broadly zonal circulation systems extending in a mirror-fashion polewards from the equator, the ITCZ or Intertropical Convergence Zone. Such an effect might either reinforce or tend to negate the general climatic tendency for each hemisphere in its effect on low latitudes (and here the Sahara region is frequently cited, cf. Rognon and Williams 1977), but could extend into lower-middle latitudes such as the Mediterranean and Middle East region in more extreme cases. Thus in a cold period in the northern hemisphere, the climatic belts might broadly move south, with a tendency for the arid Sahara to migrate south into the savannah zone; but if the southern hemisphere ice cap was far more extended than the Arctic, the pressure for displacement from the south to the equator would outweigh these effects by shifting the ITCZ northwards, allowing equatorial rains to persist in the south Sahara fringes and creating a compressed Sahara desert zone.

One further specialised effect, *Model Four*, can be proposed, especially when considering situations such as Model Three, where unusual proximity of the normally remote westerly and equatorial rain systems is created, or Model Two, where meridional flow might likewise bring into proximity these two rainfall sources. On analogy with present-day processes – though feeble in magnitude and significance now – it has been suggested that interactions might take place between these two systems, especially at changeover seasons such as spring and autumn, which would bring rainfall to intermediate regions such as the central Sahara, normally deprived of major precipitation by their distance from either source (cf. Sudan-Sahel depressions, and the suggestions of Flohn and Nicholson 1979, and Rognon and Williams 1977).

In the remainder of this paper, I shall discuss the broad lines of the environmental, archaeological and historical evidence relating to major climatic fluctuations in the east Mediterranean region, from a mature phase of the Holocene up to the last few centuries of relative warming. This period is treated in terms of the major subdivisions widely recognised as reflecting significant secular climatic changes. (For a discussion of possible factors behind these shifts, especially the semi-regular c. 2000-year and 1000-year cycles detectable during the Holocene and final Glacial period, see Lamb 1977 and 1978a, b.)

Sub-boreal period, c. 5450–2950/2700 BP (3500–1000/750 bc)

In the scientific literature for this period from north-west Europe, there is a clear difficulty in interpreting the environmental indicators in simple climatic terms. A similar difficulty from variety of indicators characterises the east Mediterranean region, and may in fact be characteristic for a particular régime of blocked and variable weather.

In the Levant, the first half of the period represents archaeologically a major phase of expansion into the southern deserts and generally an advance in settlement. We have the same effects and time-range in north Africa and Syria. There is evidence for this humid phase lasting till the latter part of the third millennium bc in the Negev (Price-Williams 1973) and the Khabur basin (Oates 1976). Likewise the Jordan alluvial phase described by Vita-Finzi and Copeland (1978) dating back probably to Chalcolithic times, has a date of 3950 BP (2000 bc) in its upper levels. The Dead Sea may have been higher from 5000–4250 BP (3500–2300 bc) (Crown 1972) and therefore cooler or in a moister catchment, or both. In fact there is some evidence from studies off the Israeli coast (Magaritz and Kaufman 1973) for cooler sea temperatures between 4950 and 2950 BP (3000 and 1000 bc).

Price-Williams (1973) suggests that the Middle and Late Bronze Age and Iron Age occupations of the south Levant deserts were not primarily agricultural, but concerned with trade routes and defence, although Evenari has argued for the MBA at least being partly agricultural in character and the first to have applied run-off systems on a large scale (1971). But it does seem as if there was a clear decline in land use in the region through the second millennium bc and beyond. Just north of the Negev, a study of wood charcoal from archaeological sites (Lipschitz 1979) distinguishes between the Late Bronze Age and the Iron Age, giving a shift from more Mediterranean to more Saharan vegetation c. 3150 BP (1200 bc), the earlier period thus being moister than now (or merely cooler?). However, no allowance was made for the importation of wood from varying distances. In Syria, despite possible fluctuations noted above, pollen spectra furnish in general a semi-arid climate comparable to that of today (Bottema 1977).

Moving into the northern region we find, as with the preceding Atlantic period, a continued improvement in moisture recorded by increasingly full or climax woodland conditions. In Turkey pollen diagrams show climax woodland achieved by the end of this period, and in Greece the climax was reached in the latter part of the Atlantic (Van Zeist and Bottema 1977, 1980; Bottema 1978). Some possible wider implications might be drawn from the Persian Gulf core data, which could be read to indicate a dry early, and moister late, Sub-boreal, reflecting upland precipitation around the Mesopotamian Plain (Diester-Haass 1973). The change from aggradation to incision in the Deh

Luran section of that plain (Kirkby 1977) is taken by that author to suggest a moister climate, with greater vegetation mat and reduced run-off, possibly correlating with the Gulf indications.

In Arabia, present-day arid conditions are already established, and the indications from Red Sea isotope studies are appropriately dry, although the data for the Gulf of Aden could be read to show fluctuations of dry to moister conditions (Deuser 1976, Schoeli 1978, Olausson and Olsson 1969).

Possible interpretations

'After about 3000 BC the circulation seems to have become weaker, permitting some drier periods and colder winters in central and northern Europe and Asia. In northern Turkey . . . the change was to moister conditions . . . probably an early symptom of a return to more meridional circulation patterns and a winter trough in the upper westerlies near longitude 20–40°E' (i.e. the east to central Mediterranean) (Lamb 1977, p.390).

In north-west Europe, after the Piora decline, forests regained ground, but in the latter part of the period, especially after 3450 BP (1500 bc), they decline in altitude and yield to peat growth and podzolisation (Lamb 1977, p.416). Although there are indications of greater warmth, comparable to Boreal times (hence the term Sub-boreal), there are also clear recurrent fluctuations, especially of rainfall such that: 'More variable, and presumably more meridional, circulation patterns than in Atlantic times seem an obvious interpretation' (*op. cit.*, p.373). Underlying this pattern, for Lamb, would be blocking situations arising from a weakened circulation. In the earlier half of the period he ascribes this to extreme retreat of the ice sheets and northern advance of the belts of climate, but for the latter period there is sufficient evidence from glacier advance and treeline depression, and supportive environmental indicators, for an overall shift of climatic belts south again as a prelude to the Sub-atlantic climate. (For northern hemisphere glacier advances see Hecht (1979), between 3450-2450 BP (1500–500 bc); in the Swiss Alps, a climatic decline based on pollen evidence and glacier stratigraphy, see May (1979), between 3350–3250 and 2850–2250 BP (14–1300 and 9–300 bc); for a cooler climate between 3450–3100 and 2750–2650 BP (1500–1150 and 8–700 bc), on European oak density studies see Rothlisberger (1979); in the White Mts of California tree-ring studies show climate decline c. 3250 BP (1300 bc) after La Marche (1974).)

The implications for the Mediterranean latitude are not clearcut. One might expect from the Piora fluctuation onwards a marked variability at different longitudes of the Mediterranean (*Model Two*) with unusually dry zones adjacent to unusually wet zones, and a generally expanded subtropical anticyclone belt interrupted by 'bitrack' depressions steered round them. 'Bitrack depressions' are cyclonic disturbances envisaged as being diverted both north and south of a dominant, blocking anticyclone, rather like a stream around a rock in its path. In the latter half of the period, however, a general advance of the depression belt further south into the Mediterranean winter might be expected, and a retreat of the monsoons.

In the Levant and inland Syria the indications of a cooler and moister climate occur in the earlier part of the Sub-boreal, perhaps as a continuation of the Piora conditions. This is difficult to relate to the north European situation, unless we assume a bitrack concentrated in the south-east Mediterranean. Seemingly the later shift of the depression belt on a broad front into the Mediterranean, as predicted above, had no significant effect on this area. The indications of precipitation increase in the Mesopotamian Plain's mountainous hinterlands are perhaps significantly concentrated in the latter half of the period, coincident with the suggested rainfall increase throughout the Mediterranean (*Model One*).

In the rest of the northern part of the region, the continued rise of woodland is recorded, seemingly reflecting a continued rise in moisture. Whereas this is reasonable for the latter part of the period with its supposed increase in rainfall, the earlier Sub-boreal might have been supposed to be associated with a dry interval, unless bitrack conditions favoured the regions where palynology has been concentrated. There does seem to be a problem here with an overall early Sub-boreal interpreted as a major northward shift of the location of winter rainfall, and at present the north-east Mediterranean data is more consistent with a continual southward shift of cyclonic depressions from Sub-boreal into Sub-atlantic times, with minor moves in the opposite direction that do not seem to be registered in the woodland record.

Such a conclusion would also be consistent with the evidence from the Nile headwaters and the south Sahara, with the monsoon in serious decline, as with the equatorial rains (Rognon and Williams 1977). Although the general retreat of the monsoon to present levels of northward migration is seen as occurring by 3950 BP (2000 bc) (Rognon and Williams 1977, Butzer 1978), this may not be merely a reflection of an early Sub-boreal with a generally contracted northern hemisphere circumpolar vortex, for there may be a phase of Antarctic cooling that could have created an ITCZ displacement northwards from 8–4000 BP (6–2000 bc). Certainly the decline of the monsoon is recorded by the continual fall in Nile levels in Egypt during the third millennium bc, and again after some recovery in the latter part of the second millennium bc. The serious political implications of this decline for the prime subsistence basis of Egyptian civilisation have been excitingly explored by Barbara Bell (1971, 1975). Likewise the decline of the monsoon, especially from c. 3950 BP (2000 bc), has been plausibly linked to the collapse of the Indus civilisation of north-west India and west Pakistan (McGhee 1979).

Particular attention has been paid by climatologists, historians and archaeologists, to the possible role of climatic fluctuations in precipitating the collapse of the Mycenaean and Hittite civilisations around 1200 BC. The initial drought hypothesis of Carpenter (1966) was given support from research by Bryson, Lamb and others into modern parallels for a mosaic of drought and normal rainfall over the east Mediterranean as postulated by Carpenter from historical and archaeological evidence (Lamb 1967, Bryson 1974, Lamb 1977).

Such a pattern was not uncommon this century and was primarily a consequence, in its short-term manifestations, of the distribution of relief in the region. However, the continued operation of such a climatic pattern over a matter of centuries to enforce the post-civilisational collapse of the Dark Ages, was tentatively ascribed in one paper to a blocking régime across the westerlies created by a southward displacement of the north hemisphere climatic belts (Bryson 1974). In any case the climatologists have shown that Carpenter's initial drought theory assumed a general warm climate with subtropical aridity extending further north after a retreating winter rainfall belt, whereas in fact the mosaic of wet and dry areas is most plausibly, on present analogues, due to an expanded polar high that blocks winter rainfall from a smooth progression through the east Mediterranean. Archaeological objections have been raised to the reality of the mosaic pattern, in terms of settlement continuities and discontinuities (Dickinson 1974), which have more weight than the apparent absence of change in Aegean woodlands (Wright 1968). The latter data give no evidence for any perturbations of climate in this or the Sub-atlantic period, contrary to very clear indications from historical and geomorphic data. One must conclude that at the level of fluctuations *within* the major Holocene periods, woodland evidence is only notably sensitive in marginal environments, for example desert margins of the south Levant, upper treeline margins in northern Europe. In the intermediate situation, such as the north-east Mediterranean, the lesser-scale changes may be insufficient to disturb established woodland. As we have seen, there is in fact good evidence for climatic decline in the northern hemisphere from 3450 BP (1500 bc) onwards, which could be appropriate for the blocking situation discussed by Bryson and Lamb. The resolution of the discussion must await more detailed information to clarify these opposing claims, but it may be difficult to find environmental data in the east Mediterranean sensitive enough to the correct chronological scale and locally varying effects involved. Perhaps new historical sources may appear to resolve the issue.

Sub-atlantic period: c. 750 bc–present

The general environmental and archaeological evidence from the Levant is of a climate comparable to the present day, less extreme in either cold/moist or hot/dry conditions than earlier such phases such as the Copper Age. However, it is not always clear whether the development of human cultural skills and initiative is sufficient an explanation for the perseverance of settlement and agriculture in areas of minimal rainfall such as the Negev, or that a habitat was milder owing to a minor climatic oscillation.

The southern deserts show little evidence for resettlement until the rise of the Nabataeans in the closing centuries BC. From then until the collapse of the Byzantine civilisation in the region in the sixth–seventh centuries AD, and possibly till the eighth–ninth centuries AD (Evenari 1971) there is a remarkable flourishing of agricultural settlement, tied to the increasingly sophisticated run-off systems carefully investigated by Israeli archaeologists. It cannot merely be claimed that the Arab invasion of these regions was sufficient to create settlement decline, as Dayton (1975) has convincingly shown, for in Arabia and Jordan the Islamic period in the longer term saw continuing settlement and considerable irrigation systems constructed, together with settlement advance into marginal areas. Was there a climatic element? Dayton argues that increasing drought marks this change of cultural control, for which there is some historical support in the southern Arabian peninsula, with migration of tribes to Tunisia and clear accounts of drought. On the other hand, Goldberg (1980) has drawn attention to considerable deposition of fluvial silts, now in terraces incised up to 4–5 m high, over the Negev and Sinai, associated with radiocarbon dates of 1700 and 600 BP (ad 250 and 1350) and traces of more substantial vegetation than today. While noting the links to Byzantine activity, Goldberg raises the possibility of climatic change, comparing his alluvia with the 'Younger Fill' around the Mediterranean of Vita-Finzi (1969a), broadly dated by the latter from AD 400–1800.

But these dates and the evidence of the 'Fill' itself point, if anything, to a change to a much moister climate throughout the Mediterranean (which could conceivably be linked to the Late Roman/Early Byzantine climax of desert occupation), and the decline of the Levant must in fact be associated with cultural discontinuity, even if there are areas where the Arab encroachment was not economically disastrous. One need only recall the cultural and political gesture of resettlement of the Negev in the late nineteenth century, and in recent decades (Price-Williams 1973, Evenari 1971), times of no consistent precipitation improvement, often rather of decline, to be wary of attributing too much to the presence of settlement where developed civilisations are concerned.

Dayton (1975) fails to distinguish between possible drought in the Levant, under the influence of cyclonic rain, and the Arabian peninsula, under opposing cyclonic and monsoon rain. His best drought evidence seems to be from the monsoon zone and its northern margins. One might perhaps correlate a possible rise in winter rainfall for the south Levant 'Younger Fill' with a monsoon decline to the far south. According to Vita-Finzi (in De Cardi *et al.* 1975), the Younger Fill is also found in Arabia, but may be medieval in inception.

The Younger Fill is virtually the only well-attested feature of possible climatic significance in Syria at this period (Besançon 1980), and its universality and clear indications of its origins in erosion/run-off/rainfall are more acceptable than localised explanations such as that of Brice (1978), with the alluvial burial of ancient Antioch ascribed to earth movements.

In the north of the eastern Mediterranean, vegetational history shows no significant changes attributed to climate; which would agree with the gradual rise to modern precipitation by the later Sub-boreal and its overall maintenance to the present day. But the record is increasingly difficult to interpret because of human interference with woodland distribution. More sensitive indicators stem from geomorphic activity. In Iran the historical alluvium or 'Younger

Fill' has been well studied (Vita-Finzi 1969b, 1975; Brookes and Dennell 1977) and conforms to the general time span elsewhere for this formation of c. AD 400–1800 or later. But Brookes indicates what could be drier intervals within this long period of supposedly cooler and moister climate. Similar signs may be observable from the Persian Gulf cores (Diester-Haass 1973) in which the Sub-atlantic is associated with generally moister conditions interrupted by drier intervals. In the Mesopotamian Plain in general, a peak of complex agriculture based on run-off and canal systems is dated to later Roman and early Islamic times (cf. Kirkby 1977), which might perhaps have been aided by the same moister climate indicated by the Younger Fill. In the Iraqi sector, notable flooding of the lower Plain around AD 600 might conform, but there is evidence also from historical sources for an unusually warm period c. AD 1000 in the same region (Oates 1976). Finally, ocean cores from the Gulf of Aden cover only the early part of the period, and suggest a dry climate, with no unusual extension of the monsoons (Olausson and Olsson 1969).

In Turkey, once again, the woodland record offers little apparent sensitivity to changes detectable in river régimes and other geological evidence. The historical Younger Fill is well represented (Vita-Finzi 1969c). There is evidence from glacier development, for example from Mt Ararat, that seems to record the worldwide climatic cooling of the Little Ice Age (c. AD 1550–1850) (Farrand 1979). The more plentiful historical records now available suggest the following phases of unusual climate or secular changes of climate: after a climate in Roman times comparable to that of today, higher rainfall is suggested from c. AD 750–1300, but with drier intervals associated with frequent droughts (Erinc 1978). Likewise there is unusual wetness in the fifteenth and seventeenth centuries AD, also associated with pronounced drought years (Eisma 1978, Griswold 1979).

In Greece, too, the pollen record provides little indication of climatic fluctuation, and the prime evidence for such stems from the abundant Younger Fill alluvium (Vita-Finzi 1969a; Bintliff 1975, 1977; Dufaure 1976), dated in most exposures from Late Roman to recent times. A number of recent papers critical of the chronology of the Younger Fill (Raphael 1973; Eisma 1964; Davidson 1971, 1976, 1980) may be criticised in their turn for confusing it with earlier colluvial and deltaic deposits (Bintliff 1977, 1981; and for some realisation of this see Eisma 1978).

The best historical evidence for Greece, at least in terms of scholarly accessibility, refers to the period of Classical and Hellenistic Greece, from after 700 to 200 BC. Careful study of literary sources gives strong evidence for a climate during this era comparable to that of the present day (Meigs 1961, Guinis 1976), but rather curiously the assumption is made that therefore the Greek climate has not changed *since* the Classical period. In fact the prime evidence to disprove that assumption stems from the period of the Younger Fill, later than these carefully studied sources.

Possible interpretations

We might first consider the evidence from other parts of the Mediterranean. Little data are available for the period before the Roman Empire. The Imperial Roman period seems generally to have been one of warmth and precipitation comparable to or slightly drier than that of today. The post-Roman centuries, or Dark Ages of the West, have been associated with severe drought in the Byzantine Empire by Carpenter (1966) without adequate evidence, but in Spain there is data from which to deduce seasons of severe drought in the sixth to seventh centuries AD (Barcelo 1979). On the other hand, in all the lands of the central and west Mediterranean the Younger Fill is well represented (Vita-Finzi 1969a), implying moister and cooler conditions for much of the Dark Ages and medieval era. The apparently contradictory evidence may be reconcilable (see below) and Lamb points out that during the Little Ice Age period the Spanish historical sources clearly indicate frequent juxtapositions of severe drought and flooding seasons (1977, p.468). The Mediterranean counterpart to the north European 'Early Medieval Warm era' of c. AD 900–1200 has not hitherto been clearly demonstrable, except for interludes in deposition of Younger Fill about this time, which may mark drier conditions (cf. for example, Barker 1978, Potter 1979). On the other hand, Lamb has suggested that the Mediterranean continued to benefit from rainfall above recent levels, in some longitudes, during this warming era, because of 'bitrack' depressions, and relates this to indications of more active river flow in Sicily and peat growth in the Azores (1977, p.428). The subsequent Little Ice Age is the best documented climatic change over Europe as a whole during the Holocene, and historical evidence for cold, wet conditions abounds throughout the west and central Mediterranean (often coupled with drought reports, as noted above) (Lamb 1977, p.466ff; Pichard 1979), until the nineteenth-century warming period, and contemporary with the latter part of the Younger Fill.

Historical sources have their obvious weaknesses, although they should assist in the identification of the most extreme years. Nonetheless it is clear from the last two centuries that individual years of climatic extremity can stand isolated amid a consistent period of different norms. An examination of Weikinn's (1958) historical listing of years of remarkable climate in Europe not surprisingly offers only a general impression of a greater incidence of more northerly-type climate in southern Europe, coincident with similar but better attested phases in north-west Europe. Lamb claims a better match but the agreement is patchy (1977, p.427). How are we to evaluate, for example, the isolated information that in 829 and 1011 there was ice on the Nile (loc. cit.)? The former date would fall into the transition from a colder to warmer climate in north-west European terms, and the latter was in fact also a year of severe cold in much of Europe north of the Alps, but within a well-established *warm* era there.

In north Africa, the Nile flood fluctuations and the inferences concerning the expansion and contraction of monsoon/equatorial rains to be drawn from them, do seem to be in accordance overall with the predictions one might make from the behaviour of the westerly circulation for north-west Europe (Lamb 1977, Brooks 1949): from the seventh century AD to c. 800, low Nile levels, followed by a rise corresponding to the climatic improvement of the European 'early medieval warm era'; then a decline c. AD 12–1400 and c. AD 15–1600 comparable to the Little Ice Age and its late medieval precursor; even the milder era c. AD 1500 may be represented by a higher Nile flow. However, from the latter part of the Little Ice Age into the present era, Nile floods are high; but this contrary prediction to north European events may be connected to a displacement of the ITCZ, owing to the delayed decline of the corresponding Little Ice Age in the southern hemisphere (Lamb 1977, 449ff).

Since the last century, the extensive traces of Roman settlement and agriculture (field systems, irrigation works), thoughout north Africa, have inspired theories of climatic decline to account for subsequent abandonments and less intensive land-use and settlement (Shaw 1978). The study of classical references to the area seems to have supported such ideas, but makes no allowance, for example, for surviving fossil water (Lamb 1977, p.387). On the other hand, it is, as with the south Levant, precisely during the later period of Roman occupation and the subsequent 1400 years in north Africa, that the extensive Younger Fill was largely being deposited (Vita-Finzi 1969a), which, though possibly assisting late Roman agriculture and that of the sub-Roman cities and their cultural successors under Islamic rule, should also have offered an incentive for equally widespread land use till recent times. Once again, climatic change may have been important for the maintenance of an already successful adaptation, but was less powerful than cultural factors in the long-term survival of intensive agriculture. The references of Arab sources to moister than present-day climate in north Africa overlap with the 'early medieval warm era' of north-west Europe, and are seen as further support for a localised bitrack depression series (Lamb 1977, p.440ff.) The juxtaposition of humid indicators and drought in literary sources for the Little Ice Age period in north Africa compares well with the other evidence for the same phenomenon, both in other parts of the Mediterranean and north of the Alps (Lamb 1977, pp.469; 1979).

This general survey of the Mediterranean and Near Eastern data for the Sub-atlantic period does seem to bring out some broad consistencies in climatic trends over the whole region. A climate comparable to that of the present day, perhaps warmer and drier, predominates until late Roman times, followed by a period up to 150 BP (AD 1800) or so, in which abundant evidence exists from historical sources and geomorphic data for greater rainfall, often associated with suggestions of cooler climate but also for severe drought. Less clear is a possible interval of warmer conditions around 950 BP (AD 1000).

It is well worth comparing this summary with Lamb's reconstruction of the climatic sequence, based predominantly on north-west European evidence:

> There was a gradual, fluctuating recovery of warmth and a tendency towards drier climate in Europe over the 1000 years after 600 BC, particu-

> larly after 100 BC, leading to a period of warmth . . . around AD 400. After some reversion to colder and wetter climates in the next 3–4 centuries, sharply renewed warming from about AD 800 led to an important warm epoch which seems to have culminated around AD 900–1200 in Greenland and AD 11–1300 in Europe. In these few centuries the climates in the countries concerned evidently became briefly nearly as warm as in the postglacial warmest times . . . (but) the Little Ice Ages centuries . . . followed. (1977, p.374)

It is important for the Little Ice Age that Lamb argues for conditions 'when the extent of ice on the Arctic seas and of ice and snow on land seems to have been greater than at any time since the last major glaciation' and with weather features which 'indicated a significantly wide range of year to year variability in the Little Ice Age, which seems to have been associated with a reduced frequency of westerly winds in Europe and increases in the frequency of winds from most other directions', producing 'alternations of extreme seasons' (Lamb 1979).

In general, Lamb considers the Sub-atlantic to be marked by a southward shift in the belts of climate, but with pronounced fluctuations of warmth and cold, dryness and moistness, associated both with fluctuations in this zonal shift (*Model One*), and with the effects of blocking of the westerlies, either by expanded subtropical anticyclones in warming phases, or polar highs in cooling phases (*Model Two*). Compare, for example, his analysis of the Early Medieval Warm Era:

> All these observations of the medieval period could probably be explained by a circulation pattern in which the northern hemisphere subtropical anticyclones were on the whole displaced somewhat to the north during the time of warm climate in Europe, Greenland and North America. During most of the time the middle latitudes westerly winds were presumably weaker and less prevalent in latitudes between 40° and 60°N than now or than they became from AD 1200–1300 onwards. While central and northern Europe were enjoying more frequent anticyclonic influence, and rather sluggish westerlies or more variable winds, the Mediterranean zone . . . may well have experienced more frequent cyclonic activity of various types – e.g. slow moving cut-off cyclones and khamsin depressions [cf. our 'bitrack' and 'Sudan-Sahel' trans-Sahara depressions]. (Lamb 1977, p.440)

If one is seeking confirmatory evidence of northern hemisphere – and indeed global – cooling, and hence expansion of the circumpolar vortex in the Dark Ages and the later Medieval to Early Modern period, the evidence is impressive (May 1979, La Marche 1974, Porter 1979).

Finally, some further discussion of the interesting phenomenon of the Younger Fill is required. Despite accumulated criticism of this seemingly too simple alluvial formation, the continuing accretion of consistent dates for the Fill (cf. recently Roberts 1979) appears to be stimulating a rethink in favour of Vita-Finzi's original dating, allowing for more localised earlier formations

(Eisma 1978; Davidson, pers. comm.). Tentative diachronic appearance of the Fill in different latitudes has also led Vita-Finzi to elaborate on his southward cyclonic displacement model, with the most extreme displacement belonging to the time of the Little Ice Age and hence suiting the first clear traces of the Fill in Arabia (Vita-Finzi 1976).

But the origin of the Fill cannot simply be assigned to stormtrack displacement south, for, as we have seen, this could be argued to have occurred recurrently throughout the Holocene in the Mediterranean latitudes. This may be an opportunity to seek some middle ground between a purely climatic causation and those who have persistently ascribed the Fill to human erosion. The obvious criticism of the erosion viewpoint has been the clear evidence from archaeology and history of considerable deforestation and continual slopewash from agricultural activity, dating well back into the Atlantic period in most countries concerned, long before the main dates for alluvial deposition.

Martin Bell's research (see this volume) into the history of English chalkland hillwash is a major contribution to the source and chronology of colluvia, and to a lesser extent alluvia. But there are a number of problems apparent from his exposition to which I would like to draw attention. First, from the viewpoint of an archaeologist, if major land clearance and widespread mixed farming were seen to be responsible for the bulk of the European colluvia and alluvia, I would expect this to be rampant in the Neolithic era, the later fourth and throughout the third millennia bc; but dates obtained on both types of deposit commence generally in the second millennium and increase into the first and beyond. Yet the North American sediment-supply graphs discussed by Martin Bell exhibited a remarkable peak of erosion immediately after clearance then a drop to a much lower level hereafter: there will be many Neolithic specialists who won't take kindly to a vision of Neolithic southern Britain populated by a few busloads of people living in small clearings in the primeval woodlands! Now we have exactly the same sequence in the Mediterranean region, with clear evidence for major forest clearance and dense farming populations from the Neolithic onwards, but the vast bulk of the alluvial aggradations in valleys dated to Late Roman times and later. And we now also have well-dated colluvial deposits there from the Bronze Age onwards.

Secondly, I think we now have to move much further into understanding the processes involved in erosion, slopewash, and river alluviation. Martin Bell seemed to indicate that erosion downslope was a direct precursor of river alluviation. In fact this is commonly not the case, and colluvial deposits accumulate and remain up against walls as lynchets, or stabilise at a certain angle of repose on hillslopes. But even if there is enough later sediment or run-off, pushing these further, colluvial sediment that reaches river systems need not be deposited as a terrace deposit or aggradation. In fact, in my experience in Britain, and that of many other people interested in British river terraces, most sediment now entering streams is in quantities within the competence of those bodies of water to shift continually downstream to base level, a lake or the sea. So at the present day we are not usually seeing erosion building up river aggradation, and the late prehistoric and historic alluvial material exists as a freestanding terrace above the presently incised course. Only if the input of sediment is far beyond stream capacity will alluviation normally develop along the full length of a river system. Likewise, Mediterranean Younger Fill is a fossil deposit above modern incising streams.

It is in response to these considerations that, as part of an interdisciplinary project in central Greece, we have been trying to achieve a more detailed explanation of the subtle interaction of soil erosion, colluviation, alluviation, human activity and climatic change. We now believe that from the first clearance of open woodland in Greece, and even before in the driest regions, there existed exposed soils that were available for rain and wind erosion. Human cultivation and grazing would have furthered the natural processes of hillwash, creating a continual creep of colluvial sediment on all but the gentler slopes. In many areas terracing will have been an early adaptation to this threat, but elsewhere the material either came to rest as it accumulated at a shallower angle on the hillslope, or at the break of slope below, or else found its way into the river systems. But the extremely limited exposures of inland alluvial sediments dating to the pre-Classical period, in contrast to the dense build-up at the coast, argues for the amounts in stream bedload being within stream capacity to transport onwards.

All this changes dramatically in Late Roman and Medieval times, with the build-up along virtually every Mediterranean stream of a continuous sequence of well-bedded alluvium generally 1–3 metres high. We can be fairly certain that this is not the time of too dense a rural population and an unparalleled intensity of agriculture, ruling out the direct ploughwash theory. Some have suggested that the known late antique depopulation meant massive field abandonments and neglect of terrace walls, thus releasing centuries if not millennia of pent-up soil to choke streams. Our project botanists reject this, as it is clear that abandoned terraces are very rapidly colonised and stabilised by the ever-present ruderal plants and scrub that occupy terrace peripheries. A possible key may lie in our observations in 1980 in the 'Theban Badlands': here we can see a district of soft rock hill-land, quite typical for deposits favoured by early European farmers, betraying the massive erosion cones of Badlands topography. It is clear that till recently there was very active movement on all these slopes into the valley below. But also clear is the fact that all this has now stopped and vegetation is colonising and stabilising the whole area. It is my hypothesis at present that in the not too distant past the local climate was highly variable, with severe droughts inhibiting scrub colonisation and loosening the topsoil, alternating with dramatic rainfall, producing these great colluvial sediment flows; such a climate may have characterised the latter part of the Little Ice Age in the Mediterranean up till the middle of the last century; the current less extreme climate is encouraging scrub growth and is insufficient to push further sediments downhill. Archaeological evidence suggests that this colluvial sequence is largely post-Classical in date. The juxtaposition of abnormal wet and dry seasons we have already seen to be both feasible for earlier periods of deteriorating climate in Europe and a recorded feature of the Mediterranean historical record.

The peak periods of British hillwash and river alluviation, may, perhaps, reflect a similar interaction of a pronouncedly variable Sub-boreal climate, a possible concentration of wet conditions in the early Sub-atlantic and mid first millennium AD, and accumulated field erosion and slopewash.

Finally, what link, if any, could be made between Mediterranean civilisational decline and climatic change? Both Vita-Finzi and I (Vita-Finzi 1969a; Bintliff 1977, 1981), have suggested that the loss of hill-land and valley fields due to enhanced erosion, poorly controlled, aggrading rivers, and the decline in warmth that could have had deleterious effects on crops (cf. the frost killing of Provence oranges and olives during the Little Ice Age cited by Lamb 1977, p.466; Pichard 1979), must have been significant in the decline of the Roman and Byzantine empires. The suggestions of Lamb on pronounced meridional flow and blocking régimes, to be associated with this southward displacement, whilst accounting for apparent contradictions in the Mediterranean evidence for this period, also indicate a further source of problems for human communities, with the unparalleled and unpredictable shifts from year to year of drought and flooding, parching and freezing.

REFERENCES

Barcelo, M. (1979) Locust plagues in mid-west Hispania in the 6th and 7th centuries as a climatic factor. Paper presented at the 1979 *International Conference on Climate and History,* University of East Anglia.

Barker, G. *et al.* (1978) A Classical landscape in Molise, *Papers of the British School at Rome* 46, 35-51.

Bell, B. (1971) The Dark Ages in Ancient History: 1. The First Dark Age in Egypt, *Am. J. Archaeol.* 75, 1-26.

— (1975) Climate and the history of Egypt: the Middle Kingdom, *Am. J. Archaeol.* 79, 223-69.

Besançon, J. (1980) Stratigraphie et chronologie du Quaternaire continental du Proche Orient. Paper given at the 1980 *Lyons Symposium on the Prehistory of the Near East.*

Bintliff, J. L. (1975) Mediterranean alluviation: new evidence from Archaeology, *Proc. Prehistoric Soc.* 41, 78-84.

— (1977) *Natural Environment and Human Settlement in Prehistoric Greece.* British Archaeological Reports, Suppl. Ser. 28 (1-2), Oxford.

— (1981) Archaeology and the Holocene evolution of coastal plains in the Aegean and Circum-Mediterranean, in Brothwell, D. & Dimbleby, G. (eds) *Environmental Aspects of Coasts and Islands.* British Archaeological Reports, Int. Series, 94, Oxford.

Bottema, S. (1977) A pollen diagram from the Syrian Anti Lebanon, *Paléorient* 3, 259-68.

— (1978) The Late Glacial in the eastern Mediterranean and the Near East, in Brice, W. C., ed. (1978) 15-28.

Brice, W. C., ed. (1978) *The Environmental History of the Near and Middle East.* London: Academic Press.

Brookes, I. A. & Dennell, R. W. (1977) Spatial and temporal relations between geomorphic elements and human occupation in part of Central West Iran. Paper presented to the 10th INQUA Congress, Birmingham.

Brooks, C. E. P. (1949) *Climate Through the Ages*. 2nd ed. London.
Bryson, R. A. *et al.* (1974) Drought and the decline of Mycenae, *Antiquity* 48, 46-50.
Butzer, K. W. (1978) Environmental history of the Near East since the Last Pleniglacial. Paper given at the Tübingen Conference on *The History of Environmental Conditions in South West Asia*.
Carpenter, R. (1966) *Discontinuity in Greek Civilisation*. Cambridge: University Press.
Crown, A. D. (1972) Towards a reconstruction of the climate of Palestine 8000 BC–0 BC, *J. Near Eastern Studies* 31, 312-30.
Davidson, D. A. (1971) Geomorphology and prehistoric settlement of the plain of Drama, *Rev. Géomorph. Dyn.* 20, 22-6.
— *et al.* (1976) Erosion and prehistory in Melos: a preliminary note, *J. Archaeological Science* 219-27.
— (1980) Erosion in Greece during the first and second millennia BC, in Cullingford, R. A. *et al.* (eds) *Timescales in Geomorphology*, 143-58. London: John Wiley.
Dayton, J. (1975) The problem of climatic change in the Arabian Peninsula, *Proc. Seminar for Arabian Studies* 5, 33-60.
De Cardi, B., Vita-Finzi, C. & Coles, A. (1975) Archaeological survey in Northern Oman, *East and West* 25, 9-75.
Deuser, W. G. *et al.* (1976) Glacial and pluvial periods: their relationship revealed by Pleistocene sediments of the Red Sea and Gulf of Aden, *Science* 191, 1168-70.
Dickinson, O. T. P. K. (1974) Drought and the decline of Mycenae: some comments, *Antiquity* 48, 228-30.
Diester-Haass, L. (1973) Holocene climate in the Persian Gulf as deduced from grain-size and pteropod distribution, *Marine Geology* 14, 207-23.
Dufaure, J. J. (1976) La terrasse holocène d'Olympie et ses equivalents méditerranéens, *Bull. Assoc. Géogr. Franç.* 1976, 85-94.
Eisma, D. (1964) Stream deposition in the Mediterranean area in historical times, *Nature* 203, 1061.
— (1978) Stream deposition and erosion by the eastern shore of the Aegean, in Brice, W. C. (ed.) *The Environmental History of the Near and Middle East*, 67-81.
Erinc, S. (1978) Changes in the physical environment in Turkey since the end of the Last Glacial, in Brice, W. C. (ed.) *The Environmental History of the Near and Middle East*, 87-110.
Evenari, M. *et al.* (1971) *The Negev*. Harvard: University Press.
Farrand, W. R. (1979) Blank on the Pleistocene map, *Geogr. J.* May 1979, 548-54.
Flohn, H. & Nicholson, S. (1979) Climatic fluctuations in the arid belt of the 'Old World' since the last glacial maximum. Paper circulated at the 1979 *International Conference on Climate and History*, University of East Anglia.
Goldberg, P. (1980) Late Quaternary stratigraphy of Israel: an eclectic view. Paper given at the 1980 Lyons *Symposium on the Prehistory of the Near East*.
Griswold, W. J. (1979) Climatic variation and the social revolutions of seventeenth century Anatolia. Paper given at the 1979 *International Conference on Climate and History*, University of East Anglia.
Guinis, S. C. (1976) New evidence on the stability of the Greek climate in historical times, *Praktika tes Akademias Athenon* 51, 323-9.
Hecht, A. D. (1979) Palaeoclimatic research: status and opportunities, *Quaternary Res.* 12, 6-17.

Kirkby, M. J. (1977) Land and water resources of the Deh Luran and Khuzistan Plains, Appx. 1, in F. Hole (ed.) *Studies in the Archaeological History of the Deh Luran Plain, The Excavation of Chagha Sefid*, Memoirs of the Museum of Anthropology, University of Michigan, 9.

La Marche, V. C. (1974) Palaeoclimatic inferences from long tree-ring records, *Science* 183, 1043-8.

Lamb, H. H. (1967) Review of Rhys Carpenter, *Discontinuity in Greek Civilisation*, *Antiquity* 41, 233-4.

— (1977) *Climate: Present, Past and Future. 2. Climatic History and the Future.* London: Methuen.

— (1978a) The variability of climate, in Fryendahl, K. (ed.) *The Nordic Symposium on Climatic Changes and Related Problems*, 116-44. Copenhagen.

— (1978b) Towards an understanding of climatic change, in Frydendahl, K. (ed.) *The Nordic Symposium on Climatic Changes and Related Problems*, 181-204. Copenhagen.

— (1979) An approach to the study of the development of climate and its impact on human affairs. A paper given at the 1979 *International Conference on Climate and History*, University of East Anglia.

Lamb, H. H. & Dickinson, R. R. (1975) Recent hydrometeorological events in the North Atlantic sector, *Bird Study* 22, 142.

Lipschitz, N. *et al.* (1979) Fluctuations in the aridity line in Israel during the Late Bronze Age. Paper given at the 1979 *International Conference on Climate and History*, University of East Anglia.

McGhee, R. (1979) Archaeological evidence for climatic change during the past 5000 years. Paper given at the 1979 *International Conference on Climate and History*, University of East Anglia.

Magaritz, M. & Kaufman, A. (1973) Changes in the isotopic composition of East Mediterranean seawater during the Holocene, *Nature* 243, 461-4.

May, R. M. (1979) Arctic animals and climatic changes, *Nature* 281, 177-8.

Meigs, P. (1961) Some geographical factors in the Peloponnesian War, *Geogr. Rev.* 31, 370-81.

Oates, J. & D. (1976) *The Rise of Civilisation*. Oxford: Elsevier-Phaidon.

Olausson, E. & Olsson, I. U. (1969) Varve stratigraphy in a core from the Gulf of Aden, *Palaeogeogr., Palaeoclimat., Palaeoecol.* 6, 87-103.

Pichard, G. (1979) The part played by climate in the social and agricultural stagnation of Provence 1680-1718. Paper given at the 1979 *International Conference on Climate and History*, University of East Anglia.

Porter, S. C. (1979) Glaciological evidence of Holocene climate change. Paper given at the 1979 *International Conference on Climate and History*, University of East Anglia.

Potter, T. W. (1979) *The Changing Landscape of South Etruria*. London: Elek.

Price-Williams, D. (1973) Environmental archaeology in the Western Negev, *Nature* 242, 501-3.

Raphael, C. (1973) Late Quaternary changes in coastal Elis, Greece, *Geogr. Rev.* 63, 73-89.

Roberts, N. (1979) The location and environment of Knossos, *Ann. British School at Athens* 74, 231-41.

Rognon, P. & Williams, M. A. J. (1977) Late Quaternary climatic changes in Australia and North Africa: a preliminary interpretation, *Palaeogeogr., Palaeoclimat., Palaeoecol.* 21, 285-327.

Rothlisberger, F. (1979) Dendroclimatological chronologies in the Holocene period. Paper given at the 1979 *International Conference on Climate and History*, University of East Anglia.

Schoeli, M. & Faber, E. (1978) New isotopic evidence for the origin of Red Sea brines, *Nature* 275, 436-8.
Shaw, B. D. (1978) Climate, environment and prehistory in the Sahara, *World Archaeology* 8, 133-49.
Vita-Finzi, C. (1969a) *The Mediterranean Valleys*. Cambridge: University Press.
— (1969b) Late Quaternary alluvial chronology of Iran, *Geol. Rundschau* 58, 951-73.
— (1969c) Late Quaternary continental deposits of central and western Turkey, *Man* 4, 605-19.
— (1975) Quaternary deposits in the Iranian Makran, *Geogr. J.* 141, 415-20.
— (1976) Diachronism in Old World alluvial sequences, *Nature* 263, 218-19.
Vita-Finzi, C. & Copeland, L. (1978) Archaeological dating of geological deposits in Jordan, *Levant* 10, 10-25.
Van Zeist, W. & Bottema, S. (1977) Palynological investigations in Western Iran, *Palaeohistoria* 19, 19-85.
— (1980) Palynological evidence for the climatic history of the Near East, 50,000–6000 B P. Paper given at the 1980 Lyons *Symposium on the Prehistory of the Near East*.
Weikinn, C. (1958) *Quellentexte zur Witterungsgeschichte Europas*, Vol. 1. Berlin: Akademie Verlag.
Winstanley, D. (1973) Recent rainfall trends in Africa, the Middle East and India, *Nature* 243, 464-5.
Wright, H. E. (1968) Climatic change in Mycenaean Greece, *Antiquity* 42, 123-7.

Environmental conditions and land cultivation during the Urnfield Bronze Age in central Europe

The increasing significance of unintentional and unwanted environmental problems, as well as of the methodical and systematic moulding of the environment in the historical present, provides to an increasing degree a subtle knowledge of the relationships between human society, especially production, on the one hand, and the natural environment of this society and its production on the other. A continuous 'exchange of material between society and nature' (cf. Neef 1969) is bound up with the production process, independent of the stage of its development, and this mutual correlation between society and nature is, along with production, subject to continual development. With the precise investigation of these relationships and their development, not only are deeper insights won into the causality of the sequence of events in landscape history and the socio-economic basis of past phases of social evolution, but at the same time we obtain glimpses into the natural reaction models of particular intentional and unintentional attacks on the 'natural budget'. These glimpses are invaluable for trend analyses on the present-day development of cultural landscapes and therefore for prognostic statements about future environmental conditions. The intensive investigation of environmental relationships of prehistoric and early historic populations through the routine incorporation of scientific evidence is therefore of fundamental importance – and not only for the specialist disciplines participating, that is, not only for prehistoric archaeology and sciences devoted to landscape history, but also beyond and above this, for the solution of present-day environmental problems and for a methodical moulding of the environment in both present and future – matters that are highly topical both socially and in terms of political economics.

The increasing international topicality and importance of such considerations is complemented when, for example, within the framework of the tasks of the International Union for Quaternary Research (INQUA), its Subcommission for the Euro-Siberian Holocene devoted its own Symposium in Uppsala to the theme 'To study the past – predicting the future' (1975). Fundamental aspects of matters considered there can be grasped with exceptional clarity through the example of the central European Urnfield Bronze Age.

Their systematic investigation embraces two separate tasks:

1) The influencing of social circumstances and developments by natural effects and changes;

2) The moulding and changing of geographical circumstances by social factors.

The investigation of these must take account of the fact that both in the

Figure 1. Buried humus horizons of rendzina profiles from a sequence of Holocene calcareous freshwater deposits (freshwater carbonates of tufa type) in the Pennickental near Jena-Wöllnitz (district Jena, Thuringia). Not far from the foot of the adjacent slope bordering the valley on the north, scree from the lower shelly limestone seals the Holocene layers. This scree, covering the earlier Holocene deposits, peters out towards the valley centre. By contrast both the humus horizons that underlie the scree continue right across the valley profile. From the lower of these two humus horizons, as well as from the fill of pits cut from this soil into the calcareous freshwater deposit, comes datable settlement pottery of the Urnfield Bronze Age (Schrickel 1957; Mania & Preuss 1975, 27).

development of human society and in the changes of its natural environment, independent regularities are at work which are only able to acquire influence on each other as a result of the raw material exchange between society and nature (mentioned above). For the central European Urnfield Bronze Age these circumstances can now, as a result of new research results, be outlined.

The first contribution in this connection was through the systematic stratigraphic investigation of the sequence of layers of Holocene calcareous freshwater deposits in central Europe by Jäger (1965a); by means of which differentiated *statements about climatic history* for the Holocene landscape development in the dry areas of the central European interior were possible. These assertions rely on the fact that calcareous freshwater deposits themselves represent subaquatic depositions whose development was interrupted during specific periods in the Holocene warm period on numerous occasions, when it was superseded by periods of terrestrial soil formation. This interchange between subaquatic sedimentation and terrestrial soil formation exhibits in numerous deposits of Holocene calcareous freshwater sediments, attributed to various

Figure 2. Buried humus horizon of a rendzina profile in a sequence of Holocene calcareous freshwater deposits (freshwater carbonates of tufa type) near the site of Evetesi Malom, not far from Jabloňov (district Rožňava) in the south Slovak Karst, archaeologically datable by settlement pottery of the Urnfield Bronze Age.

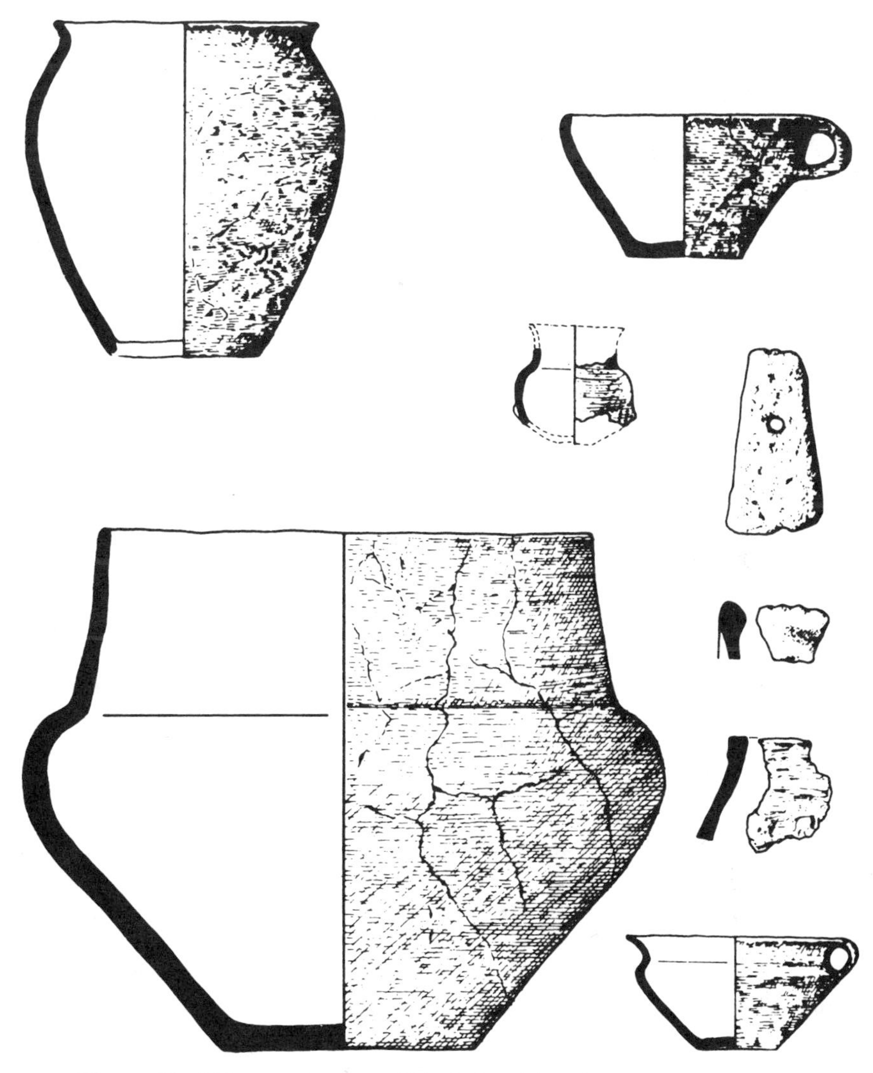

Figure 3. Urnfield pottery from a pit fill in the Pennickental sequence near Jena-Wöllnitz (district Jena, Thuringia). After Schrickel 1957.

types and regions in central Europe, a widespread synchroneity which can only be explained through climatic causes.

The interpretation of this finding in terms of climatic history by Jäger (1965, 1970) proceeds from the assumption that terrestrial soil formation in a previously subaquatic sedimentation area presupposes in all cases its drying-out, that is in the case of standing water a lowering of the water level, in the case of flowing water a reduced water flow which, for its part, must go back to reduced spring output. This interpretation permits three possible explanations for the observed widespread synchroneity of such processes, namely

Figure 4. The travertine knoll of Banická, near Hozelec (district Poprad, Slovakia), where a buried humus horizon of a rendzina profile is dated by Urnfield pottery.

1) through reduction of the mean (annual and especially summer) precipitation aggregates;

2) through increase in the mean (especially summer) evaporation figures;

3) through a combination of both factors.

This interpretation in climatic history terms of lithostratigraphic and pedostratigraphic findings, whose synchronisation can preferably be assured by means of the archaeological dating of buried soil horizons in the sequence of Holocene calcareous freshwater sediments (figures 1–4), is justified by its ability to be correlated with other lithostratigraphic, pedostratigraphic and biostratigraphic observations of central European Holocene research:

1) The demonstration of synchronous displacements of the relative shares of wood species in pollen diagrams that are determined to be indicative of moist or dry situations (e.g. alder or pine) in those areas of central Europe where calcareous freshwater sediments are either not available for stratigraphic investigation or have not been so investigated (Müller 1969).

2) The demonstration of changing and synchronously fluctuating ground water levels through dated pedostratigraphic finds in river meadows and valleys in the north central European inland plain (Breddin and Buck 1970; Jäger and Laser 1971; a case in point in figure 5).

3) The demonstration of synchronous coast-line displacements and sea-level changes in the coastal areas of north-west central Europe (Hageman and Jäger 1969, Jäger and Kliewe 1969, Jäger and Hageman 1971).

Holocene depositional sequences in scree accumulations at the foot of steep rock walls, and around cave mouths in karst landscapes of the central European highland zone, demonstrate further a repeated change between strengthening and weakening of rock fall processes in the Holocene, and indicate their possible arrangement into the same chronological contexts (Kukla and Ložek 1968).

To the findings of Holocene stratigraphy can be added the observations of archaeological research in central Europe:

Figure 5. Profile at the site of Barzlin, near Lübbenau in the Spreewald (Breddin and Buck 1970). Buried settlement horizons of the Urnfield Bronze Age and Early Iron Age partially overlie one another in the exposed profile; in places one can observe the intercalation of fluviatile sand. In addition a G_0 horizon (not clearly visible in a black-and-white photograph) at the top level of the Urnfield (lower) settlement horizon is cut by settlement pits of the Early Iron Age (upper) settlement horizon, showing a temporally restricted high groundwater table that falls chronologically between the two.

1) The phases of Holocene landscape development in central Europe indicated as dry periods manifest themselves as times of a) preference for fortifications (figures 6 and 7), b) preference for the settlement of floodplains and depressions, frequently with settlements below present-day ground water-level (figure 5), and c) preference for cave utilisation.

2) The so-called lake-dwellings in the central European Alpine foothills fall mostly in the same period of time.

3) In particular central European landscapes with sensitive ground-water régimes, for instance as a result of karst development, particular sections of prehistoric and early historic settlement development are, according to the findings especially of Paret (1961) in the Swabian Alb, represented by dense find distributions only in valleys, while others occur only on upland plateaux. Here the finds originating in the valleys represent the dry phases of Holocene climate development in central Europe.

From the preceding data, an indication of fluctuations in dryness in post-glacial landscape development in central Europe, attested both stratigraphically and in terms of settlement history, is derived. This characterises the Urnfield Bronze Age with especial clearness. This period of time is represented

Figure 6. The Házmburk (Hasenburg) near Klapý (district Litoměřice) in the central Bohemian massif. This site not only has the prominent remains of a medieval fortification on its summit, but has also produced on its slopes rich Urnfield material of the Knovíz culture (Bouzek and Koutecký 1966). This is one of the many Urnfield hill-forts that, in the Carpathians, reach into the montane zone at heights up to and above 1000 m.

in the deposition sequences of Holocene calcareous freshwater sediments on many sites by especially strongly marked soil formation. In all cases we are dealing in soil-typological terms with an A/C soil on a carbonate substratum, that is a rendzina (cf. Kubiena 1953, pp.211–29, pl.xiii–xvi). Other dry phases in the central European inland Holocene are also stratigraphically attested by means of the humus horizons from rendzina profiles, but the earlier ones, and especially the Neolithic dry horizons, are attested less often and in many instances with less strongly developed humus horizons (figures 1–4).

This especially frequent and intensive formation of Urnfield-period dry soils in the depositional sequences of Holocene calcareous freshwater sediments in central Europe corresponds to a notable frequency of archaeological finds in the humus horizon, that is of human occupation of floodplain and other valley sites near water at a time which stretches in terms of south German Bronze Age chronology from about the end of period Br D up to the beginning of Ha C in Reinecke's (1911, 1924) terminology. The pedological findings permit alternative interpretations: they could be taken as documenting either an unusual intensity or an above-average duration of this dry period. Archaeological datings so far available permit one to come down in favour of the latter interpretation without necessarily ruling out an unusual intensity of this dry

Figure 7. An example of increased soil erosion and scree accumulation in the Urnfield period from Litoměřice (north Bohemia). A buried humus horizon of a chernozem profile from Holocene loess-derived deposits is datable by two pottery associations: the horizon itself contained decorated Slavic pottery of the ninth to tenth centuries (at least one sherd), while from the underlying layer came pieces of redeposited basalt from the central Bohemian massif as well as settlement pottery of Urnfield to Hallstatt date. This provides dated evidence for the redeposition of the basalt scree.

phase as well.

In agreement with synchronous coastline displacements in the north-western part of continental Europe it has been found from a survey by Hageman and Jäger (1969) that Holocene dry phases in central Europe normally last for a few decades to centuries, whereas those of the Urnfield period between c. 1250 and 650 BC (historical) embraced more than half a millennium. On the other hand towards its end it too can be subdivided by means of a short-lived damp phase. It was on the basis of these findings that Jäger's (1969) attempt to limit the chronostratigraphical term 'Sub-boreal' to just this period was founded, while the usual period of Holocene landscape development traditionally assigned to the Sub-boreal, as a result of particular climatic factors held in common with the late Atlantic, of the same tradition as the so-called Epi-atlantic, should be combined in a separate stratigraphic unit. This is marked in the mollusc diagrams by the largest number of woodland species and the simultaneous extinction of elements of the *Ruderatus* fauna, and can consequently be set parallel to the woodland optimum of the Postglacial (Ložek 1974). It is noteworthy that in the chernozem areas the molluscan fauna never achieved the level of the woodland optimum, a fact that relates to its Neolithic settlement. A precise biostratigraphic definition of the Epi-atlantic can of course only be given after a corresponding phasing of this period by means of pollen diagrams.

The attribution of the central European Urnfield period in terms of climatic history thus leads to the discovery that this period of prehistoric cultural and settlement development in central Europe constitutes the longest and probably also the most intensive dry phase of the Postglacial.

Such an attribution has initially two implications:

1) In comparison with other periods of postglacial climatic development one must reckon with a reduced availability of moisture for the duration of the Urnfield Bronze Age. This is especially so by comparison with the preceding Tumulus Bronze Age which, according to lithostratigraphic and biostratigraphic findings, embraces an especially damp period of Holocene landscape development, in complete contrast to the Urnfield period.

2) The relevance for landscape history and ecology that the changed moisture supply at the change from Tumulus to Urnfield Bronze Age brought may be considered greatest above all in those areas of central Europe where a disadvantage in terms of present-day precipitation can also be recognised. This is especially true for areas with average annual precipitation rates under 500 mm that are today characterised by chernozem soils. Under agricultural conditions without the possibility of modern techniques like irrigation the availability of land and its potential for plant production must have been considerably restricted in areas with a relatively short moisture supply by a further reduction. In the case of the Urnfield Bronze Age this effect must have been especially noticeable since a particularly wet period preceded it; on the other hand this would have permitted a widespread agricultural development in those regions that appear at a disadvantage in terms of rainfall, both today and in prehistory.

In connection with these assertions one can point especially to the naturally unfavourable situation of the Pannonian Basin as far as present-day precipitation rate is concerned, for this area has been claimed on the basis of archaeological observations, above all by Kimmig (1964), as the area of origin of the Urnfield movement with all its historical implications. In fact the Pannonian Basin belongs precisely to those areas of central Europe in which a dry phase must have had especial ecological relevance. A comparable effect is, however, to be observed not only in the Pannonian Basin but also in other chernozem areas of central Europe. This invariably concerns early settlement landscapes in which for example a full development of woodland communities in the molluscan fauna has never taken place (Vašátko and Ložek 1973). In spite of this, relatively numerous woodland species appear even in these landscapes during the Epi-atlantic woodland maximum, which, however, finally disappear during the Urnfield period and never again emerge, while during the same period steppe species, including modern invaders, become dominant. Things are similar on the edges of the chernozem area, where the woodland species are replaced by open ground communities (e.g. Velký Hubenov in north Bohemia – Smolíková and Ložek 1973); and in the warm dry hilly areas that are characterised by a change to steppe-like conditions – a phenomenon that turns up in places in wooded areas today (e.g. the Slovak Karst – Prošek and Ložek 1956; the Bohemian Karst – Ložek 1974). In isolated mountain groups inside the chernozem areas the woodland fauna was extensively destroyed at this time (Pavlov Hills – Vašátko and Ložek 1971). If one goes to higher elevations, however, these phenomena become less noticeable, a fact that relates to the faunal sequences as well as to sediment and soil development. In the montane zone of the Carpathians the climatic changes we have described are no longer – with few exceptions – clearly represented and are indicated mostly by a gradual fall in the numbers of woodland species – a fact that can of course be attributed to other climatic factors, such as a drop in temperature.

This undramatic development in the montane zone or at even higher elevations can be explained by supposing that these high altitudinal zones remained sufficiently damp even during dry fluctuations in the Sub-boreal, including the period of the Urnfield Bronze Age, for favourable living conditions to be available for a closed upland wood. This situation is in complete contrast to that in the immediately adjacent submontane zone whose original middle Holocene woods fell victim to grassland expansion in many places during the Late Bronze Age, and on plateaux with favourable bedrock (limestone, dolomite) gave way to typical xerophilous species. The best examples of this are the karst heathlands of the Slovak Karst or the Drevěník in the Zips area. In other areas the comparable steppe formation only took place later, above all in the early Slav period or during the medieval Wallachian settlement phase (Slovakian central Carpathians – the Choč Mountains, Sul'ov Rocks etc.) (figure 8).

Certain stratigraphically fixed Holocene finds deserve further mention in this connection, for instance in the comparison of the sequence of layers of Holocene calcareous freshwater sediments in the Thuringian Saale area and in the south Slovakian Karst which could be taken as implying that the duration and/or intensity of the dry phases increased directionally towards continental south-east Europe, that is in the case of central Europe towards the Pannonian Basin. These findings, however, require further investigation. Still, one can, from the results presented here, gather the extent to which Holocene stratigraphy can contribute to the classification of the causes of the Urnfield movement. No less important, however, are the possibilities these Holocene stratigraphies provide for investigating their consequences. Paret (1946, 1961) has already pointed to settlement displacements in connection with pre- and proto-historic climatic fluctuations in central Europe, using the example of the Swabian Alb. In the same area Seitz (1951, 1952, 1956) was the first to demonstrate, more than twenty years ago, the regular interchange of subaquatic sediments and terrestrial soils in the layer sequence of Holocene calcareous freshwater deposits, whose widespread validity for central Europe was demonstrated by means of the more recent investigations by Jäger (1965a, 1970). However, the alteration of settlement boundaries through earlier popu-

Figure 8. View of a karstified landscape, showing the characteristic vegetation that has existed since the drastic deforestation of the Urnfield and Hallstatt periods, near Hrhov (district Rožňava), in the Turňa valley in the south Slovak Karst. In the foreground extends a calcareous tufa accumulation in whose deposition sequence the Urnfield dry phase is attested by a buried humus horizon of a rendzina profile.

lations achieved special dimensions in two stages of postglacial settlement history in central Europe, namely during the course of medieval land improvement on the one hand and during the Urnfield Bronze Age on the other. In the fringe areas of central Europe, which were temporarily included in the Roman Empire, this period can be included as a third, comparable phase into this process of alteration. Holocene stratigraphic sequences and the evidence of intensified settlement activity have been subjected to the first systematic investigations: for the Roman period by Vita-Finzi (1969) and for the Medieval period by Jäger (1962, 1973). For the Urnfield Bronze Age, on the other hand, matters have rested with the discovery by Jäger (1962) of striking analogies to the medieval land improvement.

However, a more precise characterisation of the consequences of the Urnfield movement in central Europe, both in terms of settlement history and in terms of the cultural landscape, is already possible. It requires the conjunction of archaeological knowledge and recent scientific investigations over a regional Holocene landscape development into an overall picture, which may be outlined here by way of conclusion. Several very informative building blocks for this overall picture are already available:

1) The migration of population groups from the subcontinental to the continental loess areas in south-eastern central Europe, and especially from the

Pannonian Basin (Kimmig 1964).

2) Increased density of settlement in the westerly situated basins of the central European highland zone (*Mittelgebirgszone*) (e.g. in north-west Bohemia: Bouzek 1966, 1969a, 1969b, pp.84ff.), as well as the opening up of new settlement areas in both Old- and New-moraine landscapes of north-western central Europe, with their suboceanic to oceanic conditions, brought about by the incorporation of relatively dry sandy soils (Redlich 1958).

3) More widespread inclusion of valleys near water in the settlement area (e.g. in south-west central Europe: Paret 1961), including those which survive at present below the ground-water level, especially on the north central European lowlands (Breddin and Buck 1970; Jäger and Laser 1971) (figure 5).

4) The erection of shore settlements (the so-called 'lake-dwellings') in the lake-shore areas of the central European Alpine foothills.

5) The partial desertion of plateau areas naturally poor in water on karst-developed pre-Quaternary limestones in the central European highland zone (e.g. Swabian Alb: Paret 1961).

6) Clear expansion of the settlement area, especially in hilly regions, also in the central European highland zone (e.g. Saxon Vogtland: Coblenz 1954), as well as in the montane zone of the central European high mountains (e.g. western Carpathians: Ložek 1973, Horedt 1974).

7) More widespread erection of fortifications in all settlement areas (with a so-called 'fort-horizon' (*Burgenhorizont*) in Neumann's (1954) sense), through the incorporation of mountain ranges in the montane altitudinal zone (Horedt 1974) (figures 6, 7).

8) More widespread occurrence of regionally foreign cultural elements and groups in differing areas of central Europe (e.g. the so-called 'Fremdgruppen' period in Saxony: Grünberg 1943, Coblenz 1952).

9) The introduction of a cultigen new to the region, the broad or horse-bean (*Vicia faba* L.), which after a distribution that was previously Mediterranean and Sub-Mediterranean achieved within a few centuries a distribution over the whole of central Europe (Jäger 1965b), reached as far as Scandinavia (Hjelmqvist 1955) and in particular areas of central Europe (like the Lower Lausitz) is connected remarkably often not with settlement finds but with graves (Jäger 1965b) (figure 9).

10) Increased erosion in the newly incorporated settlement areas especially in higher elevations, but also in the lowlands, recognisable by virtue of the increased fine clastic sedimentation of the rivers draining the areas, demonstrating the colonisation or extension of areas used for agriculture (Jäger 1962).

11) Increased deposition of coarse scree in mountainous regions through the incorporation of higher settlement elevations up to the montane zone, which points to an extension of deforestation and the conversion to pasture of the higher mountain ranges (Ložek 1976; cf. Vašátko and Ložek 1973) (figure 10).

12) More widespread occurrence of retrograde soil development, especially in the warm-dry black earth areas on loess and their fringes, conditional on the

Figure 9. Seeds of the broad or Celtic bean (*Vicia faba* L.) from a grave vessel of the final Bronze Age at Tornow (district Calau), in the lower Lausitz. The distribution of this pulse spread in the Urnfield period over wide areas of central Europe as well as Scandinavia (Jäger 1965b, Hjelmqvist 1955).

Figure 10. View of a lapiés field in the area of the Hallstatt and La Tène hill-fort of Zadiel' (district Rožňava) in the south Slovak Karst, showing the karstification effected by prehistoric deforestation.

erosion-dependent exposure of fresh subsoil as well as on the cumulative covering of soils developed in earlier warm phases by a fresh substratum of clastic sediments (Ložek 1976, Smolíková and Ložek 1973).

13) Clearings in the former woodland both in the subcontinental to continental areas of south-eastern central Europe and in the suboceanic to oceanic parts of the north-west, partly as a direct consequence of a natural drying-out of the affected woodland zone, partly brought about by an intentional pushing back of the wood for the benefit of arable and pastoral agriculture by the Urnfield population (Jäger 1962, Ložek 1976).

14) In places a retrograde development of whole groups of species, partly as a result of clearings in the vegetation cover, partly effected and increased both by retrograde soil development and by direct anthropogenic impacts (Ložek 1976).

Overall, therefore, the Urnfield Bronze Age appears not only as a period of considerable settlement displacement, but also of fundamental landscape changes whereby fluctuations in climatic history and (partly dependent thereon) anthropogenic influences affected the landscape formation and development in the same direction, especially in those drier areas of central Europe that face a disadvantage in terms of precipitation. The Urnfield settlement distribution, clearly altered by comparison with that in the Tumulus Bronze Age, can easily be construed, together with the population movements that are recognisable in the archaeological repertoire at the beginning of the Urnfield period, as a reaction to a changed environment. In its turn, however, it led to further processes of landscape change for the population of the time and in many places exacerbated the ecological effects of this highly significant climatic change. A withdrawal from hydrologically unfavourable areas is recognisable as the basic tendency of these population displacements (that is, from areas with relatively high continentality: the warm-dry basins of the central European central highland zone and of the western Carpathians, the karstified upland limestone plateaux), among which special significance in historical interpretation attaches to the Pannonian Basin as the starting-area for the Urnfield movement (Kimmig 1964).

(Translated by A. F. Harding. This article originally appeared in Coblenz, W. and Horst, F. (eds) *Mitteleuropäische Bronzezeit* (1978), 211–29. Berlin: Akademie-Verlag.)

REFERENCES

Bouzek, J. (1966) The history of the Knovíz settlement, in Bouzek, J., Koutecký, D. & Neustupný, E., *The Knovíz Settlement of North-West Bohemia*, Fontes archaeologici Pragenses 10, 100-7.

— (1969a) Zwei Hypothesen zu den Anfängen der Lausitzer Kultur – Diskussionsbeitrag, *Beiträge z. Lausitzer Kultur*, Beiheft 7 d. Arbeits- u. Forschungsberichte Dresden, 25-9.

— (1969b) *Homerisches Griechenland im Lichte der archäologischen Quellen*. Acta Universitatis Carolinae Philosophica et Historica, Monographia XXIX. Prague.

Breddin, R. & Buck, D. W. (1970) Untersuchungen auf der befestigten Siedlung von Lübbenau, Kr. Calau, *Veröffentlichungen d. Museums f. Ur- u. Frühgeschichte Potsdam* 5, 113-17.

Coblenz, W. (1952) *Grabfunde der Mittelbronzezeit Sachsens*. Dresden.

— (1954) Keramik mit Knoviser Anklängen aus dem Vogtland, *Arbeits- u. Forschungsberichte z. sächsischen Bodendenkmalpflege* 4, 337-92.

Grünberg, W. (1943) *Die Grabfunde der jüngeren und jüngsten Bronzezeit im Gau Sachsen*. Berlin.

Hageman, B. P. & Jäger, K.-D. (1969) Activities, progresses, and future lines of action of the Subcommission on the Study of the Holocene of INQUA regarding the Holocene stratigraphy against the background of the excursions during the period 1965-1969, *Bulletin of the Subcommission on the Study of the Holocene of the INQUA* 3, 50-3.

Hjelmqvist, H. (1955) Die älteste Geschichte der Kulturpflanzen in Schweden, *Opera botanica a Societate botanica Lundensi* 1, 3. Lund.

Horedt, K. (1974) Befestigte Siedlungen der Spätbronze- und der Hallstattzeit im innerkarpatischen Rumänien, in *Symposium zu Problemen der jüngeren Hallstattzeit in Mitteleuropa*. Bratislava, 205-28.

Jäger, K.-D. (1962) Über Alter und Ursachen der Auelehmablagerung thüringischer Flüsse, *Praehistorische Zeitschrift* 40, 1-59.

— (1965a) *Holozäne Binnenwasserkalke und ihre Aussage für die nacheiszeitliche Klima- und Landschaftsentwicklung im südlichen Mitteleuropa*. Unpublished dissertation, University of Jena.

— (1965b) Verkohlte Samen aus einem bronzezeitlichen Grabgefäß von Tornow, Kr. Calau – Ein Beitrag zur Anbaugeschichte der Ackerbohne (Vicia faba L.) in Mitteleuropa, *Ausgrabungen u. Funde* 10, 131-8.

— (1969) Climatic Character and Oscillations of the Subboreal Period in the Dry Regions of the Central European Highlands, in *Quaternary Geology and Climate* (Proceedings of the VII Congress of the International Association for Quaternary Research, 16), Washington, D.C., 38-42.

— (1970) Mitteleuropäische Klimaschwankungen seit dem Neolithikum und ihre siedlungsgeschichtlichen Auswirkungen, in *Actes du VIIe Congrès International des Sciences Préhistoriques et Protohistoriques* – Prague 21-7 Aug. 1966, 668-73.

— (1973) Holozänstratigraphische Befunde als Zeugnisse für den Landesausbau im slawischen und deutschen Mittelalter, in *Berichte über den II. Internationalen Kongreß für Slawische Archäologie*, Bd. III, 75-88.

Jäger, K.-D. & Hageman, B. P. (1971) Correlation between Changes of Sea Level in N-W Europe and Climatology of Central Europe during the Holocene, *Quaternaria* 14, 101.

Jäger, K.-D. & Kliewe, H. (1969) Regionale Zusammenhänge und Differenzierungen in der Holozänstratigraphie Mitteleuropas, *Petermanns Geographische Mitteilungen* 113, 129-34.

Jäger, K.-D. & Laser, R. (1971) Die siedlungsgeschichtliche Aussage stratigraphischer und bodenkundlicher Untersuchungen im Gelände der kaiserzeitlichen Ansiedlung bei Wüste Kunersdorf, Kr. Seelow, *Veröffentlichungen d. Museums f. Ur- u. Frühgeschichte Potsdam* 4, 11-22.

Kimmig, W. (1964) Seevölkerbewegung und Urnenfelderkultur, in *Studien aus Alteuropa* (Beihefte der Bonner Jahrbücher, Bd. 10), Teil I, 220-83.

Kubiena, W. (1953) *Bestimmungsbuch und Systematik der Böden Europas*. Stuttgart.

Kukla, J. & Ložek, V. (1968, 1971) Význam krasových oblasti pro poznání poledové doby, *Československý Kras* 20, 35-49.

Ložek, V. (1973) K historii eroze půdy v holocénu, in Šilar, J. *et al.*, *Ochrana a tvorba životního prostředí (Ukoly geologických věd)* – Sborník referatů symposia konaného 26. dubna 1972 k 10. výročí založení Ústavu geologických věd prírodovědecké fakulty University Karlovy, 16-25.
— (1974) Pěnovce v Krabině a jejich význam pro palaeogeografii Českého krasu, *Československý Kras* 25, 7-17.
Ložek, V. (1976) Klimaabhängige Zyklen der Sedimentation und Bodenbildung während der Quartärs im Lichte malakozoologischer Untersuchungen, *Rozpravy ČSAV řada MPV* 86/8, 1-97.
Mania, D. & Preuss, J. (1975) Zu Methoden und Problemen ökologischer Untersuchungen in der Ur- und Frühgeschichte, in *Symbolae Praehistoricae*, Festschrift f. Friedrich Schlette, Berlin, 9-59.
Müller, H. M. (1969) Die spätpleistozäne und holozäne Vegetationsentwicklung im östlichen Tieflandbereich der DDR zwischen Nördlichem und Südlichem Landrücken, in *Berlin – Die Hauptstadt der DDR und ihr Umland* (Wissenschaftliche Abhandlungen der Geographischen Gesellschaft der Deutschen Demokratischen Republik, Bd. 10), Gotha and Leipzig, 155-65.
Neef, E. (1969) Der Stoffwechsel zwischen Gesellschaft und Natur als geographisches Problem, *Geographische Rundschau* 21, 453-9.
Neumann, G. (1954) Sieben Gleichbergburgen nach dem Forschungsstand von 1952, in *Frühe Burgen und Städte* (Wilhelm Unverzagt zum 60. Geburtstag), Berlin, 7-16.
Paret, O. (1946) *Das neue Bild der Vorgeschichte*. Stuttgart.
— (1961) *Württemberg in vor- und frühgeschichtlicher Zeit*. Stuttgart.
Prošek, F. & Ložek, V. (1956) O změnách přírodních poměrů Jihoslovenského krasu v nejmladší geologické minulosti, *Ochrana přírody* 11, 33-42.
Redlich, Cl. (1958) Zum Problem der Siedlungsverschiebungen am Ende der Bronzezeit, *Praehistorische Zeitschrift* 36, 71-117.
Reinecke, P. & Schumacher, K. (1911) Erläuterungen zu Taf. 1-69 der *Altertümer unserer heidnischen Vorzeit* V. Mainz.
Reinecke, P. (1924) Zur chronologischen Gliederung der süddeutschen Bronzezeit, *Germania* 8, 43-4.
Schrickel, W. (1957) Eine Abfallgrube der Unstrutgruppe von Jena-Oberwöllnitz, *Ausgrabungen u. Funde* 2, 116-20.
Seitz, H. J. (1951) Die Süßwasserkalkprofile zu Wittislingen und die Frage des nacheiszeitlichen Klima-Ablaufes, *Berichte d. Naturforschenden Gesellschaft Augsburg* 4, 1-132.
— (1952) Die Süßwasserkalkprofile zu Wittislingen. Ergänzungen und Neuergebnisse, *Berichte d. Naturforschenden Gesellschaft Augsburg* 5, 28-36.
— (1956) Zur Altersfrage der Bandkeramik und weitere Neuergebnisse aus den Profilen zu Wittislingen (1952-56), *Berichte d. Naturforschenden Gesellschaft Augsburg* 7, 5-33.
— (1963) Der Lauf der Egau in vorgeschichtlicher Zeit, *Jahrbuch d. Historischen Vereins Dillingen a. d. Donau* 64/65, 21-32.
Smolíková, L. & Ložek, V. (1964) The Holocene Soil Complex of Litomerice, *Sborník geologických věd, řada A (antropozoikum)* 2, 41-56.
— (1973) Der Bodenkomplex von Velký Hubenov als Beispiel einer retrograden Bodenentwicklung im Laufe der Nacheiszeit, *Časopis pro mineralogii a geologii* 18, 365-77.
Vašátko, J. & Ložek, V. (1971) K postglaciálnímu vývoji malakofauny Pavlovských vrchů, *Zprávy Geografického ústavu ČSAV* 8, 4, 20-4.

Vašátko, J. & Ložek, V. (1973) Der Holozäne Bodenkomplex von Pavlov und seine Bedeutung für die Landschaftsgeschichte des südmährischen Tschernosemgebietes, *Zprávy Geografického ústavu ČSAV* 10, 7, 1-10.

Vita-Finzi, Cl. (1969) *The Mediterranean Valleys – Geological Changes in Historical Times*. Cambridge: University Press.

Climatic changes and central European prehistory

The paper presented here is – in many ways – a result of collaboration with my colleagues Klaus-Dieter Jäger, a quaternary geologist from Dresden, and Vojen Ložek, a malacologist from Prague. The first report of our studies was presented to the prehistoric congress at Nice in 1976 (Bouzek, Jäger and Ložek 1976). Other evidence has been collected since by the present author and both his colleagues, but this contribution intends to go beyond the technical side of this work (still in progress) and also sketch the implications of the elaborated model for European prehistory in general. For such a task, a detailed knowledge in various specialisations is as necessary as the elaboration of a sensible synthetic model. The mutual interaction between man and nature must also be considered: unlike the situation in earlier times, the Holocene environment was affected – since the beginnings of agriculture – by man's activities (Jäger and Ložek 1977).

It seems to be useful to divide this paper into three sections, the first of which will be devoted to the methods used, the second should sketch a tentative picture of climatic development in central Europe, pointing out its strong and weak parts, and the last section should discuss the implications of climatic development for man's history.

Methods

As compared with the earlier ice ages, climatic changes during the Holocene were less substantial, and took longer to be discovered. The geological dating usual in earlier periods cannot be applied here; the date of Holocene deposits can only be established either from radiocarbon dates (or by other, usually less accurate, scientific methods, like thermoluminescence or paleomagnetism), or from archaeological finds, that is human artefacts. The latter are preferable, since they directly link the environmental and archaeological evidence together, but the interdisciplinary collaboration must be direct – the lack of direct collaboration was one of the main obstacles to me, when I started studying climatic changes (Bouzek 1969a, 1969b).

Geologists are not particularly interested in keeping all the pottery fragments from their deposits, while post-Palaeolithic archaeologists tend to show little interest in geological features, or in collecting snail shells or undisturbed samples for pollen analysis. The C^{14} dating method has its limitations and mistakes can happen; malacological and pollen samples can hardly be taken on the same spot, since the two materials are preserved under different conditions. Pollen analyses, moreover, are mostly undertaken on samples from upland bogs, where small fluctuations in the precipitation rate hardly affect the local flora, whereas a 20 per cent decrease of rainfall, for example, can have a very marked effect in agricultural lowlands with much lower average precipitation rates. Examples in our territory are north-west and central Bohemia, southern Moravia, Thuringia and Hungary.

Besides this, both archaeology, and many branches of natural science have reached the stage where opposing views on particular issues are held by different persons; sound and unsound theories can hardly be distinguished by a person not specialised in a particular field, since the distinction between scientific and pseudoscientific argumentation is, in such matters of detail, difficult to achieve.

We must, therefore, use different methods independent of each other, try to correlate them into a sensible whole, and examine critically all possibilities of alternative conclusions.

1) The methods of world-wide significance may be mentioned first, though they only give a framework to the investigations in central Europe. The cyclical sea-level fluctuation theory has often been criticised, but the critics were only able to show irregularities in Fairbridge's curve, whereas nearly all the more detailed investigations in the Mediterranean, Black Sea and the Atlantic confirmed the existence of transgressions and regressions which correlate with periods of transgression and regression in other parts of the world (cf. Bintliff 1977; Richards and Fairbridge 1965, 1970). The finely elaborated Dutch sequence can best be compared with the central European development (figure 1): the transgressions seem to mark a dryer, more continental climate in central Europe and *vice versa* (Hageman and Jäger 1969; Jäger and Hageman 1971; figure 1). Samples from stratigraphic drillings in the arctic ice in Greenland (Camp Century) form another parallel to the methods about to be described (cf. Pleiner and Rybová 1978, Kral 1977).

2) Among the methods applied to central Europe directly, the study of the sequence of subaquatic calcareous sediments and terrestrial conditions (humus horizons) in open space areas is especially significant. This sedimentation in central Europe is strictly connected with warm (dry) periods in the regional climatic development. Exceptions to this rule are rare and occur mainly in the vicinity of present-day or former thermal springs. Some examples of stratigraphical evidence from Thuringia (Pennickental near Jena-Wöllnitz, Backsteinländer near Jena-Ammerbach, Johannisberge bei Jena-Loberda), the Swabian Alb (Vittislingen), the Bohemian Karst (Svatý Jan pod Skalou, Tetín) and from the Slovakian Karst (Jabloňov, Háj, Hrhov) are mentioned in the report to the Nice congress (Bouzek *et al.* 1976, cf. Seitz 1956) and new investigations in these places enabled a more exact correlation of archaeological, geological and malacological evidence.

3) Clastic sequences in Holocene river-sides with pedological features point to changes of the ground-water level in coincidence with regional climatic fluctuations, mainly by gleying phenomena and the existence of buried humus horizons. The dating of these features is based, again, on archaeological

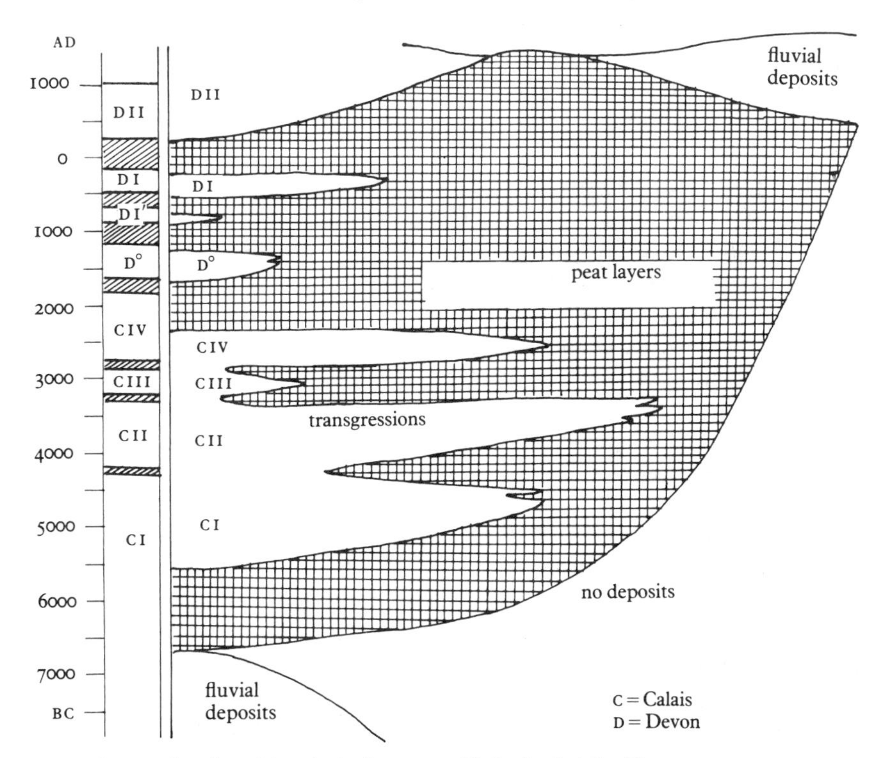

Figure 1. Stratigraphic units in the western Netherlands (after Hageman and Jäger 1969).

discoveries. Characteristic, for example, is the relatively low ground-water table during the Urnfield period in the riversides of the Brandenburg region and elsewhere (Breddin and Buck 1970, Jäger and Laser 1971).

4) The relation of prehistoric settlements lying close to rivers to their flood plain, and to water sources that inundated settlements while still occupied. These cases must, again, be studied jointly by geologists and archaeologists; they show a similar development to that of the ground-water-level fluctuation.

5) The changes in malacofauna, especially in samples dated by archaeological finds. Most important are changes during the Neolithic and Late Bronze Age (Urnfield) periods: in both cases new xerothermic species appear. The latter mark a rapid retreat of woodland species in more densely populated areas and a spread of grass land-snails. Long established xerothermic species and those which only migrated into central Europe during the Neolithic, like *Capea vindobonensis* (Fér.) and *Oxilichus inopinatus* (Ul.) spread rapidly over these territories. The sub-mediterranean *Zebrina detrita* (Müll.) first appeared in central Europe, and the mesic species which prefer park landscapes accelerated their spread (Ložek 1967, Jäger and Ložek, this volume).

6) Palynological analyses are more instructive when coming from the lowlands with fertile soils (chernozem and similar) or from their periphery; the

tests from the mountainous zone are less informative (see above). The relationship of the *Pinus* and *Alnus* curves seems to be important, and especially the *Pinus* frequency. It is also worth mentioning the fact that *Vicia faba* advanced during the Urnfield period towards all parts of northern central Europe (Jäger 1975).

7) The frequency of settlement traces in caves in relation to the subaquatic sedimentation in other periods. The two peaks of cave settlements are Linear Pottery Neolithic and Final Bronze Age (Urnfields), whereas, in most other periods (except, to a certain degree, Late Únětice) the caves were merely used for cult purposes. This phenomenon could be tested personally during the dry summer of 1975, which enabled an agreeable stay in many caves from which, in the damper conditions of other years, one normally returned like a boar from a mud-bath.

8) The variation of human settlement density and its pattern. This question will be discussed more specifically below, so only the basic points will be mentioned here. The Urnfield period (the end of the second millennium BC most specifically) marks a peak of agricultural settlement density not reached again until the Early Medieval colonisation, while some parts of Neolithic, Classical Únětice, Late Hallstatt and Late La Tène periods mark other, less high peaks. Some areas were settled in central Europe only during climatic optima, and were otherwise without any permanent settlements altogether.

The main lines of Holocene climatic development in central Europe

It must be stressed again that what can be presented here is a tentative sketch only. Even if the general line of development appears very probable, much more investigation will be necessary for confirming and improving the details of the picture. The Neolithic and Late Bronze Age optima are best documented, whereas in other cases much less is known for sure. Warm and dry periods need not always be the same, and the drying out of the soil usually started earlier in areas of steppe-like character (like the Hungarian plain) than in Bohemia and Thuringia, and, as is clearer for the Urnfield period, the dry phase follows the warm climatic optimum with its prolonged growing season only after some time, probably also being caused (at least on this occasion, cf. below p. 188) by soil exhaustion and deforestation as a result of the previous 'population explosion' and rapid increase of settlement density.

The Early Neolithic in central Europe (especially the Early Linear pottery culture) marked an exceptionally warm period enabling the settlement of areas in relatively high altitudes, uninhabited during most parts of later prehistory; it was probably this optimum that lured the colonists so far north. The Late Neolithic (Late Linear pottery culture, *Stichbandkeramik* and Painted wares) became cooler, and the Eneolithic, as a whole, had a rather cool climate, even if the Middle Eneolithic (Báden, Jevišovice, Řivnáč) may have been an exception. The Late Eneolithic (Corded Ware, Bell Beakers) and Early Únětice with a cooler climate were followed by an optimum lasting from classical Únetice until the age of the Věteřov, Mad'arovce and Tószeg hill settlements, though this was less well marked than the Neolithic and Urnfield optima. The Middle Bronze Age (Tumulus culture) was a period of higher precipitation rate and a cooler, more atlantic climate. The Urnfield period, as already mentioned above, marked a very characteristic climatic optimum with a long growing season, first warm and later also dry; after 1000 BC settlements in Bohemia move from the lowlands with low precipitation rates towards the hills, while a similar development happened probably rather earlier in Hungary.

The eighth/seventh centuries BC were a time of rapid climatic worsening, tending towards cool and atlantic, but there are two later less pronounced warmer subperiods during the Hallstatt and La Tène Iron Ages: the first of them in the sixth/fifth centuries BC (Late Hallstatt and Early La Tène), the second in the second/first centuries BC, during the flourishing of the central European *oppida*. The age of the Roman empire is marked again by a more atlantic climate, with expansion of forests. The next warmer period is generally well known: it is the time of Germanic and Slavonic migrations during and after the fall of the Western Roman empire.

At the close of this section, it is also interesting to compare the central European development with the situation in the Mediterranean, better known from historical records. The peak of Urnfield prosperity coincides with the breakdown of Mediterranean Bronze Age civilisation and with the Dark Age there, the eighth/seventh century recession in central Europe with the rise of Classical Greek civilisation and a further period of central and north European prosperity with the collapse of the west Roman empire. If we proceed backwards, the central European Middle Bronze Age (Tumulus culture) was contemporary with the zenith of the Mycenaean civilisation, and the late third millennium BC destructions were roughly contemporary with the rise of the central European Bronze Age. From this survey it seems that climatic ups and downs in central Europe and in the Mediterranean are complementary to each other (cf. Bouzek 1969a, 1969b).

The impact of climate on prehistoric evolution in central Europe

One of the special subjects of examination mentioned in the previous section was the study of population density (cf. Smolla 1974). For this purpose I have chosen here as representative the area of north-west Bohemia, which is well known archaeologically (Bouzek, Koutecký and Neustupný 1966, Buchvaldek 1966, Pleiner and Rybová 1978, Pleinerová 1966–7, Plesl 1965) though other parts of central Europe will also be mentioned.

Up to the industrial revolution the lowland part of this area was typical corn-producing country, in most parts famous for its fertility since the Early Middle Ages. The present yearly average of rainfall fluctuates between 50–500 mm, but it is so evenly distributed throughout the year that agriculture is possible without irrigation. The hills there, the Bohemian Central Massif, however, are bare; the soil was washed away here after deforestation and only grass, dry in the summer, grows there. The density of settlement varies considerably during the prehistoric period (figures 2, 3). The Neolithic (Linear

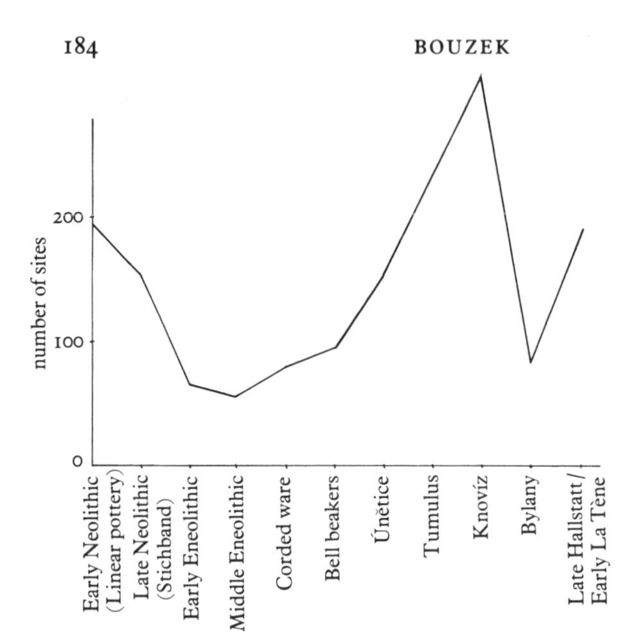

Figure 2. Fluctuations in the number of prehistoric settlements in north-west Bohemia: sequence of the cultures, including not precisely datable unexplored sites.

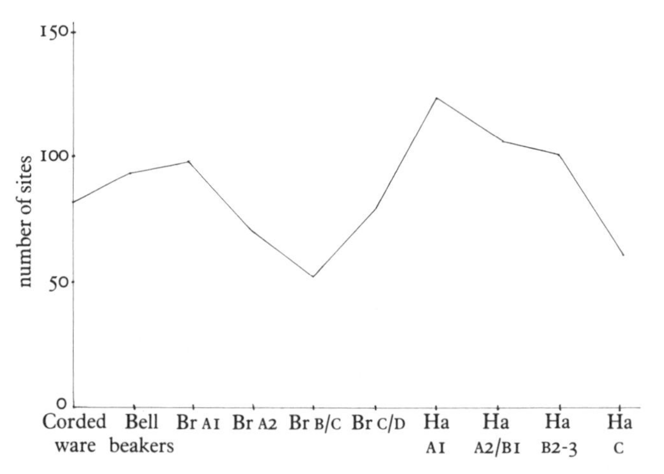

Figure 3. Fluctuations in the number of prehistoric settlements in north-west Bohemia: sequence of closer time-units, excluding not precisely datable sites.

Ware) settlement is rather dense, though this may partly be due to the migrations of villages over a larger territory in a cycle lasting several decades, as supposed by many specialists. The Eneolithic population density (mainly known from graves, since with some Eneolithic cultures, like the Corded Ware, we know of no settlements at all, is smaller, and it becomes substantially larger only with the Classical Únětice culture. During the Middle Bronze Age Tumulus culture it sinks again, whereas the Urnfield period marks a peak of settlement density never reached again (less than 5 km^2 per one known site). The absolute peak of settlement density was reached in Hallstatt A, as in most parts of central Europe, especially at low altitudes in river valleys. A rapid increase can be seen in the Lausitz culture area in the northern part of Czechoslovakia, Poland and East Germany, where there were only few Middle Bronze Age forerunners. Later the settlement density sank and some villages moved towards the hills. The decrease of rainfall may have been one reason for this shift, since Ha B also marks the peak of frequency of cave occupation in Bohemia. Nearly all existing settlements were abandoned towards the end of Ha B, and Ha C, with few settlement traces and more richly equipped graves, meant a substantial diminishing of the population total. The settlement, again, became more dense in Ha D (sixth/fifth centuries BC), whereas the time of the Celtic migrations in the fourth and third centuries BC marks another decrease of population, apparently in connection with a climatic deterioration. The only clear interruption was during the second/first centuries BC at the time of the flourishing of Celtic *oppida* in central Europe. Their end, and an invasion of Germanic tribes from the north, was connected with the spread of the typically Sub-atlantic, cooler, climate, already mentioned.

Knowing from both settlements and cemeteries that an average Urnfield settlement has c. 50–150 inhabitants, and that this figure may have been the same for the Únětice, Early Hallstatt and Late La Tène villages, whereas the Tumulus culture and most of the Eneolithic settlements were probably smaller in size, we may tentatively estimate the population numbers in north-west Bohemia, as follows:

Neolithic (Linear Ware)	c. 15–20,000
Eneolithic (average)	c. 10–15,000
(for the Corded Ware rather less)	
Únětice (Classical)	c. 20–30,000
Middle Bronze Age Tumulus Culture	c. 15–20,000
Urnfield (maximum)	c. 70–100,000
Ha C (Bylany culture)	c. 15–20,000
Ha D/La Tène A	c. 40–60,000

The mid-eighteenth-century population of this area was about 250,000. What can be said about one small territory where there was a possibility of working with approximate figures corresponds to the general development in most parts of central Europe. Arable agriculture and cattle breeding had been the two basic means of subsistence since the Neolithic, but the system brought to central Europe by Early Neolithic settlers had to be adapted. A few years of bad harvest led to hunger and death, and therefore one of the main functions of the Bronze Age temple and palatial economic systems in the Near East was this storage of grain and its redistribution in times of misfortune. The story of Joseph's deciphering of Pharaoh's dream suggests that seven years' reserve meant the absolute maximum capability of palatial redistribution. Other stories about droughts are graphically described in ancient writings. Dionysos of Halicarnassus (1, 23, 2–3) reports of the Pelasgians:

> The first cause of the desolation of their cities seemed to be a drought which laid waste the land, when neither any fruit remained on the trees until it was ripe, but dropped while still green, nor did such of the seed corn as sent up shoots and flowered stand for the usual period until the ear was ripe, nor did sufficient grass grow for the cattle; and of the waters some were no longer fit to drink, others shrank up during the summer, and others were totally dried up. And like misfortunes attended the offspring both of cattle and of women. For they were either abortive or died at birth, some by their death destroying also those that bore them; and if any got safely past the danger of their delivery, they were either maimed or defective or being injured by some other accident, were not fit to be reared. The rest of the people also, particularly those in the prime of life, were afflicted with many unusual diseases and uncommon deaths. (Loeb translation)

Many migrations in the Mediterranean were caused by drought and hunger: either of the whole population, or of one half of it, as Herodotus reports for the Lydians and Etruscans (Herodotus I, 94); famine in overpopulated Greek cities was also one of the most important reasons for Greek colonisation, which was preceded by a rapid increase of population during the eighth century BC (Camp 1979). Many reports of droughts from other parts of the world, even from periods and places far removed like nineteenth-century Brazil or China, show a similar picture and similar depopulation figures (Carpenter 1966). We must admit that the possibilities of storing grain among the more primitive prehistoric populations of central Europe were more limited than those from the ancient Near East. A certain amount of grain could be stored in pits for several years. The Urnfield people used this system on a very wide scale, but they hardly had sufficient surplus for more than two years, and normally less than that. They could not buy corn in the United States or Canada as most countries do after a bad harvest nowadays, and it was also difficult for them to use other varieties of seed-corn when the climate became dryer or cooler. But if they wanted to survive, they had to move elsewhere or to adapt their system to the changing conditions.

From central European prehistory we know that they did both things. When, for example, during Ha A2–B1 the decreasing precipitation rate and perhaps also soil exhaustion (cf. Kristiansen 1980) caused smaller crop yields in the lowlands, many settlements moved towards the hill country, with its poorer brown soils, but sufficient rainfall. In other cases, the changes must have been more profound, though they were apparently not accomplished within one decade, since our archaeological timing in central Europe can only exceptionally distinguish closer time units than two to three generations.

Agriculture with a prevalence of grain production functions well in dryer and warmer times, when a longer growing period operates even at higher altitudes; but it is impractical there in periods with a rather atlantic climate. The combination of cooler summers and milder winters, with little snow, however, enabled more cattle and sheep to be kept even during the winters (the storage of hay, if any, was never sufficient in past ages) and both the settlement pattern and other evidence suggest that alternative agricultural systems existed, sometimes even contemporaneously, side by side. Some settlements in high altitudes reflect mining, others are poor and may reflect a Vlach-type agriculture with a few small fields and a predominance of cattle-breeding. The Púchov culture in northern Slovakia may be an example of this, and it is reported for many Germanic tribes by Roman authors. But there is also evidence pointing to other patterns. For some periods, especially the Middle Bronze Age and Hallstatt times, there are many tumuli high up in the hills, but only very modest traces of temporary settlements there. These people may well have been transhuming pastoralists. The hills were their own country and they buried their dead there, but for winters they had to come to the lowlands, where there was little or no snow cover, to keep their cattle (and sheep) alive. As we know well from Mediterranean parallels, both ancient and modern (for the former, remember Isaac's difficulties in buying land and wells in the fertile coastal lowland), there was a tension everywhere between transhuming pastoralists and settled farmers. This concerned equally the 'horizontal' transhumance between semi-desert and coast, and the 'vertical' transhumance between mountains and lowlands, both in the Mediterranean and along the Atlantic coastland. But there was also a kind of *modus vivendi* between the two groups. The cattle-breeding communities were militarily stronger than the arable farmers, who had to work harder on their fields, but in most cases the farmers were more numerous (cf. Dehn 1974, Hammond 1976, Sandars 1978).

Cultures with cattle-breeding prevailing (including also sheep and/or goats) were probably the majority of Eneolithic groups (especially Globular Amphorae, Corded Ware, Bell Beakers, but possibly also Baalberg and Salzmund) which largely differ in their character from cultures with an agricultural system of Near Eastern affiliation. Proportionately less settlement than grave finds are among the characteristics of the former, as well as the more frequent use of non-ceramic vessels of organic materials, and therefore in preserved finds either only cooking pots of clay (Middle Bronze Age 'Kumpfkeramik', Slavonic pottery during the migration of the Slavs) or pottery strongly influenced by non-ceramic vessels: as for instance Baalberg, Salzmünd, Globular Amphorae, Corded Ware and Bell Beakers in the Eneolithic, later the notched decoration (Kerbschnitt) of the Middle Bronze Age Tumulus culture, the sack-shaped bowls and sharp profiles on biconical and other carinated vessels decorated with notches that recall woodworking techniques, dating to the transition between Early Lausitz and its much more richly represented Middle Stage (Bouzek 1969b). The cultures with arable agriculture predominant tend to have more a sophisticated and independent ceramic tradition, though they naturally differ at different stages of prehistoric development, gradually more sophisticated shapes appearing in subsequent epochs.

Accepting our tentative model of different agricultural systems existing side by side can also provide an explanation to some crucial problems of chronology, like the coexistence of Řivnáč settlements and Globular Amphorae or late Maďarovce and Věteřov fortified settlements with the same bronzes as the earliest Tumulus Culture graves; there is an analogous situation in Bronze Age D (cf. Rulf 1980).

But the following point seems to be even more important. Any climatic change was critical for the population. The effect was not only an adaptation, but also tensions, migrations and wars. A positive change resulted in a rapid increase of population, a negative change was followed by its decrease. The establishing of a new alternative agricultural system or alternatively, of two or more complementary systems in different parts of the country, at different altitudes, was followed by its refinement, an optimisation of the system. Such an optimal system was, however, highly specialised and collapsed with any new climatic change. The whole cyclical path of Europe's prehistoric development with its many ups and downs is intimately connected with the climatic rhythm of Mother Earth, and this aspect cannot be overlooked in any real tracing of its history.

As time went on, many climatic-type changes were more or less affected by human activity; deforestation caused denudation and drying out of the soil, soil exhaustion by agricultural overpopulation must also have played its part in preparing the collapse of systems connected with climatic optima. Nowadays we can see not only the drying out of the savannah belt south of the Sahara causing many political changes, but also degradation of soils by fertilisers and by high erosion in many parts of the world. Many civilisations perished because they destroyed their soils, and this should also teach us to protect our present environment from the destructive powers which no civilisation before our own has developed to such a high degree.

But let us return to European prehistory. The Early Neolithic climatic optimum opened the way to Neolithic colonists, its end meant a crisis embracing the peripheral European groups in the Neolithic world and hastening the distribution of the plough and different new combinations of grain-producing and cattle and sheep breeding. Early Bronze Age (Únětice) settlement in the fortified sites towards the end of the Early Bronze Age reaches a cultural level nearly comparable with that of the Mediterranean countries, but the barbarian Tumulus Culture tribes destroyed this world and lived in a more primitive way with a prevalence of cattle-breeding until the new climatic optimum of c. 1300 BC enabled an agricultural colonisation of large areas that previously had virtually no permanent dwellings. After a 'population explosion' with no more land to be settled and the drying out of the lowlands, movements in various directions, to Italy, Greece, southern France, Spain and the Ukraine, started. The climatic deterioration in the eighth century BC and climatic changes in the Eurasian steppes opened the way to the eastern 'Cimmerian' nomads, just as later similar changes enabled the Scythian raids and the Hun, Avar and Hungarian invasions to take place. Another development resembling the end of the Urnfields and the subsequent migrations led the Celts to move southwards in the fourth and third centuries BC and the Ger-

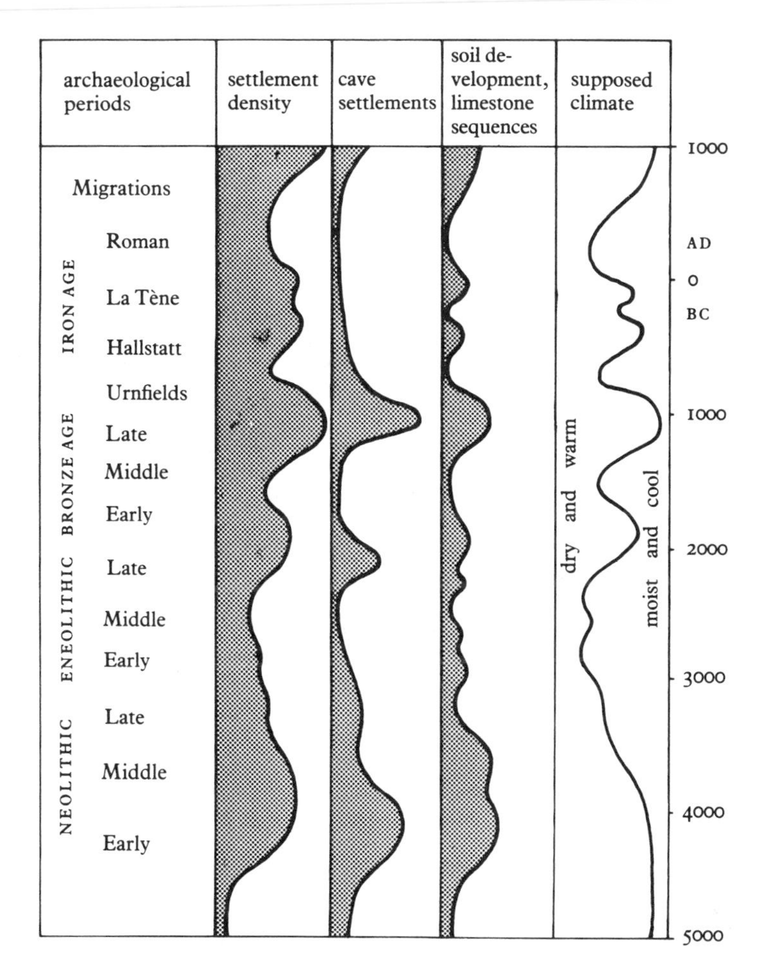

Figure 4. Correlation of the settlement density, number of cave settlements, datable soil developments in limestone sequences and supposed climatic changes in central Europe. The figures are only approximate, and the relatively high number of Neolithic settlements may be partly caused by the supposed shifting agriculture.

manic and Slavonic peoples in the fourth to seventh centuries AD to move in similar directions. Figure 4 summarises these developments.

The peaks of prosperity in central (and northern) Europe and in the Mediterranean are complementary to each other, the optima in the north meant usually pessima in the south and *vice versa*; even the collapse of the Early Bronze Age cities in the late third millennium BC and the rise of the Early Bronze Age culture in central Europe probably reflects the same cyclical change. The rhythm of climatic changes is, in general terms, identical with the cyclic development of European history as a whole.

REFERENCES

Bintliff, J. L. (1977) *Natural Environment and Human Settlement in Prehistoric Greece, based on original fieldwork*. British Archaeological Reports, Suppl. Series 28.

Bouzek, J. (1969a) *Homerisches Griechenland im Lichte der archäologischen Quellen*. Prague.

— (1969b) Zwei Hypothesen zu den Anfängen der Lausitzer Kultur, in *Beiträge zur Lausitzer Kultur*, 25-9. Dresden.

— Sluneční vůz a vůz s kotlem – Sonnenwagen und Kesselwagen, *Arch. Rozhledy* 29, 197-202.

Bouzek, J., Jäger, K.-D., & Lozek, V. (1976) Climatic and Settlement Changes during the Central European Bronze Age. Summary in: IXe congrès UISPP Nice 1976, résumés des communications, 437, the whole text in press in the *Actes* of the Congress.

Bouzek, J., Koutecký, D. & Neustupný, E. (1966) *The Knovíz settlement of Northwest Bohemia*, Fontes Archaeologici Pragenses 10.

Breddin, R. & Buck, D. W. (1970) Untersuchungen auf der befestigten Siedlung von Lübbenau, Kr. Calau, *Veröffentlichungen des Museums f. Ur- und Frühgeschichte Potsdam* 5, 113-17.

Buchvaldek, M. (1967) *Die Schnurkeramik in Böhmen*. Prague.

Camp, J. McK. (1979) A drought in the late 8th century BC, *Hesperia* 48, 397-411.

Carpenter, R. (1966) *Discontinuity in Greek Civilisation*. Cambridge: University Press.

Dehn, W. (1974) Einige Bemerkungen zur Gesellschaft und Wirtschaft der Späthallstattzeit. 'Transhumance' in der westlichen Späthallstattkultur?, in Baumann, H. (ed.) *Historische Forschungen für W. Schlesinger*, 1-18. Köln-Wien.

Firbas, F. (1967) Pflanzengeographie, in *Lehrbuch der Botanik*, founded by E. Strassburger *et al.*, 29th edition by D. v. Danffer *et al.*, 679-707. Stuttgart and Jena.

Hageman, B. P. & Jäger, K.-D. (1969) Activities, progress and future lines of action of the Subcommission on the study of the Holocene of INQUA regarding the Holocene stratigraphy against the background of the excursions of the period 1965-1969, *Third Bulletin of the Subcommission on the study of the Holocene of the INQUA*, Haarlem, 50-3.

Hammond, N. G. L. (1976) *Migrations and Invasions in Greece and the Adjacent Areas*. Park Ridge.

Jäger, K.-D. (1975) Verkohlte Samen aus einem bz. Grabgefäss von Tarnau, Kr. Calau. Ein Beitrag zur Anbaugeschichte der Ackerbohn (*Vicia faba* L.) in Mitteleuropa, *Ausgrabungen u. Funde* 10, 131-8.

Jäger, K. D. & Hageman, B. P. (1971) Correlation between changes of sea level in NW Europe and climatology of Central Europe during the Holocene, *Quaternaria* 14, 101.

Jäger, K.-D. & Laser, R. (1971) Die siedlungsgeschichtliche Aussage stratigraphischer und bodenkundlicher Untersuchungen in Gelände der kaiserzeitlichen Ansiedlung bei Wüste Kunersdorf, Kr. Seelow, *Veröff. des Museums f. Ur- und Frühgeschichte Potsdam* 4, 11-22.

Jäger, K.-D. & Ložek, V. (1977) Indications of Holocene stratigraphy concerning the changing natural structure and metabolism of landscape in consequence of human impact, in *Proceedings of the Working Session on Holocene – INQUA (Eurosiberian Subcommission) Tatranská Lomnica – Bratislava 1976*, 93-110.

Kral, F. (1977) On the evidence of postglacial oscillations of climate in pollen profiles from the Alps, in *Proceedings of the Working Session on Holocene – INQUA (Eurosiberian Subcommission) Tatranská Lomnica – Bratislava 1976*, 117-22.
Kristiansen, K. (1980) Besiedlung, Wirtschaftsstrategie und Bodennutzung in der Bronzezeit Dänemarks, *Präh. Zeitschrift* 55, 1-37.
Ložek, V. (1967) Beiträge der Molluskenforschung zur prähistorischen Archäologie Mitteleuropas, *Zeitschrift für Archäologie* 1, 88-138.
— (1976) Zur Geschichte der Bodenerosion in den mitteleuropäischen Lösslandschaften während des Holozäns, *Letters on Stratigraphy* 5(1), 44-54.
Pleiner, R. & Rybová, A., eds (1978) *Pravěké dějiny Čech*. Prague.
Pleinerová, I. (1966-7) Únětická kultura v oblasti Krušných Hor a v jejich sousedství, Part I, *Památky arch.* 57, 339-458, Part II, *Památky arch.* 58, 1-36.
Plesl, E. (1965) Otázky strědobronzového osídlení v sz. Čechách, *Památky arch.* 56, 457-512.
Richards, H. G. & Fairbridge, R. W. (1965) *Annotated Bibliography of Quaternary Shorelines, 1945-1964*. Philadelphia.
— (1970) ibid., *Supplement 1965-9*. Philadelphia.
Rulf, J. (1980) K sídelní kontinuitě v neolitu a eneolitu Čech, *Praehistorica VIII* (Festschrift J. Filip), 55-8.
Sandars, N. K. (1978) *The Sea Peoples, Warriors of the Ancient Mediterranean*. London: Thames and Hudson.
Seitz, H.-J. (1956) Zur Altersfrage der Bandkeramik und weitere Neuergebnisse aus den Profilen zu Wittislingen, *Berichte der Naturforschenden Gesellschaft Augsburg* 7, 5-35.
Smolla, G. (1974) Prähistorische Bevölkerungszahlen, in *Bevölkerungsbiologie*, 333-43. Stuttgart.
Torbrügge, W. (1958) Geographische und historische Fundlandschaften der Oberpfalz: Korrekturen zum Fundbild der Bronzezeit, *Germania* 36, 10-28.
Vita-Finzi, Cl. (1969) *The Mediterranean Valleys–Geological Change in Historical Times*. Cambridge: University Press.

Climate, grazing and man: notes towards the definition of a relationship

The reality of climatic change in most of the British Isles spanning the transition from the second to first millennium bc can hardly be doubted. The bulk of British studies have been concerned with increased peat growth both in lowland raised bogs and in upland blanket bogs (reviewed recently by Turner (1981) and Tinsley (1981)) suggesting both decrease of temperature and increase in rainfall. Isotope studies on lake sediments on Gotland in the Baltic (Mörner and Wallin 1977) and on polar ice cores in Greenland (Dansgaard *et al.* 1969) seem to confirm the same general trend, and there is a general consensus that a drop of up to 2°C in summer temperatures and an increase in annual rainfall (generally unspecified) may be in order (e.g. Lamb 1977, Taylor 1980). It is worth noting that this picture is imprecise. There may be regional west-east variation, starting with evidence for wetter conditions by 3950 BP (2000 bc) in Ireland but not elsewhere, and perhaps visible later in different dates for renewed peat growth on either side of the Pennines (Tinsley 1981). This provides a long period, from 3350 to 2550 BP (1400 to 600 bc), over which changes were spread, and isotope studies also support this. Nor is the seasonal distribution of changes yet explained, though attempted in some detail for Wales by Taylor (1980). Despite such imprecision, the prehistorian is confronted with the problem of accommodating changes of this nature into wider explanations of contemporary change in the archaeological record. The temptation – as in much else – has been to react with simple rather than complex hypotheses, and in exploring contemporary social and economic change to invoke a rather crude environmental determinism. In this way conditions have been widely seen as automatically more difficult for a variety of activities such as cereal cultivation and animal husbandry (Fleming 1976; Coles and Harding 1979, pp.475, 493; Burgess 1974, p.195; 1980, p.157) cross-Channel sea crossings (Piggott 1972–3) and even astronomical observation and dry-land religion (Burgess 1974). Perhaps because it has seemed so clearly to have changed, climate has then been used in a variety of ways, to 'explain' the nature of the Later Bronze Age (from the Acton Park phase in Burgess 1974, but only from the Penard phase in Burgess 1980), shifts in economy and settlement, or more specifically reduced cross-Channel contact from the Hallstatt D phase onwards. Sometimes straightforward muddy catastrophe seems to be envisaged (Burgess 1974) sometimes a significant tipping of the scales is suggested (Burgess 1980), but there has been a general tendency in accounts of this kind to give observed climatic change a decisive role in all activities, at all seasons, and over the country as a whole.

This paper proposes instead that prehistorians should investigate changes of this kind with far greater subtlety and discrimination, by actually exploring the effects of climatic shift on the economic activities involved rather than merely assuming them, and by giving due consideration to the place of these activities in contemporary society.

My main interest is in the uplands of the country, here defined as over about 210 m above sea level, a substantial part of the British land mass (e.g. Pearsall 1971, fig. 12). I have made the working assumption – to be justified later in the paper – that the lowlands, including therefore much of the Wessex chalk downland, were not radically affected by either temperature drop or rainfall increase of the magnitude discussed since economic activities potentially at risk would not have been near critical environmental thresholds. There is considerable evidence that cereal cultivation is not likely to have been affected: field systems and cereal remains can be documented on various areas of the chalk downland more or less continuously from the beginning of the later Bronze Age right on into the Iron Age (e.g. Bowen and Fowler 1978), and linear boundaries, which have been connected with pastoral activities because they disrupt previously established field systems, do not in fact provide ubiquitous evidence in a late phase of the Bronze Age for a pastoral interlude, apart from being datable to a wide timespan (Bowen 1978). Pasture may have been improved in the lowlands by an increase in rainfall, though initial growth would have been slowed by a decrease in temperature (see below). There is evidence from contemporary studies that grass productivity can be increased by as much as a factor of 2.5 by increased rainfall (Evans 1960) and even now in part of eastern England there is a 'soil moisture deficit' for grasses, which are shallower-rooted than cereals (Limbrey 1978). For well-watered situations such as Romney marsh, figures of 10 to 12 sheep per acre all year round have been quoted (Hoskins 1978). Increased rainfall may thus have been welcome. Exceptions have been proposed as on the East Anglian fen edge around 2950 BP (1000 bc) where it has been suggested that a rising water table affected not so much the summer grazing in the fens themselves but the winter grazing or holding land on its edge (Pryor 1980). Even here one could suggest the likelihood of a retreating fen edge rather than the total collapse of the fenland grazing system, and for each possible loss of this kind there were gains to be made from new coastal grazings (e.g. Cunliffe 1980) themselves with rich pasture (van Zeist 1974).

Turning to the uplands themselves, difficulties for cereal cultivation through shorter growing seasons, colder and wetter conditions and lower altitudinal limits have been outlined by Fleming (1976). It is possible that there was much abandonment of upland agriculture though this has to be proved rather than assumed. Johnson (1980) has noted a quantity of sites in south-west England above 180 m with continuity well into the first millennium bc, and upland sites on the west Yorkshire limestone pavement are not certainly pre-Iron Age (Fleming 1976). It may anyway be argued that agriculture was a minor component of upland exploitation (see below). My aim here is therefore to investigate animal economies in the uplands, in order to go beyond simple assumptions of decline as a result of 'rougher grazing' consequent upon climatic change. It is necessary to look closely at the possible changes in grazing quality, at the conditions in which environmental change could be accommodated and the scale of social adjustment required, and conversely at the role of contemporary social arrangements in the course of changes in economy.

The state of upland vegetation in the second millennium bc prior to the climatic deterioration must first be considered, to give proper perspective on the problem, for there was no simple shift after it from rich grassland to rough blanket peat. There seems rather to have been a mosaic of different sorts of vegetation in the second millennium uplands. The treeline was evidently high, perhaps up to 760 m (Pennington 1974) and there was plenty of woodland surviving. This can be seen through wood buried in peat profiles of second or first millennium bc date in the Pennines, the Lake District and elsewhere (Pennington 1974) or through pollen diagrams which show greatest woodland clearance in the first millennium bc, as on the North York Moors (Atherden 1976). There was already also a substantial quantity of cleared ground. Some woodland had perhaps been replaced naturally by blanket bog, soils having become progressively waterlogged since as far back as the Atlantic period, as suggested for Upper Teesdale (Turner *et al.* 1973) and other parts of the Pennines (Conway 1954). Other woodland had been cleared by man; the process extends back to the Mesolithic period, perhaps locally on an extended scale (e.g. Jacobi *et al.* 1976), was continued in the Neolithic period (5950–3950 BP (4000–2000 bc)) and accelerated in the second millennium bc itself, as again in the mid-Pennines (Tinsley 1976) or on Dartmoor (Simmons 1969). Under open conditions there were a variety of soils, from brown earths, to acid brown earths and podzols, themselves considered to be of both natural and anthropogenic origin (H. Keeley, this volume and references), as well as peat profiles above the mineral soil. Grassland may have varied from *Festuca-Agrostis* grassland on the base-rich soils, to *Nardus-Molinia* grassland on leached, podzolised or slightly peaty soils, to *Callunetum* on peat profiles (Pearsall 1971, Gimingham 1972), though the problems of reconstruction of this kind must not be overlooked, since vegetation composition is greatly affected by land-use generally (Pearsall 1971). Above all, considerable regional variation can be stressed, in the extent of surviving woodland and in the composition of the mosaic. The Upper Teesdale study for example, in an area above 460 m with mixed limestone and drift soils, suggested that most of the present blanket peat in the area had already been started by about 2950 BP (1000 bc) (Turner *et al.* 1973), while studies in other areas (quoted by Tinsley 1981, p.215) suggest extended growth and spread from about this date.

What resources then would these uplands have offered? There were undoubtedly possibilities for cultivation but on the basis of field evidence it may be suggested that these were localised. Cultivation on Dartmoor for example seems largely to have been confined to the parallel reave system, around the

230 m contour and as much at the head of the valleys as on the moor itself (Fleming 1978). It is plausible that the bulk of field remains are connected with grazing, including the irregular field systems and cairnfields common in many areas, but often with poorly developed lynchets (e.g. Barrett 1980, p.80). The field evidence thus appears to match the observation that the uplands offered far greater potential for grazing. The yield of woodland browse (Mellars 1976) should certainly be noted as a useful resource, but more attention should be paid to open grassland whose yields are superior. These may be approached particularly *via* the considerable number of studies of sheep grazing and upland productivity conducted since the earlier years of this century and especially since the last war. It is fortunate that these include studies not only of 'improved' breeds like the Cheviot and Blackface but also of the Soay sheep of St Kilda (Jewell *et al.* 1974) which may be akin to prehistoric sheep. It is unfortunate that there are far fewer studies of cattle in the uplands (e.g. Nicholson *et al.* 1970) but for working purposes the figure of five sheep to one cow is often quoted (e.g. Darling and Boyd 1964). It is possible that sheep were the dominant animal in upland exploitation, since cattle have higher feeding requirements (Evans 1960) and have been observed to grow badly on high pasture though they can be maintained by *Festuca-Agrostis* and *Molinia* grassland (Pearsall 1971). There are few properly recorded upland faunal assemblages in the archaeological record of this period to test this; the percentages of cattle and sheep vary considerably, often in favour of the former (Cunliffe 1978).

Recent studies of sheep show a great variety of stocking rates. One study in the Cheviots of south-east Scotland recorded a rate of 1 sheep per 1.6 acres, better than the Scottish modal rate of 1 sheep per 2.5 acres (Hunter 1962). Sheepwalks in Snowdonia in north-west Wales and in mid-Wales had densities ranging from 5.9 to 0.26 ewe units per acre (Hughes 1958, table 8). In general terms it can be seen that such densities vary according to changes in underlying geology and soils, drainage, vegetation type, and to some extent altitude and aspect. Thus the Lower Old Red Sandstone of the Gairs heft was considered significantly richer in bases than many other Scottish upland pastures (Hunter 1962) and in the Conway valley it was found that glacial drift soils carried approximately one ewe unit per acre less than the basic terrains (Hughes 1958, p.182). Further variation in density has been studied in detail in Snowdonia with the highest (excepting a patch of formerly cultivated ground) – around 3.5 ewe units per acre – being recorded on reasonably drained, basic soils with medium rainfall (Dale and Hughes 1978, tables 1 and 2).

From the sheep's point of view these variations seem to be largely a matter of the varying nutritive quality of the sward carried by the terrain and much attention has been paid to the vegetational composition of different areas of grazing. Gairs heft for example was dominated by *Molinia caerulea*, *Festuca-Agrostis* and *Pteridium* swards, with a smaller amount of *Nardus stricta* and *Calluna vulgaris*, and a minor component of *Eriophorum vaginatum*, *Deschampsia* and *Juncus* spp. Soils included flushed gleys around *p*H 6, brown forest soils from *p*H 5 to 5.5 and podzolic brown earths and podzols falling below *p*H 5; a basic distinction was made between mull swards dominated by *Festuca-Agrostis* and mor swards with *Molinia, Nardus, Calluna* and the rest (Hunter 1962). Similar variation has been observed in the Snowdonia studies and indeed in the whole of upland Britain (e.g. Tansley 1968, Pearsall 1971). Three criteria of the nutritive value of pasture are digestibility measured in fibre content, protein content measured through the nitrogen content, and the mineral content measured through the quantities of trace elements such as calcium and phosphorus. A useful basic account is set out by Pearsall (1971). For example, *Poa annua, Festuca-Agrostis* and *Nardus* are in that order increasingly fibrous, and the more fibre the less protein-rich green living cell. The nitrogen content in the leaf is a useful index of the valuable protein constituents (necessary for building flesh) since they contain about 16 per cent nitrogen. Without specifying his source Pearsall quotes the following values (table 8, p.111):

	Alluvial pasture	*Festuca-Agrostis*	*Nardus*
Fibre	21.5	24.6	31.2
$N \times 6.5 =$ protein	18.75	13.12	10

Mineral content such as calcium and phosphate necessary for bone building also often seems to rise and fall in a parallel manner in the uplands, but more detailed studies, as on St Kilda (Milner and Gwynne 1974, table 11.5) do suggest considerable variation with high values possible for *Molinia* and *Calluna*, for example. Studies already quoted as in Snowdonia bring us back to the general relation with soils; in general terms the better the soil the better the pasture. Sheep, perhaps not surprisingly, are able to make suitable discrimination between the different swards on offer, and this 'comparative grazing intensity' has been much observed. The St Kilda study of Soay sheep for example records (as well as the 'home range' behaviour of particular groups) a concentration on the best species of grass available per season (Grubb and Jewell 1974, fig.7.12). It has also been noted that the poorer the pasture, the greater the energy expenditure needed by the animal to exploit it (Evans 1960). Seasonal variation is however important and better species such as *Festuca* and *Agrostis* are not the most grazed at all times of the year. In winter and early spring especially, *Nardus* and *Calluna* are important at a time when other species have died back more or are slower to return to growth (e.g. Hunter 1962, Milner and Gwynne 1974, Dale and Hughes 1978). It can be seen therefore that where stock are to be maintained in one area right through the year winter feeding quality will be a strong constraint and that variety of pasture sufficient to include reasonable winter-early spring grazing is an advantage.

Climatic change on the scale discussed above may be argued to have had two sorts of effect on pasture, producing on the one hand changes in vegetational composition, and leading to changes in growing season and ecological productivity on the other. First, it has been seen that blanket peat was extended in many parts of the country in the later second–earlier first millennium bc, and this would have entailed both a loss of minerals from the soil-pasture cycle and also probably an overall loss of ecological productivity (e.g. Smith and Forrest 1978). Compared with many kinds of grassland, blanket peat can support less sheep. A figure of 1.35 ewes per acre was recorded for blanket peat areas in the Conway area, but it was pointed out also that some non-blanket peat areas of Snowdonia have similar densities (Hughes 1958, p.182). It may also be noted that carrying capacity compared to upland woodland is unknown but not necessarily at a disadvantage, and again that the winter advantages of such a shift – in moderation – would be perceptible. Increased leaching and podzolisation because of higher rainfall on grassland would also have led to mineral loss which would have lessened pasture value. Though this variable is hard to quantify, we may note again the figures from Snowdonia, with less sheep per acre in the areas of highest rainfall (Dale and Hughes 1978, tables 1 and 2). Thirdly, it is likely on the basis of present-day observation of the relationship between soil and pasture that there would also have been qualitative changes in pasture type with increased leaching and podzolisation, most notably from *Festuca-Agrostis* mull sward on brown earths to *Molinia-Nardus* mor sward on more acidic peaty or podzolic soils. Such putative change would have varied in degree since varieties of *Festuca-Nardus* or *Agrostis-Nardus-Molinia* sward for example are commonly observed today (e.g. Hughes 1958), but the general shift in pasture type is likely to have been towards poorer quality. The process however may not have been simple since it has often been observed that land-use and grazing pressure themselves exert strong pressure on vegetation (e.g. Pearsall 1971, Tansley 1968). A relaxation of grazing for example may encourage *Nardus* to spread rather than *vice versa*, with the thicker sward progressively hindering decomposition (Limbrey 1976, p.168). It is also notoriously difficult for the pollen analyst to distinguish different grass species. Some differentiation in the basis of size has recently been tried (Caseldine 1981) and further attempts, which might lead ultimately to pasture quality diagrams as well as simple gross pollen diagrams, would be of considerable use to the prehistorian. Reduced stocking rates are presumably implied in such a change, but two qualifying factors should be noted. First, 'comparative grazing intensity' measures stock preference as well as grazing value in itself and there is still scope for a sward underused in a situation of choice to provide reasonable stocking rates if called upon. Secondly as far as summer grazing goes, general under-use of up to seventy per cent of pasture has been noted because of the burst of summer growth (Gimingham 1972, p.171), so that in certain circumstances qualitative differences between pasture types may have been less crucial than overall abundance.

Changes in the length of the growing season may have been more critical. Plant growth is generally considered to begin when the mean (air) temperature reaches 5.6°C. Though light is also a critical variable once growth has started (Grant 1968) and one which might have been affected by climatic change, discussion will concentrate on temperature for which more data are available.

As a generalisation mean temperature tends to decrease with height above sea level and a crude rate of 1 deg C per 154–165 m has been quoted (Gloyne 1968). Time-lapse figures for northern England/southern Scotland at the present day of about thirteen days per 100 m are quoted (Manley 1945, Gloyne 1968). Such time-lapse can be seen empirically in studies of the onset and abundance of grass growth at different altitudes (e.g. Alcock and Lovett 1968; Smith and Forrest 1978, fig.8) with later and slower growth at higher altitudes. Simple extrapolation therefore from the postulated 2 deg C drop involved in climatic change would require the lowering of altitudinal thresholds by about 300 m and a reduction in the growing season at higher altitudes of about 40 days.

The simple nature of these figures must be stressed. There is often a confusion between air and soil temperatures (Gloyne 1968); at least one study suggests a temperature of 10°C (air?) for the start of upland grasses (Grant 1968). There is variation in lapse-rates between the maritime uplands of the west, where they are steeper, and the east of the country, where they are gentler (Harrison 1974). Harrison has also pointed out considerable temporal and spatial variation in lapse-rates, that is between different seasons and different areas. Studies in north-west Wales for example show that the fall in temperature with height was least in spring, especially in March and May (ibid., p.53) and greatest in late autumn and winter, and the general applicability of standard lapse-rates has been questioned altogether.

A reduced growing season and lengthened winter would obviously produce harsher conditions for animal husbandry in the winter. The study of Soay sheep on St Kilda showed that body weight of both rams and ewes fluctuated through the year and was lowest in winter (Doney et al. 1974, fig.4.10). Birth and lactation tend to coincide with or precede the onset of grass growth (Grant 1968) and on St Kilda ewes with the lowest body weights and their lambs, which also tended to be the smallest, had the worst chances of survival (Grubb 1974, fig.10.6). There would also be a shorter period for summer weight replacement (Brasher and Perkins 1978). Climatic change in these respects could have produced serious constraints on upland exploitation, and with worse consequence than the supposed shift to 'rougher grazing' but considerable variation between seasons and regions must also be allowed for.

It remains to consider what the capacity of such changes might have been to cause major changes in contemporary society. The scale of upland grazing before climatic change, that is in the earlier and mid second millennium bc, was probably varied from region to region but regularly extensive (if not, there is little point to the discussion at all since we are not dealing with a critical resource). Pollen and field wall evidence both point in this direction, even if as on Dartmoor much land division may have overlapped the period of climatic change since for example there are now dates going back to 3450–3350 BP (1500–1400 bc) from the Shaugh Moor enclosure (Wainwright and Smith 1980). Of greater concern is the organisation of such land-use. Two possibilities at extremes from each other may be contrasted. On the one hand the evidence could reflect localised domestic production, the result of the commonly envisaged population overspill on to marginal land, which operated entirely without reference to other environmental zones or areas. On the other hand the scale of land division suggests more strongly communal involvement, with the possibility also of hierarchies of control, and it is difficult moreover to see areas such as Dartmoor as closed systems. An alternative would be to see them, however organised locally, as part of 'regional economies', defined as linking different areas such as lowland and upland through division of labor and interchange of products, not necessarily on an equal basis (Rowlands 1980, pp.32–8). According to this hypothesis upland areas such as Dartmoor may have been involved by the second millennium bc not just in local subsistence but in the production of animal surpluses which were important in regional terms in the creation of wealth, either as livestock or for transference to other media. Faience beads in cairns on Shaugh Moor (Wainwright *et al* 1979) certainly indicate exchange beyond Dartmoor itself. Other examples of regional economy could include central-southern England in the Early Bronze Age with the Wessex chalk linked to other areas; the Fenland too of East Anglia with its intensive grazing systems may have been part of a wider system of interaction. Further afield it is interesting to note increased penetration of the highlands in north-east Scotland (e.g. O'Sullivan 1974) at roughly the same date as prestige items such as Beaker pottery and early metalwork in the surrounding lowlands.

Climatic change could have entailed two sorts of effect, severe curtailment or abandonment of upland activity, and adjustment to varying degrees. In the former case actual peat encroachment would be one of the more dramatic situations. The best candidate for this event is actually from lowland Co. Mayo around 3950 BP (2000 bc) (Caulfield 1978) since elsewhere it is not clear whether peat encroachment was the direct cause or the consequence of abandonment. The effect of such encroachment would be greatest on localised domestic exploitation since in this mode there would be least room for manoeuvre, whereas for the regional economy peat uplands would still be a useful resource, as subsequent Iron Age and medieval use demonstrates.

It is important to explore other sorts of adjustment, for in the environmental and social conditions outlined it seems that this would regularly have been possible. Most societies have the capacity to absorb environmental changes since they have to face, even in the best possible conditions, some degree of fluctuation. All farmers must face the nuisance value of the weather or fail to be farmers at all (Oliver 1967). There is a broad range of first millennium bc sites in the uplands of England, Wales and Scotland (Cunliffe 1978), which suggest that adjustment was indeed possible. One way to counter vegetational changes would be by greater management of grazing; Hunter's chief recommendation (1962) was to encourage equal use of mull and mor swards, and some prehistoric land division at least might have been directed to such an aim, which would also have been achievable with the use of close shepherding. There would be scope for increased differentiation of species used in the uplands (as seen in the last 150 years with first Cheviots then the hardier Blackface dominant (Carlyle 1979); it may be no accident that sites like Staple Howe (Brewster 1963) flanking the lowlands have greater percentages of cattle than would be predicted for upland use proper. A third strategy would be a greater degree of transhumance. Winter retreat and lowland use could even have led paradoxically to more intensive use of the uplands in summer with greater numbers of stock made possible by better winter holdings. Higher grazing intensity helps to maintain or improve sward quality, and pollen diagrams quoted above from the North York Moors or Upper Teesdale show renewed woodland clearance into the first millennium bc, perhaps again to improve the quality of pasture or browse. A transhumant strategy would also have been easier to accommodate into a regional rather than local economy. It may also have helped to regularise animal husbandry by spreading risks, if Ingold's (1980) generalisation that pastoralists suffer inherent instability because of periodic irruptions in animal numbers is valid.

Environmental constraints accentuated by climatic change may have posed problems for many communities but for the most part necessary adjustments could have been absorbable. This is not to deny that they were contributory to general processes of social change, such as greater emphasis on conflict, raiding and defence, or again the regional economy. But for the most part the archaeological record shows continuity not abrupt hiatus, and it is misleading to single out the Penard phase of the twelfth/eleventh centuries BC as the countrywide watershed of this period (Burgess 1980). Radical change in upland use in some areas may be indicated, but dates vary and other factors are likely to be involved. Could the reduction of activity on Dartmoor for example reflect not climatic changes but changes in social conditions and the creation of wealth as the Later Bronze Age Atlantic regional economy ended (cf. Rowlands 1980) and iron replaced bronze? Could the reduced contact between Britain and the continent alleged for the Ha D period (c. 600–450 BC) not reflect a turning by European communities to the Mediterranean (Rowlands 1980, p.45) rather than stormier sea crossings as some scholars have suggested? Could the abandonment of the Fengate winter grazings and their replacement by mixed farming settlements (Pryor 1980) be connected with other, social, changes in the region such as may be seen in the changing patterns of the use and deposition of bronze wealth (Gardiner 1980)? It is to questions of adjustment to environmental constraint within the wider framework of social change that prehistorians should now turn.

Acknowledgements

I should like to thank the conference participants for useful comment and particularly Seamas Caulfield and David Maguire for supplying further references included here.

REFERENCES

Alcock, M. B. & Lovett, J. V. (1968) Analysis of environmental influence on productivity, in Hunt, I. V. (ed.) *Hill-land productivity*, 20-9. Brit. Grassland Soc. Occ. Symp. no.4.

Atherden, M. A. (1976) The impact of late prehistoric cultures on the vegetation of the North York Moors, *Trans. Inst. Brit. Geographers* 1 (N.S.), 284-300.

Barrett, J. (1980) The evolution of Later Bronze Age settlement, in Barrett, J. & Bradley, R. (eds) *Settlement and Society in the British Later Bronze Age*, 77-100. British Archaeological Reports 83.

Bowen, H. C. (1978) Celtic fields and ranch boundaries in Wessex, in Limbrey, S. & Evans, J. G. (eds) *The Effect of Man on the Landscape: the Lowland Zone*, 115-23. CBA Research Report 21.

Bowen, H. C. & Fowler, P., eds (1978) *Early Land Allotment in the British Isles*. British Archaeological Reports 48.

Brasher, S. & Perkins, D. F. (1978) The grazing intensity and productivity of sheep in the grassland ecosystem, in Heal, O. W. & Perkins, D. F. (eds) *Production Ecology of British Moors and Montane Grasslands*, 354-75. Ecological Studies 27. Berlin: Springer.

Brewster, T. C. M. (1963) *The Excavation of Staple Howe*. Scarborough.

Burgess, C. (1974) The Bronze Age, in Renfrew, C. (ed.) *British Prehistory: a New Outline*, 165-232. London: Duckworth.

— (1980) *The Age of Stonehenge*. London: Dent.

Carlyle, W. J. (1979) The changing distribution of breeds of sheep in Scotland 1795-1965, *Agricultural History Review* 27, 19-29.

Caseldine, C. J. (1981) Surface pollen studies across Bankhead Moss, Fife, Scotland, *J. Biogeogr.* 8, 7-25.

Caulfield, S. (1978) Neolithic fields: the Irish evidence, in Bowen, H. C. & Fowler, P. J. (eds) *Early Land Allotment in the British Isles*, 137-43. British Archaeological Reports 48.

Coles, J. M. & Harding, A. F. (1979) *The Bronze Age in Europe*. London: Methuen.

Conway, V. (1954) Stratigraphy and pollen analysis of southern Pennine blanket peats, *J. Ecol.* 42, 117-32.

Cunliffe, B. (1978) *Iron Age Communities in Britain* (2nd edition). London: Routledge & Kegan Paul.

Cunliffe, B. W. (1980) The evolution of Romney Marsh: a preliminary statement, in Thompson, F. H. (ed.) *Archaeology and Coastal Change*, 37-55. Society of Antiquaries Occasional Paper (N.S.) 1. London.

Dale, J. & Hughes, R. E. (1978) Sheep population studies in relation to the Snowdonian environment, in Heal, O. W. & Perkins, D. F. (eds), *Production Ecology of British Moors and Montane Grasslands*, 348-53. Ecological Studies 27. Berlin: Springer.

Dansgaard, W., Johnsen, S. J., Møller, J. & Langway, C. C. (1969) One thousand centuries of climatic record from Camp Century on the Greenland Ice sheet, *Science* 166, 377-81.

Darling, F. Fraser & Boyd, J. Morton (1964) *Highlands and Islands*. London: Collins.

Doney, J. M., Ryder, M. L., Gunn, R. G. & Grubb, P. (1974) Colour, conformation, affinities, fleece and patterns of inheritance in the Soay sheep, in Jewell, P. A., Milner, C. & Boyd, J. Morton (eds) *Island Survivors: the Ecology of the Soay Sheep of St Kilda*, 88-125. London: Athlone Press.

Evans, R. E. (1960) *Rations for Livestock* (Ministry of Agriculture, Fisheries and Food, Bulletin no.48). London: HMSO.

Fleming, A. (1976) Early settlement and the landscape in west Yorkshire, in Sieveking, G., Longworth, I. H. & Wilson, K. E. (eds) *Problems in Economic and Social Archaeology*, 359-73. London: Duckworth.

Fleming, A. (1978) The Prehistoric landscape of Dartmoor. Part 1. South Dartmoor, *Proc. Prehistoric. Soc.* 44, 97-123.

Gardiner, J. (1980) Land and social status – a case study from Eastern England, in Barrett, J. & Bradley, R. (eds) *Settlement and Society in the British Later Bronze Age*, 101-14. British Archaeological Reports 83.

Gimingham, C. H. (1972) *Ecology of Heathlands*. London: Chapman & Hall.

Gloyne, R. W. (1968) Some climatic influences affecting hill-land productivity, in Hunt, I. V. (ed.) *Hill-land Productivity*, 9-15. Brit. Grassland Soc. Occ. Symp. no.4.

Grant, S. A. (1968) Temperature and light factors limiting the growth of hill pasture species, in Hunt, I. V. (ed.) *Hill-land Productivity*, 30-4. Brit. Grassland Soc. Occ. Symp. no.4.

Grubb, P. (1974) Social organisation of Soay sheep and the behaviour of ewes and lambs, in Jewell, P. A., Milner, C. & Morton Boyd, J. (eds) *Island Survivors: the Ecology of the Soay Sheep of St Kilda*, 131-59. London: Athlone Press.

Grubb, P. & Jewell, P. A. (1974) Movement, daily activity and home range of Soay sheep, in Jewell, P. A., Milner, C. & Morton Boyd, J. (eds) *Island Survivors: the Ecology of the Soay Sheep of St Kilda*, 160-94. London: Athlone Press.

Harrison, S. J. (1974) Problems in the measurement and evaluation of the climatic resources of upland Britain, in Taylor, J. A. (ed.) *Climatic Resources and Economic Activity*, 47-63. London: David & Charles.

Hoskins, W. G. (1978) *One Man's England*. London: British Broadcasting Corporation.

Hughes, R. E. (1958) Sheep population and environment in North Wales, *J. Ecol.* 46, 169-90.

Hunter, R. F. (1962) Hill sheep and their pasture: a study of sheep grazing in south-east Scotland, *J. Ecol.* 50, 651-80.

Ingold, T. (1980) *Hunters, Pastoralists and Ranchers. Reindeer Economies and their Transformations*. Cambridge: University Press.

Jacobi, R. M., Tallis, J. H. & Mellars, P. A. (1976) The Southern Pennine Mesolithic and the ecological record, *J. Archaeol. Science* 3, 307-20.

Jewell, P. A., Milner, C. & Morton Boyd, J., eds (1974) *Island Survivors: the Ecology of the Soay Sheep of St Kilda*. London: Athlone Press.

Johnson, N. (1980) Later Bronze Age settlement in the south-west, in Barrett, J. & Bradley, R. (eds) *Settlement and Society in the British Later Bronze Age*, 141-80. British Archaeological Reports 83.

Lamb, H. H. (1977) The Late Quaternary history of the climate of the British Isles, in Shotton, F. W. (ed.) *British Quaternary Studies: Recent Advances*, 283-98. Oxford: Clarendon Press.

Limbrey, S. (1975) *Soil Science and Archaeology*. London: Academic Press.

— (1978) Changes in quality and distribution of the soils of lowland Britain, in Limbrey, S. & Evans, J. G. (eds) *The Effect of Man on the Landscape: the Lowland Zone*, 21-7. CBA Research Report 21. London.

Manley, G. (1945) The effective rate of altitudinal change in temperate climates, *Geogr. Rev.* 35, 408-17.

Mellars, P. A. (1976) Fire ecology, animal populations and man: a study of some ecological relationships in prehistory, *Proc. Prehistoric Soc.* 42, 15-46.

Milner, C. & Gwynne, D. (1974) The Soay sheep and their food supply, in Jewell, P. A., Milner, C. & Morton Boyd, J. (eds) *Island Survivors: the Ecology of the Soay Sheep of St Kilda*, 273-325. London: Athlone Press.

Mörner, N. A. & Wallin, B. (1977) A 10,000 year temperature record from Gotland, Sweden, *Palaeogeogr., Palaeoclimat., Palaeoecol.* 21, 113-38.

Nicholson, I. A., Paterson, I. S. & Currie, A. (1970) A study of vegetational selection by sheep and cattle in *Nardus* pasture, in Watson, A. (ed.) *Animal Populations in Relation to their Food Resources*. British Ecological Society Symposium no. 10. Oxford and Edinburgh.

Oliver, J. (1967) Problems of agro-climatic relationships in Wales in the eighteenth century, in Taylor, J. A. (ed.) *Weather and Agriculture*, 187-200. Oxford: Pergamon Press.

O'Sullivan, P. E. (1974) Radiocarbon-dating and prehistoric forest clearance on Speyside (East-Central Highlands of Scotland), *Proc. Prehistoric Soc.* 40, 206-8.

Pearsall, W. H. (1971) *Mountains and Moorland* (revised edition). London: Collins.

Pennington, W. (1974) *The History of British Vegetation*. London: English Universities Press.

Piggott, S. (1972-3) A note on climatic deterioration in the first millennium BC in Britain, *Scottish Archaeol. Forum* 4, 109-13.

Pryor, F. (1980) *Excavation at Fengate, Peterborough, England: the third report*. Northamptonshire Archaeology Monograph.

Rowlands, M. J. (1980) Kinship, alliance and exchange in the European Bronze Age, in Barrett, J. & Bradley, R. (eds) *Settlement and Society in the British Later Bronze Age*, 15-55. British Archaeological Reports 83.

Simmons, I. G. (1969) Environment and early man on Dartmoor, *Proc. Prehistoric Soc.* 35, 203-19.

Smith, R. A. H. & Forrest, G. I. (1978) Field estimates of primary production, in Heal, O. W. & Perkins, D. F. (eds) *Production Ecology of British Moors and Montane Grasslands*, 17-37. Ecological Studies 27. Berlin: Springer.

Tansley, A. G. (1968) *Britain's Green Mantle* (2nd edition, revised M. C. F. Procter). London: George Allen & Unwin.

Taylor, J. A. (1980) Environmental changes in Wales during the Holocene period, in Taylor, J. A. (ed.) *Culture and Environment in Prehistoric Wales*, 101-30. British Archaeological Reports 76.

Tinsley, H. M. (1976) Cultural influences on Pennine vegetation with particular reference to North Yorkshire, *Trans. Inst. British Geographers* 1 (N.S.). 310-22.

— (1981) The Bronze Age, in Simmons, I. & Tooley, M. (eds) *The Environment in British Prehistory*, 210-49. London: Duckworth.

Turner, J. (1981) The Iron Age, in Simmons, I. & Tooley, M. (eds) *The Environment in British Prehistory*, 250-81. London: Duckworth.

Turner, J., Hewetson, V. P., Hibbert, F. A., Lowry, K. H. & Chambers, C. (1973) The history of the vegetation and flora of Widdybank Fell and the Cow Green Reservoir Basin, Upper Teesdale, *Phil. Trans. R. Soc.* B, 265, 327-408.

Van Zeist, W. (1974) Palaeobotanical studies of settlement sites in the coastal area of the Netherlands, *Palaeohistoria* 16, 223-371.

Wainwright, G. J. & Smith, K. (1980) The Shaugh Moor project: second report: the enclosure, *Proc. Prehistoric Soc.* 46, 65-122.

Wainwright, G. J., Fleming, A. & Smith, K. (1979) The Shaugh Moor project: first report, *Proc. Prehistoric Soc.* 45, 1-33.

Contributors

K. E. Barber
Department of Geography, University of Southampton
Martin Bell
Department of Geography, University of Bristol
Hans-Jürgen Beug
Abteilung für Palynologie der Universität Göttingen
J. L. Bintliff
School of Archaeological Sciences, University of Bradford
Jan Bouzek
Institute for Classical Archaeology, Charles University, Prague
A. F. Harding
Department of Archaeology, University of Durham
M. Hughes
Department of Biology, Liverpool Polytechnic
Klaus-Dieter Jäger
Geological Institute, Saxon Academy of Sciences, Dresden
Marcel Joos
Laboratorium für Urgeschichte, University of Basel
Helen C. M. Keeley
Ancient Monuments Laboratory, Department of the Environment, London
H. H. Lamb
Climatic Research Unit, School of Environmental Sciences, University of East Anglia, Norwich
Vojen Lozek
Geological Institute, Czech Academy of Sciences, Prague
Michel Magny
66 rue du Bois Bourgeois, Montbeliard
P. J. Osborne
Department of Geological Sciences, University of Birmingham
J. R. Pilcher
Palaeoecology Centre, Queen's University of Belfast
Ian Shennan
Department of Geography, University of Durham
Alasdair Whittle
Department of Archaeology, University College, Cardiff

Index